1992

Dr. Thomas E. Barman
Institut National de la Sante
et de la Recherche Medicale
INSERM U 128
F-34033 Montpellier Cedex
France

Printed and bound by R.R. Donnelley & Sons, Harrisonburg, Virginia.
Printed in the United States of America.

9 8 7 6 5 4 3 2 (Second printing, 1985)

ISBN 0-387-04423-X Springer-Verlag New York Berlin Heidelberg Tokyo
ISBN 3-540-04423-X Springer-Verlag Berlin Heidelberg New York Tokyo

Contents

Contents Vol. I

<u>CARBOXYLESTERASE</u>

(Carboxylic-ester hydrolase)

A carboxylic ester + H_2O = an alcohol + a carboxylate

Ref.

<u>Molecular weight</u>

source	value	conditions	
Pig liver	150,000 - 200,000	H_2O	(2)
Horse liver	96,000	from reaction with di-isopropyl phosphoro-fluoridate	(5)

<u>Specific activity</u>

The enzyme (pig liver) has been purified to homogeneity. (2)

<u>Specificity and Michaelis constants</u>

The enzyme from a number of sources catalyzes the hydrolysis of a wide variety of aliphatic esters. The enzyme also acts as a transferase. (1)

source	substrate	V(relative)	K_m(M)	conditions	
Pig liver[a]	ethyl n-butyrate	1.00	4.4×10^{-4}	pH 7.0, 25° (titrator)	(3)
	methyl n-butyrate	0.89	4.39×10^{-4}		
	methyl chloroacetate	> 5	"large"		
Horse liver[b]	methyl n-butyrate	1.00	2.32×10^{-3}	pH 6.8, P_i, 25°	(4)
	ethyl n-butyrate	0.45	6.20×10^{-4}		
	ethylacetate	0.04	-		

[a] The observed kinetics of this enzyme do not obey the Michaelis-Menton equation and can be explained either by substrate activation or by identical interacting sites.

[b] The reaction catalyzed by this enzyme follows Michaelis-Menton kinetics.

<u>Inhibitors</u>

The enzyme is inhibited by di-isopropyl phosphorofluoridate and other organophosphates and by several lactones (e.g. 4-hydroxybutyrolactone). (1)

<u>References</u>

1. Hofstee, B. H. J. (1960) The Enzymes, 4, 486.

2. Adler, A. J. & Kistiakowsky, G. B. (1961) JBC, 236, 3240.

3. Adler, A. J. & Kistiakowsky, G. B. (1962) JACS, 84, 695.

4. Burch, J. (1954) BJ, 58, 415.

5. Boursnell, J. C. & Webb, E. C. (1949) Nature, 164, 875.

ARYLESTERASE

(Aryl-ester hydrolase)

A phenyl acetate + H_2O = a phenol + acetate

Ref.

Molecular weight

source	value	conditions	
Sheep serum	35,000-50,000	-	(1)

Specific activity

Sheep serum (385 x)   1.2 paraoxon   (pH 7.6, P_i, 37°)   (1)

Specificity and Michaelis constants

Arylesterase acts on a variety of phenolic esters. The enzyme is not inhibited by DFP but, instead, hydrolyzes this compound.   (2,3,4)

source	substrate	V (relative)	K_m(M)	conditions	
Sheep serum[a]	paraoxon	1.00	4.4×10^{-3} [b]	2.5×10^{-2} M NaHCO$_3$ + 0.162 M NaCl + 0.2% gelatin, 37°	(1,2)
	p-nitrophenyl acetate	12.00	1.87×10^{-3}		
	DFP	0.40	-		
	tabun	1.80	-		

[a] The enzyme also hydrolyzed the following compounds: paraoxon (1.00), m-nitrophenyl acetate (28.0), o-nitrophenyl acetate (1.05) and p-nitrophenyl butyrate (1.07). The following compounds were not hydrolyzed: phenyl acetate, tetraethyl pyrophosphate and triacetin.

[b] A value of 2.9×10^{-4} was obtained using crude sheep serum as the source of the enzyme.

Abbreviations

paraoxon	di-ethyl p-nitrophenyl phosphate
DFP	di-isopropyl phosphorofluoridate
tabun	ethyl -N- dimethylphosphoroamidocyanate

References

1. Main, A. R. (1960) BJ, 74, 10.
2. Main, A. R. (1960) BJ, 75, 188.
3. Aldridge, W. N. (1954) BJ, 57, 692.
4. Aldridge, W. N. (1953) BJ, 53, 110.

LIPASE

(Glycerol-ester hydrolase)

A triglyceride + H_2O = a diglyceride + a fatty acid ion

Ref.

Molecular weight

Preparations from various biological sources contain several
protein fractions of widely different molecular weights possessing
lipolytic activity. The lipase activity of bovine milk is associated
with casein micelles. (6,7)

source	value	conditions	
Bovine milk[a]	62,000; 75,000; 112,000	Sephadex G100 and G200, 0.75M NaCl + 2.5 x 10^{-2}M MgCl$_2$	(6)
Bovine milk (slime)	7,000	pH 8.5	(4)
Rat adipose tissue[a]	39,000; 47,000; 55,000; 68,000; 75,000; 200,000	Sephadex G100 and G200. 2.5 x 10^{-2}M MgCl$_2$	(6)
Pig pancreas[a]	42,000	Sephadex G100 and G200, 0.75M NaCl + 2.5 x 10^{-2}M MgCl$_2$	(6)

---

[a] Tributyrinase activity

Specificity and kinetic properties

Lipases are included in that group of esterases which hydrolyses
emulsified substrates - substrates in true solution are not attacked.
It is thought that the enzyme is adsorbed by its emulsified substrate
and that the initial rate of reaction is a function of the number
of enzyme molecules adsorbed at the interphase (8). The enzyme hydrolyses esters of glycerol or other alcohols and long chain fatty acids.

Specificity and Kinetic properties contd.

Tri- di- and monoglycerides are attacked in decreasing order of
activity (1,2,3,5). A lipase which hydrolyses "Tween" has been highly
purified from rat adipose tissue.   (10)

The enzyme isolated from several sources requires emulsifiers (e.g.
bile salts), fatty acids or various other activators for full activity.
For instance, the acid lipase of Ricinus communis (castor bean)
requires a mixture of cyclic polymers of ricinoleic acid for activity.
This mixture may be replaced by fatty acids, monoglycerides,
$\propto$-tocopherol succinate or the methyl half ester of dodecenyl succinate. (9)

References

1. Hofstee, B. H. J. (1960) The Enzymes, 4, 493.

2. Desnuelle, P. (1961) Advances in Enzymology, 23, 129.

3. Chandan, R. C. & Shahani, K. M. (1964) J. Dairy Sci., 47, 471.

4. Chandan, R. C., Shahani, K. M., Hill, R. M. & Scholz, J. J.
    (1963-64) Enzymologia, 26, 87.

5. Marchis-Mouren, G., Sarda, L. & Desnuelle, P. (1959) ABB, 83, 309.

6. Downey, W. K. & Andrews, P. (1965) BJ, 94, 642.

7. Downey, W. K. & Andrews, P. (1966) BJ, 101, 651.

8. Benzonana, G. & Desnuelle, P. (1965) BBA, 105, 121.

9. Ory, R. L., Barker, R. H. & Boudreaux, G. J. (1964) B, 3, 2013.

10. Wallach, D. P., Ko, H. & Marshall, N. B. (1962) BBA, 59, 690.

PHOSPHOLIPASE A

(Phosphatide acyl-hydrolase)

A lecithin + H_2O =

a lysolecithin + an unsaturated fatty acid ion

Molecular weight

source	value	conditions	
Naja naja venom	32-33,000	various	(2)
Crotalus adamanteus venom	30-35,000	pH 7.4	(5)

Specific activity

C. adamanteus venom (5 x) enzyme I[a] 575 } ovolecithin (di-
                          enzyme II   850 } palmitoyl-lecithin)
                                          (pH 7.4)   (5)

---

[a] Two proteins with phospholipase A activity are present in C. adamanteus venom. These have been separated.

Specificity

Phospholipase A specifically removes the fatty acid residue at the 2-position from phosphatidylcholine, phosphatidylethanolamine and phosphatidylserine to yield the corresponding lyso compounds (lyso-phosphatidylcholine etc.). The behaviour of the enzyme towards its substrates depends to a large extent on the source of the enzyme. Thus, preparations from the pancreas readily attack phosphatidylethanolamine but do not act on phosphatidylcholine unless deoxycholate or an anionic phospholipid is present. The enzyme from Crotalus adamanteus does not require an auxiliary compound to hydrolyze lecithin.   (1,2)

Specificity contd.

Phospholipase A from <u>Crotalus</u> <u>adamanteus</u> venom (or pig pancreas) possessed specificity properties such that the rate of hydrolysis of various types of lecithin molecules decreased in the order: 1-unsaturated 2-saturated, 1-unsaturated 2-unsaturated, 1-saturated 2-polyunsaturated, 1-saturated 2-monounsaturated, 1-saturated 2-saturated.   (3)

Phospholipase A from the venom of <u>Naja</u> <u>naja</u> hydrolyzes cardiolipin.   (4)

Michaelis constants

source	substrate	$K_m(M)$	conditions	
<u>C. adamanteus</u> venom Enzyme I or II	ovolecithin	3.9×10^{-2}	pH 7.4	(5)

References

1. Slotta, K. H. (1960) The Enzymes, 4, 552.

2. van Deenen, L. L. M. & de Haas, G. H. (1966) Ann. Rev. Biochem., 35 (1), 674.

3. Moore, J. H. & Williams, D. L. (1964) BBA, 84, 41.

4. Marinetti, G. V. (1964) BBA, 84, 55.

5. Saito, K. & Hanahan, D. J. (1962) B, 1, 521.

ACETYLESTERASE

(Acetic-ester hydrolase)

An acetic ester + H_2O = an alcohol + acetate

Ref.

Specificity and kinetic properties

Acetylesterase is a typical esterase having its greatest activity on esters of acetic acid. It is neither inhibited by nor does it hydrolyze di-isopropyl phosphorofluoridate. (1,2)

The enzyme isolated from hog kidney attacked n-propyl acetate, n-propylchloroacetate, mono-, di- and tri-acetin and p-nitrophenyl-acetate. It had a higher affinity for n-propylchloroacetate than for n-propyl acetate. (1)

An acetylesterase has been isolated from the orange which hydrolyzes mono-, di- and tri-acetin, methyl acetate, ethyl acetate, benzyl acetate, xylitol pentaacetate and tetraacetylmethyl-α-D-galacturonate. This enzyme also catalyzes the hydrolysis of acetyl-choline, albeit only at very high concentrations (K_m = 1.6 M). (3)

References

1. Bergmann, F., Segal, R. & Rimon, S. (1957) BJ, 67, 481.
2. Bergmann, F. & Rimon, S. (1960) BJ, 77, 209.
3. Jansen, E. F., Jang, R. & MacDonnell, L. R. (1947) AB, 15, 415.

ACETYLCHOLINESTERASE

(Acetylcholine hydrolase)

Acetylcholine + H_2O = choline + acetate

Molecular weight

source	value	conditions	
Electrophorus	230,000 (a)	pH 7.0	(3)
electricus	54,000 (b)	-	(3)

(a) Values in excess of 1×10^6 have been reported and are thought to have been obtained as a result of a particular isolation procedure (3). The enzyme is subject to reversible aggregation phenomena (4).

(b) Obtained by titrating the enzyme with N,N-dimethyl-S-diethoxyphosphorylthioethanolamine.

Specific activity

E. electricus (330 x) 11,000 acetylcholine (pH 7.0, P_i, 25°) (5)

Specificity and Michaelis constants

The enzyme is not specific for acetylcholine and hydrolyzes a variety of acetic esters. It possesses low activity towards propionyl- or butyrylcholine. It also catalyzes transacetylation reactions. (1)

source	substrate	$\frac{V}{(relative)}$	K_m(M)	conditions	
Bovine erythrocyte	$(CH_3)_3 \equiv N-$ $(CH_2)_2OCOCH_3$ (a)	1.00	2.68×10^{-4}		
	$(CH_3CH_2)(CH_3)_2 \equiv N-$ $(CH_2)_2OCOCH_3$	0.95	2.61×10^{-4}		
	$(CH_3)_3 \equiv N-$ $(CH_2)_2SCOCH_3$	0.83	1.31×10^{-4}		
	$((CH_3)_2CH)(CH_3)_2 \equiv N-$ $(CH_2)_2OCOCH_3$	0.75	2.92×10^{-4}		
	$(CH_3CH_2CH_2)(CH_3)_2 \equiv N-$ $(CH_2)_2OCOCH_3$	0.63	5.86×10^{-4}	pH 7.5, 26°	(6)
	$(CH_3)_3 \equiv N-$ $(CH_2CH(CH_3)OCOCH_3$	0.22	2.22×10^{-3}		
	$(CH_3CH_2CH_2)_2(CH_3) \equiv N-$ $(CH_2)_2OCOCH_3$	0.081	1.01×10^{-3}		
	$(CH_3CH_2CH_2)_2(CH_2CH_3) \equiv N-$ $(CH_2)_2OCOCH_3$	0.054	5.55×10^{-4}		
	phenylacetate	1.13	1.31×10^{-3}		

Specificity and Michaelis constants contd.

source	substrate	$\overset{V}{(\text{relative})}$	$K_m(M)$	conditions	Ref.
E. electricus	acetylcholine	–	9×10^{-5}	pH 7.00, $25°$	(9)
	acetylhomocholine	–	1.3×10^{-3}		
	acetylcholine	1.00	9.4×10^{-5}		
	dimethylaminoethylacetate	0.53	6.5×10^{-4}	pH 7.00, $25°$	(7)
	methylaminoethylacetate	0.25	7.8×10^{-3}		
	aminoethylacetate	0.26	1.56×10^{-2}		

[a] Acetylcholine. For clarity, the positive charge normally assigned to the nitrogen atom and the compensating halide ion are not given.

Inhibitors

Acetylcholinesterase is inhibited by a variety of compounds including the natural amino acids, several amides, dipeptides and esters (8); a series of n-methylphosphoramidates (10) and several trimethylammonium derivatives (9). Alkyl phosphates (e.g. tetraethyl pyrophosphate and di-isopropyl phosphorofluoridate) are potent irreversible inhibitors (1).

source	inhibitor	$K_i(M)$	conditions	
E. electricus	(3-hydroxyphenyl)TMA (bromide)dimethyl carbamate	1.2×10^{-8}	pH 7.00, $25°$	(9)
	(2-hydroxybenzyl)TMA (bromide)	2.05×10^{-8}		
	phenylTMA(iodide)	3.8×10^{-5}		
	benzylTMA(bromide)	9.1×10^{-5}		

Abbreviations

TMA   trimethylammonium

References

1. Wilson, I. B. (1960) The Enzymes, 4, 501.
2. Oosterbaan, R. A. & Jansz, H. S. (1965) Comprehensive Biochemistry, 16, 1.
3. Kremzner, L. T. & Wilson, I. B. (1964) B, 3, 1902.
4. Grafius, M. A. & Millar, D. B. (1967) B, 6, 1034.
5. Kremzner, L. T. & Wilson, I. B. (1963) JBC, 238, 1714.
6. Krupta, R. M. (1964) B, 3, 1749.
7. Wilson, I. B. & Cabib, E. (1956) JACS, 78, 202.
8. Bergmann, F., Wilson, I. B. & Nachmansohn, D. (1950) JBC, 186, 693.
9. Wilson, I. B. & Quan, C. (1958) ABB, 73, 131.
10. Neely, W. B., Unger, I., Blair, E. H. & Nyquist, R. A. (1964) B, 3, 1477.

CHOLINESTERASE

(Acylcholine acyl-hydrolase)

An acylcholine + H_2O = choline + an anion

Molecular weight

source	value	conditions	
Horse serum	$S_{20,w}$ = 9.9 84,000[a]	pH 7.0 -	(3) (3)
Human serum	300,000		(4)

[a] Obtained by titrating the enzyme with isopropylmethyl phosphoro-fluoridate.

Specific activity

Horse serum (14,000 x) 1000 acetylcholine (pH 7.5, P_i, 25°)   (3)

Specificity and Michaelis constants

The enzyme acts on a variety of choline esters.   (1)

The enzyme from Pseudomonas fluorescens also catalyzes the transfer of the acetyl group of the substrate AcPN to suitable alcohol acceptors. With n-amyl alcohol as the acceptor, the transferase activity was 12 times more rapid than the esterase activity. Acceptors were more suitable as they became longer and less branched. Primary alcohols were better acceptors than secondary or tertiary alcohols. The presence or absence of a positive charge did not affect acceptor activity.   (5)

The enzyme (horse serum) is without activity on methyl butyrate, triacetin, amyl acetate, ethyl butyrate, ethyl acetate, ethyl formate or acetyl 3-methyl choline.   (3)

source	substrate	relative velocity	$K_m(M)$	conditions	
Horse serum	butyrylcholine chloride	1.75	-		
	acetylcholine chloride	1.00	-	pH 7.5,	
	phenyl acetate	0.46	-	P_i, 25°	(3)
	tributyrin	0.14	-		
P. fluorescens	AcPN	-	5.6×10^{-6}	pH 6.2, P_i, 22°	(6)
	AcPN[a]	-	4.4×10^{-6}	pH 6.2,	
	n-amyl alcohol	-	8.3×10^{-3}	P_i, 22°	(5)
Human serum	benzoylcholine	-	4×10^{-6}	pH 7.4, P_i, 25°	(8)

Specificity and Michaelis constants contd.

(a)With n-amyl alcohol as the acceptor in the transferase reaction.

Inhibitors

The enzyme (P. fluorescens) is not inhibited by organic phosphates
(e.g. di-isopropyl phosphorofluoridate) but choline, betaine, choline
analogs (e.g. neostigmine) and carbamoylcholine all inhibit (6). Other
inhibitors are discussed in reference (8).

source	inhibitor	type	$K_i(M)$	conditions	
P. fluorescens	AcPN	complex	3.7×10^{-4}	pH 6.2,	(6)
	PN	mixed	1.9×10^{-4}	P_i, 22°	

Light absorption data

$\Delta \varepsilon(\text{AcPN-PN})$ at 273 mμ = 2200 $M^{-1}cm^{-1}$ (pH 6.2)   (7)

Abbreviations

PN   3-hydroxyphenyl trimethylammonium bromide
AcPN   acetyl ester of 3-hydroxyphenyl trimethylammonium
            bromide

References

1. Augustinsson, K-B. (1960) The Enzymes, 4, 521.

2. Oosterbaan, R. A. & Jansz, H. S. (1965) Comprehensive
   Biochemistry, 16, 1.

3. Jansz, H. S. & Cohen, J. A. (1962) BBA, 56, 531.

4. Surgenor, D. M. & Ellis, D. (1954) JACS, 76, 6049.

5. Fitch, W. M. (1964) JBC, 239, 1328.

6. Fitch, W. M. (1963) B, 2, 1221.

7. Fitch, W. M. (1963) B, 2, 1217.

8. Kalow, W. & Davies, R. O. (1959) Biochem. Pharmacol., 1, 183.

PECTINESTERASE

(Pectin pectyl-hydrolase)

Pectin + $\underline{n}$ H$_2$O = $\underline{n}$ methanol + pectate

Ref.

Specificity

Pectinesterase is a highly specific enzyme which hydrolyzes almost exclusively the methyl groups of pectic substances. The enzyme isolated from the orange, for instance, removed only methyl groups adjacent to free carboxyl groups - pectin which had been totally esterified with methanol was hydrolyzed very slowly, if at all. The hydrolysis proceeded linearly along the chain molecule as successive methoxy groups were split off. (1)

The following substrates were inactive: esters of polygalacturonatic acid with ethanol, glycol, glycerol and acetic acid and the methyl esters of galacturonic acid, methyl galacturonoside, digalacturonic acid (both mono and di-esters), methyl digalacturonoside (diester), trigalacturonic acid (tri-ester), tragacanth, alginic acid and tartaric acid. (1)

The reader is referred to reference (2) and (3) for further details of the properties of pectinesterase.

References

1. Deuel, H. & Stutz, E. (1958) Advances in Enzymology, 20, 358.

2. Lineweaver, H. & Jansen, E. F. (1951) Advances in Enzymology, 11, 267.

3. MacDonnell, L. R., Jang, R., Jansen, E. F. & Lineweaver, H. (1950) AB, 28, 260.

CHOLESTEROL ESTERASE
(Sterol-ester hydrolase)

A cholesterol ester + H_2O = cholesterol + an anion

Ref.

Equilibrium constant

The reaction is reversible. (1,2,3)

Specificity

Cholesterol esterase catalyzes the hydrolysis and formation of cholesterol esters ranging from cholesterol acetate to cholesterol stearate. The enzyme from porcine pancreas, for instance, utilized oleate (1.00), linoleate (1.09), stearate (0.44), palmitate (0.28) or linolenate (0.13) - but not myristate - in the synthesis of the respective cholesterol esters. The same enzyme could also utilize certain sterols in the place of cholesterol (1.00): dihydrocholesterol (1.09), β-sitosterol (0.39), stigmasterol (0.22) and ergosterol (0.03). The following sterols were inactive: epicholesterol, 7-dehydrocholesterol, estradiol, diethylstilbesterol, cholesteryl bromide (or chloride) and coprostanone. (1,2)

Several emulsifying agents were found to enhance cholesterol esterase activity. Of these taurocholate and cholate were the most active. (2,3)

A steroid esterase from Nocardia restricus has been described. (4)

References

1. Aldridge, W. N. (1961) Biochemist's Handbook, p278.
2. Hernandez, H. H. & Chaikoff, I. L. (1957) JBC, 228, 447.
3. Korzenovsky, M., Diller, E. R., Marshall, A. C. & Auda, B. M. (1960) BJ, 76, 238.
4. Sih, C. J., Laval, J. & Rahim, M. A. (1963) JBC, 238, 566.

CHLOROPHYLLASE

(Chlorophyll chlorophyllido-hydrolase)

Chlorophyll + H_2O = phytol + chlorophyllide

Ref.

Equilibrium constant

The reaction is essentially irreversible [F].   (1)

Specificity

The enzyme (etiolated rye seedlings) hydrolyses pheophytin a, pheophytin b, chlorophyll a, bacteriochlorophyll and chlorobium chlorophyll.   (1)

Michaelis constants

source	substrate	$K_m(M)$	conditions	
Etiolated rye seedlings	pheophytin a	1.5×10^{-5}	pH 7.5, P_i, 30°	(1)

References

1. Klein, A. O. & Vishniac, W. (1961) JBC, 236, 2544.

GLUCONOLACTONASE

(D-Glucono-δ-lactone hydrolase)

D-Glucono-δ-lactone + H_2O = D-gluconate

Specificity

Gluconolactonase from __Azotobacter__ __vinelandii__ attacks D-glucono-δ-lactone, D-glucono-γ-lactone, 6-phosphoglucono-δ-lactone, D-galactono-γ-lactone and lactobionic-δ-lactone. The following compounds were inactive: D-mannono-δ-, D-xylono-γ-, D-glycero-D-galactonoheptono-γ-, D-saccharo-δ-, D-gulono-γ-, D-glucurono-γ-, D- and L-arabono-γ-, D-talono-γ-, L-galactono-γ-, D-glycero-D-idoheptono-γ- and D-glycero-D-galactono-γ-lactones.

(1)

Michaelis constants

source	substrate	$K_m(M)$	conditions	
A. vinelandii	D-glucono-δ-lactone	8.5×10^{-6}	pH 6.0, P_i, 25°	(1)

The enzyme exhibits an absolute requirement for a divalent cation (Mg^{2+}, Mn^{2+} or Co^{2+}).

(1)

References

1. Brodie, A. F. & Lipmann, F. (1955) JBC, 212, 677.

ALDONOLACTONASE

(D(or L)-Gulono-γ-lactone hydrolase)

D(or L)-Gulono-γ-lactone + H_2O = gulonate

Ref.

Equilibrium constant

The reverse reaction has been demonstrated to occur at slightly acid pH.

(1)

Specificity and Michaelis constants[a]

source	substrate	relative velocity	K_m(M)
Rat liver	D-galactono-γ-lactone	1.00	-
	L-gulono-γ-lactone	0.064	6.0×10^{-2}
	D-glucurono-γ-lactone	0.009	-
	D-gulono-γ-lactone	0.64	1.65×10^{-2}
	a-D-glucoheptono-γ-lactone	0.028	-
	D-arabono-γ-lactone	0.159	-
	D-ribono-γ-lactone	0.055	-
	L-galactone-γ-lactone	0.25	2.1×10^{-2}
	D-mannono-γ-lactone	0.108	-
	D-mannurono-γ-lactone	0.040	-
	D-glucono-γ-lactone	0.62	-

[a]The data are from references (1) and (2). The conditions were: 0.1M $KHCO_3$, 25°.

References

1. Bublitz, C. & Lehninger, A. L. (1963) Methods in Enzymology, 6, 337.
2. Bublitz, C. & Lehninger, A. L. (1961) BBA, 47, 288.

PALMITOYL-CoA HYDROLASE

(Palmitoyl-CoA hydrolase)

Palmitoyl-CoA + H_2O = CoA + palmitate

Specificity

Palmitoyl-CoA hydrolase has not been extensively purified. A preparation from pig brain attacked hexanoyl-CoA, octanoyl-CoA, decanoyl-CoA, myristoyl-CoA and stearoyl-CoA in addition to palmitoyl-CoA.

(1)

Michaelis constants

source	substrate	$K_m(M)$	conditions	
Pig brain	palmitoyl-CoA	2.2×10^{-5}	pH 7.0, P_i.	(1)

Light absorption data

(Palmitoyl-CoA— CoA)[a] $\varepsilon, (233 \ m\mu)$ $\sim 4000 \ M^{-1} \ cm^{-1}$ (pH 7)   (1)

---

[a] Other fatty acyl CoA derivatives also have a strong absorption band at 233 mμ.

References

1. Srere, P. A., Seubert, W. & Lynen, F. (1959) BBA, 33, 313.

SUCCINYL-CoA HYDROLASE

(Succinyl-CoA hydrolase)

Succinyl-CoA + H_2O = CoA + succinate

Molecular weight

source	value	conditions	
Pig heart	$S_{20,w} = 4.5$	pH 7.6	(1)

Specificity

The enzyme (pig heart) does not hydrolyse acetyl-CoA.   (1)

Inhibitors

The enzyme (pig heart) is inhibited by PP_i and ATP.   (1)

References

1. Gergely, J. (1955) Methods in Enzymology, 1, 602.

3-HYDROXYISOBUTYRYL-CoA HYDROLASE

(3-Hydroxyisobutyryl-CoA hydrolase)

3-Hydroxyisobutyryl-CoA + H_2O =
CoA + 3-hydroxyisobutyrate

Ref.

Specificity

3-Hydroxyisobutyryl-CoA hydrolase from pig heart was active with 3-hydroxyisobutyryl-CoA (1.0) and 3-hydroxypropionyl-CoA (0.3) but the CoA thiol esters of the following acids were inactive: glycollic, DL-lactic, 2-hydroxyisobutyric, dl-3-hydroxybutyric, 3-hydroxy-3-methylglutaric, acetic, propionic, isobutyric, succinic, crotonic, senecioic and 3-methylenebutyric. The enzyme is highly specific for the thiol portion of the substrate: no activity was detected with the 3-hydroxyisobyrate thiol esters of thioglycollate, cysteine, thiomalate, glutathione or pantetheine or with the glutathione thiol esters of acetic, lactic, propionic, crotonic or butyric acids. (1)

References

1. Rendina, G. & Coon, M. J. (1957) JBC, 225, 523.

HYDROXYACYLGLUTATHIONE HYDROLASE

(S-2-Hydroxyacylglutathione hydrolase)

S-2-Hydroxyacylglutathione + H_2O = glutathione + a 2-hydroxyacid anion

Ref.

Equilibrium constant

The reaction is essentially irreversible [F].   (1)

Specificity

The enzymes hydroxyacylglutathione hydrolase (glyoxylase II) and lactoyl-glutathione lyase (glyoxylase I: 4.4.1.5) are responsible for the "glyoxylase reaction" which transforms methylglyoxal to DL-lactate with glutathione as cofactor.   (1)

Glyoxylase II catalyzes the hydrolysis of a variety of hydroxyacylglutathiones. Thus the following compounds were attacked: glycolyl-GSH, D- or L-lactoyl-GSH, mandeloyl-GSH, glyceroyl-GSH, acetyl-GSH and D- or L-alanyl-GSH. Pyruvoyl-GSH, 3-hydroxybutyryl-GSH and β-alanyl-GSH were hydrolyzed more slowly and alanylcysteine, lactoyl-cysteine, acetylthioglycollate and acetyl-CoA not at all.   (2,3,4)

Light absorption data

lactoyl-GSH ε, (240 mµ)   =   3300 $M^{-1}cm^{-1}$ (pH 6.6)   (5)

Abbreviations

GSH   glutathione

References

1. Knox, W. E. (1960) The Enzymes, 2, 271.
2. Racker, E. (1952) BBA, 9, 577.
3. Wieland, T. & Koeppe, H. (1953) Ann., 581, 1.
4. Wieland, T. & Koeppe, H. (1954) Ann., 588, 15.
5. Cliffe, E. E. & Waley, S. G. (1961) BJ, 79, 475.

ALKALINE PHOSPHATASE

(Orthophosphoric monoester phosphohydrolase)
An orthophosphoric monoester + H_2O =
an alcohol + orthophosphate

Molecular weight

Ref.

source	value	conditions	
Escherichia coli	80,000 [2]	various	(3,4)
Bovine milk	190,000	Sephadex G200, pH 5.0, 7.5 or 9.5	(5)
Bovine liver	190,000	Sephadex G200, pH 8.8	(6)
Calf intestine	100,000	pH 8.7	(10)

Specific activity

E. coli (~6 x)	24.8[a]	NPP (pH 8.0, 25°)	(7,8,18)
Bovine milk	854[b]	NPP (pH 10.0, carbonate-bicarbonate, 25°)	(5)
Bovine liver (40,000)	200	NPP (pH 10.1, carbonate-bicarbonate, 20°)	(6)
Calf intestine	350	phenylphosphate (pH 10.25, carbonate-bicarbonate, 20°)	(10)

[a] In the presence of 1M Tris the specific activity = 48.
[b] Derived from phosphorylation experiments. It was assumed that the molecular weight of the enzyme = 190,000.

Specificity and Michaelis constants

Alkaline phosphatase catalyzes the hydrolysis of a variety of phosphate esters including esters of primary and secondary alcohols, sugar alcohols, cyclic alcohols, phenols and amines. Phosphodiesters are not hydrolyzed (1). The enzyme also catalyzes the hydrolysis of PP_i (9,16,17).

The enzyme catalyzes a variety of transphosphorylation reactions - for instance, the enzyme from E. coli catalyzes both the hydrolysis of PP_i and the transfer of a phosphoryl group from PP_i (or a number of nucleoside di- or tri-phosphates or mannose 6-phosphate) to glucose, forming glucose 6-phosphate.   (9,12)

It is difficult to compare the kinetic data available on alkaline phosphatase in the literature. Thus V and Km values are a function of the purity of the enzyme under study, the concentration of enzyme in the reaction mixture, the type of buffer employed, the pH of the reaction mixture and the nature and concentration of the metal activator. Furthermore, the pH optimum obtained with a particular enzyme is a function of the type of substrate used.   (1)

The specificity and kinetic properties of the enzyme isolated from a number of sources will be found in the following references:

Specificity and Michaelis constants contd.

source

E. coli	(11,14)
Neurospora crassa	(13)
Calf intestine	(15,17)
Bovine milk	(15)
Mammalian cell cultures	(16)

Inhibitors

Alkaline phosphatase is inhibited by orthophosphate and the alcohol moieties of several phosphate esters (1). Other inhibitors include L-phenylalanine, L-tryptophan and L-cysteine. (16)

Light absorption data

$NP^{(a)}$ $\varepsilon,(420\ m\mu)$ = 13,200 $M^{-1}\ cm^{-1}$ (pH 8.0) (18)

(a)Produced by the hydrolysis of NPP

Abbreviations

NPP   p-nitrophenyl phosphate
NP   nitrophenol

References

1. Stadtman, T. C. (1961) The Enzymes, 5, 55.
2. Hummel, J. P. & Kalnitsky, G. (1964) Ann. Rev. Biochem., 33, 16.
3. Rothman, F. & Byrne, R. (1963) J. Molec. Biol., 6, 330.
4. Schlesinger, M. J. (1964) Brookhaven Symposia in Biology, 17, 66.
5. Barman, T. E. & Gutfreund, H. (1966) BJ, 101, 460.
6. Engstrom, L. (1964) BBA, 92, 71.
7. Dayan, J. & Wilson, I. B. (1964) BBA, 81, 620.
8. Malamy, M. H. & Horecker, B. L. (1964) B, 3, 1893.
9. Anderson, W. B. & Nordlie, R. C. (1967) JBC, 242, 114.
10. Engstrom, L. (1961) BBA, 52, 36.
11. Garen, A. & Levinthal. C. (1960) BBA, 38, 470.
12. Morton, R. K. (1965) Comprehensive Biochemistry, 16, 55.

13. Kuo, M-H & Blumenthal, H. J. (1961) BBA, 54, 101.
14. Heppel, L. A., Harkness, D. R. & Hilmoe, R. J. (1962) JBC, 237, 841.
15. Morton, R. K. (1955) BJ, 61, 232, 240.
16. Cox, R. P., Gilbert, P. & Griffin, M. J. (1967) BJ, 105, 155.
17. Fernley, H. N. & Walker, P. G. (1967) BJ, 104, 1011.
18. Malamy, M. & Horecker, B. L. (1966) Methods in Enzymology, 9, 639.

ACID PHOSPHATASE

(Orthophosphoric monoester phosphohydrolase)

An orthophosphoric monoester + H_2O = an

alcohol + orthophosphate

Ref.

Molecular weight

source	value	conditions	
Escherichia freundii	$S_{20,w}$ = 7.5	-	(3)
Human prostate	95,800	pH 7.0	(4)
Human erythrocyte	"small"	Sephadex G75, 0.14M NaCl	(2)
Baker's yeast	$S_{20,w}$ = 1.4	0.1M NaCl	(9)
Beef spleen	23,000	pH 5.6	(14)

Specific activity

E. freundii (3000 x)	93.3 NPP (pH 6.0, Tris-maleate)	(3)
	2.9 pyridoxine[a] (pH 6.0, Tris-maleate)	(3)
Human prostate	1650 NPP (25°)	(4)

[a] In the reaction

Pyridoxine + NPP = pyridoxine phosphate + NP

Specificity and kinetic properties

Acid phosphatase removes P_i from a wide variety of phosphomono-esters and from phosphoproteins. The enzyme isolated from several sources attacks the pyrophosphate bond - thus that from beef spleen hydrolyzes PP_i, ATP and ADP (15). Phosphodiesters are not hydrolyzed by acid phosphatase (1).

Many biological materials possess acid phosphatases that catalyze transphosphorylation reactions (1). The carrot is an exception in that it possesses separate enzymes responsible for acid phosphatase and transphosphorylation activities (7).

It is difficult to compare the kinetic data available on acid phosphatase in the literature. Thus, V and Km values are a function of the purity of the enzyme under study, the concentration of enzyme in the reaction mixture and the type of buffer employed (1).

The specificity and kinetic properties of the enzyme isolated from various sources will be found in the following references:

<u>Specificity and kinetic properties contd.</u>   <u>Ref.</u>

<u>source</u>

Human prostate	(5)
Bovine spleen	(15)
Bovine milk	(6)
Frog's egg	(8)
Carrot	(7)
Potato	(11)
<u>Escherichia coli</u>	(2)
Baker's yeast	(9)

<u>Inhibitors</u>

The enzyme from human prostate is inhibited by a variety of 2-
hydroxy carboxylic acid.   (12)

<u>Light absorption data</u>

NP$^{(a)}$ $\varepsilon, (407\ m\mu) = 18,330\ M^{-1}cm^{-1}$ (pH 9)   (13)
Salicylate$^{(b)}$ $\varepsilon, (310\ m\mu) = 1,940\ M^{-1}cm^{-1}$ (pH 4-12)   (10)

$^{(a)}$Produced by the hydrolysis of NPP
$^{(b)}$Produced by the hydrolysis of <u>o</u>-carboxyphenylphosphate

<u>Abbreviations</u>

NPP   <u>p</u>-nitrophenylphosphate
NP   <u>p</u>-nitrophenol

<u>References</u>

1. Schmidt, G. (1961) The Enzymes, <u>5</u>, 37.
2. Georgatsos, J. G. (1965) <u>ABB</u>, <u>110</u>, 354.
3. Tani, Y., Tochikura, T., Yamada, H. & Ogata, K. (1967) <u>BBRC</u>,
    <u>28</u>, 769.
4. Ostrowski, W. & Rybarska, J. (1965) <u>BBA</u>, <u>105</u>, 196.
5. Tsuboi, K. K. & Hudson, P. B. (1955) <u>ABB</u>, <u>55</u>, 191.
6. Bingham, E. W. & Zittle, C. A. (1963) <u>ABB</u>, <u>101</u>, 471.
7. Brunngraber, E. F. & Chargaff, E. (1967) <u>JBC</u>, <u>242</u>, 4834.
8. Harris, D. L., Mizock, B. J. & Pilkis, S. J. (1966) <u>JBC</u>, <u>241</u>, 707.
9. Tsuboi, K. K., Wiener, G. & Hudson, P. B. (1957) <u>JBC</u>, <u>224</u>, 621.
10. Hofstee, B. H. J. (1954) <u>ABB</u>, <u>51</u>, 139.
11. Alvarez, E. F. (1962) <u>BBA</u>, <u>59</u>, 663.
12. Kilsheimer, G. S. & Axelrod, B. (1957) <u>JBC</u>, <u>227</u>, 879.
13. Biggs, A. I. (1954) <u>Trans. Faraday Soc.</u>, <u>50</u>, 800.
14. Glomset, J. & Porath, J. (1960) <u>BBA</u>, <u>39</u>, 1.
15. Revel, H. R. (1963) <u>Methods in Enzymology</u>, <u>6</u>, 211.

PHOSPHOSERINE PHOSPHATASE

(Phosphoserine phosphohydrolase)

L-(or D-)Phosphoserine + H_2O =

L-(or D-)serine + orthophosphate

Ref.

Molecular weight

source	value	conditions	
Mouse brain	<100,000	Sephadex G100, pH 7.5	(2)

Specificity

The enzyme isolated from chicken liver (2), rat liver (5) or yeast (6) is highly specific. Thus, sugar phosphates, ATP, ADP, AMP, phosphothreonine, phosphoethanolamine, phosphohydroxypyruvate, phosvitin and casein are not attacked by the enzyme.

The enzyme also catalyzes the transfer of a phosphoryl group from phosphoserine to acceptors that are structurally related to the substrate.

(1)

Michaelis constants

source	substrate	V(relative)	K_m(M)	conditions	
Chicken liver	L-phosphoserine	1.0	5.8×10^{-5}	pH 5.9,	
	D-phosphoserine	1.0	4.2×10^{-3}	acetate, 38°	(3)
Yeast	L-phosphoserine	1.0	4×10^{-4}	pH 7.4,	
	D-phosphoserine	1.0	8×10^{-3}	Tris, 30°	(4,6)
Rat liver	L-phosphoserine	-	5×10^{-6}	pH 7.4,	
	D-phosphoserine	-	5×10^{-3}	Tris, 37°	(5)

Inhibitors

source	inhibitor	type	$K_i(M)$	conditions	
Chicken liver	L-serine	complex	6.5×10^{-4}	pH 5.9, acetate, 38°	(1,3)
	D-serine	complex	2.7×10^{-2}		

Of a series of compounds tested, L-serine, D-serine, L-alanine
and glycine were inhibitory towards the enzyme from chicken liver,
rat liver or yeast.   (1,3)

References

1. Byrne, W. L. (1961) The Enzymes, 5, 73.

2. Bridgers, W. F. (1967) JBC, 242, 2080.

3. Neuhaus, F. C. & Byrne, W. L. (1959) JBC, 234, 113.

4. Schramm, M. (1963) Methods in Enzymology, 6, 215.

5. Borkenhagen, L. F. & Kennedy, E. P. (1959) JBC, 234, 849.

6. Schramm, M. (1958) JBC, 233, 1169.

PHOSPHATIDATE PHOSPHATASE

(L-α-Phosphatidate phosphohydrolase)

An L-α-phosphatidate + H_2O =
a D-2,3(or L-1,2)-diglyceride + orthophosphate

Ref.

Specificity

The enzyme from pig liver (microsomes) is highly specific for phospatidate in which the only bond hydrolyzed is the phosphate bond. The following compounds were inactive: diphosphatidyl glycerol, diphosphoinositide and α-glycerophosphate. β-Glycerophosphate was hydrolyzed at 10% the rate of phosphatidate. (1)

The enzyme from chicken liver hydrolyzed phosphatidate (1.00), β-glycerophosphate (0.14), DL-α-glycerophosphate (0.08) and glucose 6-phosphate (0.05). Lecithin was not hydrolyzed. (2)

Michaelis constants

source	substrate	$K_m(M)$	conditions	
Pig liver (microsomes)	phosphatidate (from hens' egg)	2.2×10^{-4}	pH 6.0, maleate, 37°	(1)

Inhibitors

Mg^{2+} and other bivalent metal ions are powerful inhibitors of the enzyme from chicken liver. (2)

References

1. Coleman, R. & Hübscher, G. (1962) BBA, 56, 479.

2. Wagner-Smith, S., Weiss, S. B. & Kennedy, E. P. (1957) JBC,
   228, 915.

5'-NUCLEOTIDASE

(5'-Ribonucleotide phosphohydrolase)

A 5'-ribonucleotide + H_2O = a ribonucleoside + orthophosphate

Ref.

Specificity and Michaelis constants

5'-Nucleotidase hydrolyzes most ribonucleoside 5'-phosphates and deoxyribonucleoside 5'-phosphates. The relative rates of hydrolysis depend on the source of enzyme. [1,2,3,4]

	Bothrops[a] atrox (venom)	Rat[b] liver	Chicken[c] liver
5'-AMP	1.00	1.00	1.0
5'-IMP	0.41	0.27	11.1
5'-UMP	0.36	0.67	1.2
5'-CMP	0.89	0.55	0.67
5'-GMP	0.42	0.26	9.7
5'-dGMP	0.33	-	7.1
5'-dAMP	0.39	0.16	-
5'-dCMP	0.62	-	-
5'-TMP	0.76	-	-
NMN	0.15	-	-
riboflavine phosphate	-	0.16	3.4
5'-XMP	-	-	-
ATP	0	-	0.55
ADP	-	-	0.55
ribose 5-phosphate	0	-	0.22

[a]From reference (4). The following compounds were not hydrolyzed: 3'-AMP, PPi, 5-phosphoribosyl 1-pyrophosphate, p-nitrophenyl phosphate, flavine mononucleotide, mononucleoside 3',5'-diphosphates and higher oligonucleotides.

[b]From reference (3). The following compounds were not hydrolyzed: 2'-AMP and 3'-AMP.

[c]From reference (2). The following compounds were hydrolyzed at very low rates: 2'-AMP, 3'-AMP, 2'-IMP, 3'-IMP, glucose 6-phosphate, β-glycerophosphate and phenylphosphate.

source	substrate	$K_m(M)$	conditions	
Chicken	5'-IMP	8×10^{-4}	pH 6.5, Tris-	(2)
liver	5'-GMP	1.3×10^{-3}	maleate, 37°	
Rat liver	5'-AMP	1.1×10^{-5}	pH 7.5, Tris, 30°	(3)

Inhibitors

The enzyme from chicken liver is inhibited by inosine and guanosine but not by adenosine or hypoxanthine. (2)

The enzyme from rat liver is inhibited by P_i and by several nucleosides. (3)

References

1. Heppel, L. A. (1961) The Enzymes, 5, 49.
2. Itoh, R., Mitsui, A. & Tsushima, K. (1967) BBA, 146, 151.
3. Segal, H. L. & Brenner, B. M. (1960) JBC, 235, 471.
4. Sulkowski, E., Bjork, W. & Laskowski, M., Sr. (1963) JBC, 238, 2477.

3'-NUCLEOTIDASE

(3'-Ribonucleotide phosphohydrolase)

A 3'-ribonucleotide + H_2O =
a ribonucleoside + orthophosphate

Specificity and Michaelis constants

3'-Nucleotidase is highly specific for 3'-nucleotides - a number of other phosphate monoesters tested were inactive (5'-nucleotides, glycerol phosphates, hexose phosphates, pentose phosphate, NAD, ADP). The enzyme possessed no diesterase activity.　　(1)

source	substrate	relative velocity	$K_m(M)$	conditions	
Rye grass	3'-adenylate	1.0	3×10^{-4}		
	3'-inosinate	0.5	-		
	3'-uridylate	0.5	2.5×10^{-3}	pH 7.5,	
	coenzyme-A	0.5	-	Tris, 37°	(2)
	3'-guanylate	0.3	-		
	3'-cytidylate	0.1	2.5×10^{-3}		

Inhibitors

The enzyme is inhibited by PP_i.　　(1)

References

1. Shuster, L. & Kaplan, N. O. (1953) JBC, 201, 535.

2. Shuster, L. & Kaplan, N. O. (1955) Methods in Enzymology, 2, 551.

GLUCOSE-6-PHOSPHATASE

(D-Glucose-6-phosphate phosphohydrolase)

D-Glucose 6-phosphate + H_2O =
D-glucose + orthophosphate

Specificity and Michaelis constants

It is thought that a single enzyme (present in rat liver and kidney microsomes) catalyzes the following reactions with equal facility:

<u>a</u>	D-glucose 6-phosphate + H_2O = glucose + P_i	
<u>b</u>	PP_i + H_2O	= 2 P_i
<u>c</u>	PP_i + glucose	= D-glucose 6-phosphate + P_i (2,6,8)

The enzyme also catalyzes the transfer of the phosphoryl group from nucleoside diphosphates or triphosphates to glucose. Glucose can be replaced by a number of other sugars. None of these reactions requires a divalent ion for activity. (4,7)

source	substrate	reaction	$\frac{V}{(relative)}$	$K_m(M)$	conditions	
Rat liver	glucose 6-phosphate	<u>a</u>	-	4.2×10^{-4}	pH 6.5, caco-dylate, 30^0	(3)
	PP_i	<u>b</u>	-	9.4×10^{-4}	pH 6.1, caco-dylate, 30^0	(3)
	glucose	<u>c</u>	-	$9 \times 10^{-2(a)}$	pH 5.2, acetate, 30^0	(4)
	PP_i	<u>c</u>	1.00	1.77×10^{-3}		
	CTP	<u>c</u>	0.59	3.08×10^{-3}		
	CDP	<u>c</u>	0.56	3.82×10^{-3}	pH 5.2,	
	ADP	<u>c</u>	0.33	1.11×10^{-2}	acetate, 30^0	(4)
	ITP	<u>c</u>	0.29	6.13×10^{-3}	with glucose	
	ATP	<u>c</u>	0.27	4.65×10^{-3}	as acceptor	
	dCTP	<u>c</u>	0.26	2.63×10^{-3}		
	GTP	<u>c</u>	0.26	3.56×10^{-3}		
	GDP	<u>c</u>	0.23	2.67×10^{-3}		

[a] With PP_i or nucleotide as phosphoryl donor.

Inhibitors

source	inhibitor	type	reaction	$K_i(M)$	conditions	
Rat liver	citrate or oxalate	C(glucose 6-phosphate)	$\underline{a}$	6×10^{-3}	pH 4.65-6.5 cacodylate, 30°	(3)
		C(PP$_i$)	$\underline{c}$	6×10^{-3}		
	P$_i$	C(glucose 6-phosphate)	$\underline{a}$	1.96×10^{-2}	pH 6.0, succinate-maleate-Tris, 37°	(5)

Citrate could be replaced only to a limited extent by other tricarboxylic acids. (3)

Glucose and a number of other sugars and sugar analogs inhibit reaction $\underline{a}$ (NC(glucose 6-phosphate)). (5,7)

References

1. Byrne, W. L. (1961) The Enzymes, 5, 73.

2. Stetten, M. R. & Taft, H. L. (1964) JBC, 239, 4041.

3. Nordlie, R. C. & Lygre, D. G. (1966) JBC, 241, 3136.

4. Nordlie, R. C. & Arion, W. J. (1965) JBC, 240, 2155.

5. Hass, L. F. & Byrne, W. L. (1960) JACS, 82, 947.

6. Nordlie, R. C. & Arion, W. J. (1964) JBC, 239, 1680.

7. Arion, W. J. & Nordlie, R. C. (1964) JBC, 239, 2752.

8. Nordlie, R. C. & Soodsma, J. F. (1966) JBC, 241, 1719.

HEXOSEDIPHOSPHATASE

(D-Fructose-1,6-diphosphate 1-phosphohydrolase)

D-Fructose 1,6-diphosphate + H_2O =
D-fructose 6-phosphate + orthophosphate

Ref.

Molecular weight

source	value	conditions	
Rabbit liver	130,000[2] (a)	sucrose gradient	(2,3)
Candidia utilis	100,000[2]	sucrose gradient	(4,5,8)

(a) Dissociation occurs in the presence of AMP and can be prevented by FDP.

Specific activity

Rabbit liver	(930 x)	22.7	FDP (pH 9.1, glycine, 22°)	(2,3)
C. utilis	(830 x)	83	FDP (pH 9.5, glycine, room temperature)	(4)

Specificity and Michaelis constants

The enzyme is highly specific for FDP. Thus, that from rabbit liver does not attack D-glucose 6-phosphate, D-glucose 1-phosphate, D-fructose 1-phosphate, D-fructose 6-phosphate, D-ribose 5-phosphate, D-ribulose 5-phosphate, D-xylulose 5-phosphate, D-ribulose 1,5-diphosphate, seduheptulose 1-phosphate and seduheptulose 7-phosphate. SDP is hydrolyzed at about 60% the rate of FDP (2,3). The enzyme from rat liver also hydro- lyses SDP but that from C. utilis (4) or spinach leaf (7) is absolutely specific for FDP.

source	substrate	$\frac{V}{(relative)}$	$K_m(M)$	conditions	
Rat liver	FDP	1.00	1.2×10^{-5}	pH 9.0, trietha- nolamine, 37°	(10)
	SDP	1.00	3×10^{-4}		
	FDP	-	$1-3 \times 10^{-6}$	pH 7.3, Tris.	(6)
Rabbit liver	FDP	-	4.3×10^{-6} (a)	pH 9.1, glycine, 22°	(2,9)
	FDP	-	2.3×10^{-6} (b)		
	Mg^{2+}	-	4×10^{-4}		
	Mn^{2+}	-	1.2×10^{-4}		
C. utilis	FDP	-	1×10^{-5}	pH 9.5, glycine, room temperature	(4)
Spinach leaves	FDP	-	3×10^{-4}	pH 8.8, Tris.	(7)

(a) In the presence of Mg^{2+}
(b) In the presence of Mn^{2+}

Ref.

Inhibitors

source	inhibitor	type	K_i(M)	conditions	
Rat liver	AMP	NC(FDP)	1.1×10^{-4}	} pH 7.3, Tris, $30°$	(6)
	dAMP	NC(FDP)	1.3×10^{-4}		
	SDP	C(FDP)	4×10^{-4}	pH 9.0, triethanolamine, $37°$	(10)
Rabbit liver	SDP	C(FDP)	1.7×10^{-4}	pH 9.1, glycine, $22°$	(9)

AMP (or dAMP), which is inhibitory, interacts with the enzyme in a co-operative manner. The effect of AMP is highly specific and the following compounds are inactive: 2'-AMP, 3'-AMP, cyclic 3',5'-AMP, UMP, GMP, CMP, IMP, ATP, GTP, UTP, CTP, UDP, GDP, CDP, NAD, PP_i, adenine, ribose 5-phosphate, adenosine, guanosine, uridine and cytidine. (6)

The enzyme from C. utilis is also specifically inhibited by AMP. (5)

The inhibitory effect of AMP can be abolished by desensitization. (5,6)

Abbreviations

FDP fructose 1,6-diphosphate
SDP sedoheptulose 1,7-diphosphate

References

1. Stadtman, T. C. (1961) The Enzymes, 5, 63.
2. Pontremoli, S. (1966) Methods in Enzymology, 9, 625.
3. Pontremoli, S., Traniello, S., Luppis, B. & Wood, W. A. (1965) JBC, 240, 3459.
4. Rosen, O. M., Rosen, S. M. & Horecker, B. L. (1965) ABB, 112, 411.
5. Rosen, O. M. & Rosen, S. M. (1966) PNAS, 55, 1156.
6. Taketa, K. & Pogell, B. M. (1965) JBC, 240, 651.
7. Racker, E. (1962) Methods in Enzymology, 5, 272.
8. Rosen, O. M., Copeland, P. L. & Rosen, S. M. (1967) JBC, 242, 2760.
9. Pontremoli, S., Luppis, B., Wood, W. A., Traniello, S. & Horecker, B. L. (1965) JBC, 240, 3464.
10. Bonsignore, A., Mangiarotti, G., Mangiarotti, M. A., de Flora, A. & Pontremoli, S. (1963) JBC, 238, 3151.

TREHALOSEPHOSPHATASE

(Trehalose-6-phosphate phosphohydrolase)

Trehalose 6-phosphate + H_2O = trehalose + P_i

Ref.

Specificity

The enzyme (Phormia regina) is highly specific. Thus mannose

6-phosphate, fructose 6-phosphate, ribose 5-phosphate, fructose 1,6-

diphosphate, glucose 1-phosphate, ATP, FMN, uridylate, 3-adenylate,

5-adenylate and PP_i are not cleaved. Glucose 6-phosphate is hydro-

lyzed at 8% the rate of trehalose 6-phosphate.   (1)

Michaelis constants

source	substrate	$K_m(M)$	conditions	
P. regina	trehalose 6-phosphate	1.4×10^{-3}	pH 7.2, Tris, $32°$	(2)

References

1. Friedman, S. (1966) Methods in Enzymology, 8, 372.

2. Friedman, S. (1960) ABB, 88, 339.

DIPHOSPHOGLYCERATE PHOSPHATASE

(2,3-Diphospho-D-glycerate 2-phosphohydrolase)

2,3-Diphospho-D-glycerate + H_2O =

3-phospho-D-glycerate + orthophosphate

Ref.

Specificity

The enzyme is highly specific; the rabbit muscle enzyme does not hydrolyze ATP, β-glycerophosphate, 3-phospho-D-glycerate, 2-phospho-D-glycerate or fructose 1,6-diphosphate. The yeast enzyme exhibits trace activities with the last three of these compounds. (1,2)

Michaelis constants

source	substrate	$K_m(M)$	conditions	
Yeast	2,3-diphospho-D-glycerate	3.3×10^{-4}	pH 5.0, acetate, 38°	(1,2)
Chicken breast muscle	2,3-diphospho-D-glycerate	1.8×10^{-3}	pH 7.0, Tris, 38°	(1,2)

References

1. Grisolia, S. (1962) Methods in Enzymology, 5, 243.
2. Joyce, B. K. & Grisolia, S. (1958) JBC, 233, 350.

HISTIDINOLPHOSPHATASE

(L-Histidinolphosphate phosphohydrolase)

L-Histidinol phosphate + H_2O =

L-histidinol + orthophosphate

Specificity

The phosphatase from Neurospora crassa is highly specific for L-histidinol phosphate which could be replaced only to a very limited extent by ethanolamine phosphate, imidazoleglycerol phosphate, imidazoleacetol phosphate or ribose 5-phosphate. (1)

Michaelis constants

source	substrate	$K_m(M)$	conditions	
N. crassa	L-histidinol phosphate	4.2×10^{-3}	pH 9.0, diethanol-amine, $30°$	(1)

Inhibitors

High concentrations of L-histidinol phosphate are inhibitory. (1)

References

1. Ames, B. N. (1957) JBC, 226, 583.

PHOSPHORYLASE PHOSPHATASE

(Phosphorylase phosphohydrolase)

$$\text{Phosphorylase a} + 4\ H_2O = 2\ \text{phosphorylase b} + 4\ P_i$$

Ref.

Molecular weight

source	value	conditions	
Rabbit muscle	50,000	sucrose gradient	(1)

Specificity

The enzyme (rabbit muscle) is active on phosphorylase a and phosphopeptides thereof but no other substrate for the enzyme has been found. (1)

Michaelis constants

source	substrate	$K_m(M)$	conditions	
Rabbit muscle	phosphorylase a	$\sim 3 \times 10^{-6}$	pH 7.4, Tris, 30°	(1)

Inhibitors

ATP inhibits but glucose 6-phosphate activates the rabbit muscle enzyme. (1)

References

1. Hurd, S. S., Novoa, W. B., Hickenbottom, J. P. & Fischer, E. H. (1966) Methods in Enzymology, 8, 546.

PHOSPHOGLYCOLLATE PHOSPHATASE

(Phosphoglycollate phosphohydrolase)

$$\text{Phosphoglycollate} + H_2O = \text{glycollate} + P_i$$

Specificity

The enzyme (tobacco leaf) is highly specific and the following were not hydrolyzed: 2-phosphoglycerate, 3-phosphoglycerate, glucose 6-phosphate, glucose 1-phosphate, PP_i, o-nitrophenyl phosphate, dihydroxyacetone phosphate, phosphopyruvate, phosphoglycolaldehyde, β-glycerophosphate, O-phosphoryl serine, propanediol phosphate, phosphocholine, O-phosphoethanolamine, acetyl phosphate, adenosine 5-phosphate, guanylate, cytidylate, ADP, ATP or phenolphthalein diphosphate. Mg^{2+} - required for maximum activity - could be replaced by Mn^{2+}, Co^{2+}, Fe^{3+} or Ni^{2+}. (1)

Michaelis constants

source	substrate	K_m(M)	conditions
Tobacco leaf	phosphoglycollate	2.5×10^{-3}	pH 6.3, Tris- (1) acetate, $30°$

References

1. Richardson, K. E. & Tolbert, N. E. (1961) JBC, 236, 1285.

GLYCEROL-2-PHOSPHATASE

(2-Phosphoglycerol phosphohydrolase)

2-Phosphoglycerol + H_2O = glycerol + P_i

Ref.

Molecular weight

source	value	conditions	
Yeast	$S_{20,w} = 1.4$	0.1 M NaCl	(2)

Specific activity

Yeast		500	2-phosphoglycerol (pH 6.5)	(2)
Wheat germ (3600 x)		200	2-phosphoglycerol (pH 5.7, acetate, 37°)	(3)

Specificity

The enzyme (yeast) hydrolyzes 2-phosphoglycerol (1.00), l-propanediol phosphate (0.76), phenyl phosphate (0.01), 3-phosphoglycerol (0.01), and PP_i (0.01), but not the following: 3-phosphoglycerate, glucose 1-phosphate, glucose 6-phosphate, ribose 5-phosphate, riboflavin 5-phosphate, yeast adenylate (2' + 3'), yeast cytidylate (2' + 3'), 5'-adenylate, ATP or diphenyl phosphate. (1)

The wheat germ enzyme is rather less specific and 3-phosphoglycerate, 2-phosphoglycerate, 2,3-diphosphoglycerate, ATP and 2-phosphoglycerol were attacked at about the same rate (3). The mung bean enzyme is specific for 2-phosphoglycerol. This enzyme requires ferric ions for full activity. (3)

Michaelis constants

source	substrate	$K_m(M)$	conditions	
Mung bean	2-phosphoglycerol	6.2×10^{-3}	pH 8.5, veronal, 49°	(3)

References

1. Schmidt, G. (1961) The Enzymes, 5, 47.

2. Tsuboi, K. K., Wiener, G. & Hudson, P. B. (1957) JBC, 224, 621.

3. Appaji Rao, N. & Vaidyanathan, C. S. (1966) Methods in Enzymology, 9, 642.

N-ACYLNEURAMINATE-9-PHOSPHATASE

(N-Acylneuraminate-9-phosphate phosphohydrolase)

N-Acylneuraminate 9-phosphate + H_2O = N-acylneuraminate + P_i

Ref.

Specificity

The enzyme (human erythrocytes) was inactive towards UTP, UDP, UMP, UDPglucose, α-glycerophosphate, glycerate 2-phosphate, glycerate 3-phosphate, phosphoenolpyruvate, dihydroxyacetone phosphate, p-nitrophenylphosphate, fructose 1-phosphate, galactose 1-phosphate, fructose 6-phosphate, erythrose 4-phosphate, mannose 6-phosphate, galactose 6-phosphate, glucose 1-phosphate, galactosamine 6-phosphate, glucose 6-phosphate, N-acetylglucosamine 6-phosphate, N-acetylmannosamine 6-phosphate, glucosamine 6-phosphate or PP_i.   (1)

Michaelis constants

source	substrate	K_m(M)	conditions	
Human erythrocytes	N-acetylneuraminate 9-phosphate	1.0×10^{-3}	pH 7, imidazole, 37°	(1)

References

1. Jourdian, G. W., Swanson, A., Watson, D. & Roseman, S. (1966) Methods in Enzymology, 8, 205.

PHOSPHODIESTERASE

(Orthophosphoric diester phosphohydrolase)

A phosphoric diester + H_2O = a phosphoric monoester + an alcohol

Ref.

Specificity and Michaelis constants

Enzyme 3.1.4.1 includes two activities: phosphodiesterase I and phosphodiesterase II. Phosphodiesterase I (e.g. from Crotalus adamanteus venom and hog kidney) attacks both polyribonucleotides and oligodeoxyribonucleotides liberating nucleoside 5'-phosphates in a stepwise manner starting at the tail end where it requires a free 3'-OH group. Phosphodiesterase II (e.g. from calf spleen) attacks both polyribonucleotides and oligodeoxyribonucleotides liberating 3'-phosphates in a stepwise manner starting preferentially at that head end which carries a free 5'-OH group. Both enzymes are therefore exonucleases. They are nonspecific with respect not only to the nature of the base but also the sugar moiety and, further, they both attack a wide variety of synthetic substrates.　(1,2)

source	substrate	specific activity	K_m(M)	conditions
Crotalus adamanteus[a] (venom) (Phosphodiesterase I)	p-nitrophenyl pT	610	5.0×10^{-4}	
	p-nitrophenyl pU	21.2	5.4×10^{-4}	
	pTpT	114	2.1×10^{-4}	
	TpT (3',5' or 5',5' diester)	4.6	5.3×10^{-4}	pH 8.9, Tris, $37°$ (2,3)
	methyl p-nitrophenyl phosphate	11.9	1.2×10^{-2}	
	benzyl p-nitrophenyl phosphate	5.3	6.8×10^{-3}	
	di-p-nitrophenyl pT	0.6	7.7×10^{-4}	
	p-nitrophenyl pT	329	4.9×10^{-4}	pH 8.0, Tris, $37°$ (2,3)
	3'-O-acetyl p-nitrophenyl pT	121	1.5×10^{-4}	

Specificity and Michaelis constants contd.   Ref.

source	substrate	specific activity	K_m(M)	conditions
Calf spleen (Phospho- diesterase II)	p-nitrophenyl thymidine-3'- phosphate	34	5 x 10^{-3}	
	ApUp	60	-	
	ApApUp	60	-	pH 5.7, ammonium acetate, 37°
	TpTp	45	-	(2,4)
	TpT	43	-	
	pTpTpT	low	-	
	Cyclo (Tp)$_2$	low	-	
	Poly A	0.7	-	

[a] Similar results were obtained with the enzyme from hog kidney.

Abbreviations

T, U, A   Thymidine, uridine and adenosine, respectively (esterified phosphoric acid is indicated by a p which is placed at the left of T etc. if the phosphoric acid is linked to the 5'-hydroxyl of the nucleoside and to the right if it is on the 3'-hydroxyl).

References

1. Khorana, H. G. (1961) The Enzymes, 5, 86.
2. Razzell, W. E. (1963) Methods in Enzymology, 6, 236.
3. Razzell, W. E. & Khorana, H. G. (1959) JBC, 234, 2105.
4. Razzell, W. E. & Khorana, H. G. (1961) JBC, 236, 1144.

GLYCEROPHOSPHORYLCHOLINE DIESTERASE

(L-3-Glycerylphosphorylcholine glycerophosphohydrolase)

L-3-Glycerylphosphorylcholine + H_2O =

choline + glycerol 1-phosphate

Ref.

Specificity

Glycerophosphorylcholine diesterase is highly specific for GPC: the only other diester hydrolyzed is GPE. Thus, the enzyme from Serratia plymuthicum was inactive with purified egg lecithin, lysolecithin, animal lecithin, sphingomyelin, dipalmitoyl-lecithin dimyristoyllecithin and several noncholine containing esters such as diphenyl phosphate, yeast RNA and polynucleotides.   (1,2)

The enzyme from rat liver was inactive with phosphorylcholine, lysolecithin and lecithin.   (3)

Michaelis constants

source	substrate	relative velocity	$K_m(M)$	conditions	
S. plymuthicum	GPC	1	1.2×10^{-3}	pH 8.85, glycylglycine, 25-27°	(1,2)
	GPE	1	2.5×10^{-3}		

Inhibitors

source	inhibitor	type	$K_i(M)$	conditions	
S. plymuthicum	GPE	C(GPC)	2.4×10^{-3}	pH 8.85, glycylglycine 25-27°	(1,2)
	GPC	C(GPE)	1.8×10^{-3}		

Abbreviations

GPC   L-3-glycerylphosphorylcholine
GPE   L-3-glycerylphosphorylethanolamine

References

1. Hayaishi, O. (1955) Methods in Enzymology, 1, 668.
2. Hayaishi, O. & Kornberg, A. (1954) JBC, 206, 647.
3. Dawson, R. M. C. (1956) BJ, 62, 689.

PHOSPHOLIPASE C

(Phosphatidylcholine cholinephosphohydrolase)

A phosphatidylcholine + H_2O =

a 1,2-diglyceride + choline phosphate

Ref.

Molecular weight

source	value	conditions	
Clostridium perfringens	$\sim 100,000$	G100 Sephadex, pH 7.6	(1)

Specificity

The enzyme (C. welchii) attacks all the major types of phospha-
tides (lecithins, sphingomyelins and kephalins) of red cell membranes. (2)

A kinetic analysis of the mechanism of haemolysis of horse, human
and rabbit erythrocytes by phospholipase C from C. perfringens is
presented in reference (3).

The enzyme requires Ca^{2+} for activity. (2,3)

References

1. Ikezawa, H., Yamamoto, A. & Murata, R. (1964) J. Biochem. (Tokyo),
   56, 480.

2. de Gier, J., de Haas, G. H. & van Deenen, L. L. M. (1961) BJ,
   81, 33P.

3. Ikezawa, H. & Murata, R. (1964) J. Biochem. (Tokyo), 55, 217.

PHOSPHOLIPASE D

(Phosphatidylcholine phosphatidohydrolase)

A phosphatidylcholine + H_2O = choline + a phosphatidate

Ref.

Specificity

Phospholipase D catalyzes the hydrolytic cleavage of the terminal phosphate diester bond of glycerophosphatides containing choline, ethanolamine, serine or glycerol with the formation of phosphatidate. Naturally occurring lecithins and a number of synthetic α-lecithins are hydrolyzed by the enzyme but β-lecithins and lysolecithin are almost inactive. The enzyme also catalyzes transphosphatidylation reactions by which the phosphatidyl group of phosphatidylcholine is transferred to one of the following alcohols: methanol, ethanol, 2-propanol, glycerol, ethanolamine or serine. Inositol, threonine, glucose and DL-glycerol 1-phosphate are inactive as acceptors. (1,2)

Anionic amphipathic substances such as dodecyl sulphate, phosphatidate, triphosphoinositide and monocetyl phosphosphate are potent activators of the enzyme (Savoy cabbage). (3)

Inhibitors

The phospholipase D of Savoy cabbage is inhibited by cationic amphipathic substances (e.g. cetyltrimethylammonium bromide). (3)

References

1. Hanahan, D. J. (1961) **Biochemists'** Handbook p267.

2. Yang, S. F., Freer, S. & Benson, A. A. (1967) JBC, 242, 477.

3. Dawson, R. M. C. & Hemington, N. (1967) BJ, 102, 76.

DEOXYRIBONUCLEASE

(Deoxyribonucleate oligonucleotidohydrolase)

DNA + (n - 1) H_2O = n oligodeoxyribonucleotides

Molecular weight

source	value	conditions	
Beef	62,000	various	(3,4)
pancreas	40,000	pH 7.0	(5)

Specificity

Pancreatic deoxyribonuclease hydrolyzes highly polymerized native or denatured DNA producing complex mixtures of many components varying from mononucleotides to hepta- or octanucleotides. Approximately 25% of all available internucleotide linkages can be hydrolyzed by the enzyme. The products terminate in 5'-phosphate. The linkage between pPu. pPy is particularly susceptible towards deoxyribonuclease. The enzyme does not hydrolyze RNA. (1,3,6)

Deoxyribonuclease attacks synthetic oligonucleotides. Thus, TpTpTpTpT is attacked to produce TpT plus pTpTpT and TpTpT plus pTpT whereas TpTpTpTpTp is attacked to produce pTp plus TpTpTpT. The compound CpApT is not attacked in spite of the presence of a pPu. pPy linkage. (1,7)

Deoxyribonuclease has also been prepared from Escherichia coli, calf spleen, yeast and Streptococcus sp. (3,8)

Abbreviations

Pu, Py, T, C, A — purine nucleoside, pyrimidine nucleoside, thymidine, cytidine and adenosine, respectively (esterified phosphoric acid is indicated by a p which is placed at the left of T etc. if the phosphoric acid is linked to the 5'-hydroxyl of the nucleoside and to the right if it is on the 3'-hydroxy).

References

1. Laskowski, M. Sr. (1961) The Enzymes, 5, 125.
2. Kurnick, N. B. (1962) Methods of Biochemical Analysis, 9, 1.
3. McDonald, M. R. (1955) Methods in Enzymology, 2, 438.
4. Gehrmann, G. & Okada, S. (1957) BBA, 23, 621.
5. Polson, A. (1956) BBA, 22, 61.
6. Privat de Garilhe, M. & Laskowski, M. (1955) JBC, 215, 269.
7. Khorana, H. G. (1959) J. Cellular Comp. Physiol, 54, Suppl. 1, 1.
8. Weissbach, A. & Korn, D. (1963) JBC, 238, 3383.

DEOXYRIBONUCLEASE II

(Deoxyribonucleate 3'-nucleotidohydrolase)

Forms 3'-nucleotides from DNA

Molecular weight

source	value	conditions	
Hog spleen	38,000	various	(3)

Specificity

Deoxyribonuclease II from calf spleen hydrolyzes DNA rapidly to polynucleotides. This first phase of the reaction is followed by a slower process the end point of which has not been defined accurately but which is thought to approach about 25 - 30% of the linkages broken. Deoxyribonuclease II produces more mononucleotides, considerably less dinucleotides and considerably more of the higher oligonucleotides than deoxyribonuclease I (3.1.4.5). All the reaction products are terminated in 3'-phosphate. (1,2)

Deoxyribonuclease from hog spleen also attacks Ca (bis-(p-nitrophenyl) phosphate)$_2$ and the p-nitrophenylesters of thymidine-, deoxyguanosine- and deoxycytidine-3'-phosphates. The enzyme is inactive with RNA. (1,4)

References

1. Laskowski, M. Sr. (1961) The Enzymes, 5, 139.

2. Koerner, J. F. & Sinsheimer, R. L. (1957) JBC, 228, 1039, 1049.

3. Bernardi, G., Appella, E. & Zito, R. (1965) B, 4, 1725.

4. Bernardi, G. & Griffe, M. (1964) B, 3, 1419.

MICROCOCCAL NUCLEASE

(Ribonucleate (deoxyribonucleate) 3'-nucleotidohydrolase)

Attacks RNA and DNA, forming 3'-nucleotides;

DNA is attacked with preference for the

adenine-thymine nucleotide pair

Ref.

Molecular weight

source	value	conditions	
Staphylococcus aureus	16,807	sequence studies	(2)
Staphylococcus pyogenes	11-12,000	pH 7.5	(6)

Specificity and Michaelis constants

The nuclease is capable of attacking both DNA and RNA forming
3'-nucleotides. DNA is attacked with preference for the adenine-thymine
nucleotide pair. The enzyme is inactive towards pyrimidine or purine
cyclic mononucleotides but synthetic poly-U and poly-C are attacked
producing exclusively mono- and dinucleotides. (1)

source	substrate	$\frac{V}{(\text{relative})}$	$K_m(M)$	conditions	
S. pyogenes	pTpTpT	1.00	5.8×10^{-5} [a]	pH 8.6, 36°	(5)
	pTpTpT	0.47	1.18×10^{-5} [b]		
	pTpTpTpT	0.43	4.5×10^{-6} [b]		
	pTpTpTpTpT	2.12	1.45×10^{-4} [b]		
	thymus DNA	1.00	36.1 [c]	pH 8.6, 36°	(5)
	wheat germ DNA	0.95	38.3 [c]		
	S. pyogenes DNA	0.45	12.0 [c]		

[a] $MgCl_2 = 1 \times 10^{-3}M$
[b] $CaCl_2 = 1 \times 10^{-3}M$
[c] 10^{-12} g ml^{-1}

Inhibitors Ref.

source	inhibitor[a]	K_i (M)	conditions	
S. aureus	thymidine 3', 5'-diphosphate	5.4×10^{-7}		
	5'-TMP	1.9×10^{-5}		
	5'-AMP	4.6×10^{-5}		
	3'-AMP	5.1×10^{-4}	pH 8.8, Tris.	(3,4)
	2'-AMP	5.1×10^{-4}		
	5'-CMP	4.2×10^{-4}		
	5'-GMP	1.1×10^{-3}		

[a]Competitive.

Abbreviations

T   thymidine (esterified phosphoric acid is indicated by a p which is placed at the left of T if the phosphoric acid is linked to the 5'-hydroxyl of the nucleoside and to the right if it is on the 3'-hydroxyl).

References

1. Laskowski, M. (1961) The Enzymes, 5, 142.

2. Taniuchi, H., Anfinsen, C. B. & Sodja, A. (1967) JBC, 242, 4752.

3. Cuatrecasas, P., Fuchs, S. & Anfinsen, C. B. (1967) JBC, 242, 4759.

4. Cuatrecasas, P., Fuchs, S. & Anfinsen, C. B. (1967) JBC, 242, 3063.

5. de Meuron-Landholt, M. & de Carille, M. P. (1964) BBA, 91, 433.

6. Anfinsen, C. B., Rumley, M. K. & Taniuchi, H. (1963) Acta Chem. Scand., 17, S270.

AZOTOBACTER NUCLEASE

(Ribonucleate (deoxyribonucleate) 5'-nucleotidohydrolase)

Attacks RNA and DNA, forming 5'-nucleotides

Ref.

Specificity

Azotobacter nuclease is an endonuclease which hydrolyzes both
RNA and DNA with the formation of oligonucleotides with 5'-phospho-
monoester end groups. Mononucleotide formation is slight. The
enzyme also hydrolyzes polyadenylate and, to a lesser extent, polyuridylate but not polycytidylate or polyguanylate. The rate of
hydrolysis of short chain oligonucleotides is much slower than that
of long chain oligonucleotides. Adenylate pentanucleotide is
cleaved to a tri- and a dinucleotide and adenylate tetranucleotide -
at a much slower rate - to two dinucleotides. Terminal phospho-
diester bonds are very resistant. (1)

References

1. Stevens, A. & Hilmoe, R. J. (1960) JBC, 235, 3016, 3023.

SERINEPHOSPHORYLETHANOLAMINE PHOSPHODIESTERASE

(Serinephosphorylethanolamine diester phosphohydrolase)

Serinephosphorylethanolamine + H_2O = ethanolamine phosphate + serine

Ref.

Specificity and Michaelis constants

source	substrate	relative velocity	$K_m(M)$	conditions
Chicken kidney	L-serine ethanolamine phosphate	1.00	3.6×10^{-3}	
	D-serine ethanolamine phosphate	1.31	2.2×10^{-3}	
	L-threonine ethanolamine phosphate	0.70	8.8×10^{-3}	pH 9.5, glycine, (1) 25°
	L-lombricine	0.58	-	
	D-lombricine	0.37	-	
	bis-ethanolamine phosphate	0.37	-	
	bis-L-serine phosphate	0.04	-	
	bis-(p-nitrophenyl) phosphate	0.08	-	

The following compounds were not hydrolysed: ATP, ADP, ethanolamine phosphate, serine phosphate, sodium β-glycerophosphate, cytidine diphosphate ethanolamine and PP_i. (1)

Inhibitors

Both of the products inhibit: that by L-serine is of the non-competitive type and that by ethanolamine phosphate of the mixed type. (1)

References

1. Hagerman, D. D., Rosenberg, H., Ennor, A. H., Schiff, P. & Inoue, S. (1965) JBC, 240, 1108.

DEOXYRIBONUCLEASE

(Deoxyribonucleate 5'-nucleotidohydrolase)

Forms 5'-nucleotides from DNA

Molecular weight

source	value	conditions	
Escherichia coli	110,000	pH 6.8	(1)

Specificity and kinetic constants

source	substrate	$V^{(a)}$	$K_m(M)$	conditions	
E. coli	p-nitrophenyl-pT	2.3	6.0×10^{-3}		
	pTpT	8.0	3.4×10^{-4}		
	pTpTpT	43.8	1.0×10^{-4}		
	TpTpT	41.6	9.0×10^{-5}	pH 9.2,	
	pTpTpTpT	82.3	1.5×10^{-4}	glycine,	(2)
	native E. coli DNA	4.3	1.7×10^{-10}	37°	
	denatured E. coli DNA	1.5	2.1×10^{-10}		
	dAT copolymer	59.0	1.9×10^{-10}		

(a) Mononucleotide formed per hour per mg enzyme protein.

The enzyme quantitatively degrades polydeoxyribonucleotides to their component 5'-nucleotides. Its initial site of attack is at the 3'-hydroxyl end of the polydeoxyribonucleotide chain and hydrolysis at the 5'-phosphoryl or 5'-hydroxyl end does not occur. It is without activity on oligonucleotides bearing 3'-phosphomonoester groups and on RNA.

The enzyme is closely associated physically with DNA polymerase (2.7.7.7) from which it has not been separated. (1,2)

Abbreviations

dAT copolymer	copolymer of deoxyadenylate and thymidylate
(pT)n	thymidine oligonucleotide. The phosphate group is designated by a p: when placed to the right of T, the phosphate is esterified at C-3' of the ribose moiety and when placed to the left, the phosphate is esterified at C-5' of the ribose moiety.

References

1. Richardson, C. C., Schildkraut, C. L., Aposhian, H. V. & Kornberg, A. (1964) JBC, 239, 222.
2. Lehman, I. R. & Richardson, C. C. (1964) JBC, 239, 233.

<u>3',5'-CYCLIC NUCLEOTIDE PHOSPHODIESTERASE</u>

(N-Ribosyl (deoxyribosyl)-purine-3',5'-cyclic phosphate

N-ribosyl (deoxyribosyl)-purine 5'-phosphate phosphohydrolase)

Adenosine-3',5'-cyclic phosphate + H$_2$O = 5'-AMP

<u>Ref.</u>

Specificity and Michaelis constants

The phosphodiesterase (dog heart) is specific for 3',5'-cyclic nucleotides with purine bases: 3',5'-cyclic nucleotides with pyrimidine bases, 2',3'-cyclic nucleotides, polyadenylate, polyuridylate, DNA, RNA or 5'-AMP were all inactive.

(1)

source	substrate	relative velocity	K_m(M)	conditions	
Dog heart	adenosine-3',5'-cyclic phosphate	1.0	4.9 x 10^{-4}		
	deoxyadenosine-3',5'-cyclic phosphate	1.3	4.7 x 10^{-4}	pH 8.6, Tris, 37°	(1)
	inosine-3',5'-cyclic phosphate	0.6	-		
	guanosine-3',5'-cyclic phosphate	0.33	-		

Inhibitors

source	inhibitor	type	K_i(M)	conditions	
Dog heart	caffeine	NC(adenosine-3',5'-cyclic phosphate)	5.0 x 10^{-2}	pH 8.6, Tris, 37°	(1)

References

1. Nair, K. G. (1966) <u>B</u>, <u>5</u>, 150.

2',3'-CYCLIC NUCLEOTIDE PHOSPHODIESTERASE

(N-Ribosyl-purine (pyrimidine)-2',3'-cyclic phosphate

N-ribosyl-purine (pyrimidine)- 3'-phosphate phosphohydrolase)

Uridine-2',3'-cyclic phosphate + H_2O = 3'-UMP

Ref.

Molecular weight

source	value	conditions	
Escherichia coli	68,000	sucrose gradient	(1)

Specificity and Michaelis constants

The phosphodiesterase from E. coli also possesses 3'-nucleotidase
activity (3.1.3.6). Thus the enzyme attacks 2,3'-cyclic nucleotides
to produce nucleosides and orthophosphate as the final products. It
is thought that both activities reside on the same protein molecule but
that separate active sites are involved. The 3'-nucleotidase activity
is the slower of the two processes. (1,2)

The enzyme is highly specific for 2,3'-cyclic ribonucleotides and
it possesses little or no activity towards ribonucleoside 2'-phosphates,
ribonucleoside 5'-phosphates, p-nitrophenylphosphate, β-glycerophosphate, fructose 1,6-diphosphate, NMN, ADP, UDP, ATP, UTP, p-nitrophenyl-
5'-UMP, E. coli RNA or spongouridine 3'-phosphate. Ribonucleoside 3'-
phosphates were hydrolyzed as follows: 3'-UMP (1.00), 3'-AMP (0.76)
and 3'-CMP (0.86). (2)

The enzyme requires Co^{2+} specifically: Mg^{2+}, Mn^{2+}, Ba^{2+} and Ca^{2+}
had little effect and Zn^{2+} and Cu^{2+} were inhibitory. (1)

source	substrate	V (relative)	$K_m(M)$	conditions	
E. coli	uridine-2',3'-cyclic phosphate	1.00	5.3×10^{-5}		
	adenosine-2',3'-cyclic phosphate	0.56	5.0×10^{-5}		
	guanosine-2',3'-cyclic phosphate	0.39	3.0×10^{-5}	pH 5.7, acetate, 37°	(2)
	cytidine-2',3'-cyclic phosphate	0.40	3.2×10^{-5}		
	di-p-nitrophenyl phosphate	0.62	2.8×10^{-4}		

References

1. Anraku, Y. (1966) in Procedures in Nucleic Acid Research (Eds. Cantoni,
   G. L. & Davies, D. R.) Harper & Row: New York. p. 130.
2. Anraku, Y. (1964) JBC, 239, 3412, 3420.

dGTPase

(dGTP triphosphohydrolase)

$$dGTP + H_2O = \text{deoxyguanosine} + \text{triphosphate}$$

Specificity and Michaelis constants

source	substrate	$\dfrac{V}{\text{(relative)}}$	$K_m(M)$	conditions	
Escherichia coli	dGTP	1.00	2.5×10^{-6}	pH 8.5, gly-	(1)
	GTP	0.39	1.5×10^{-4}	cine, 37°	

The enzyme was inactive with the deoxynucleoside triphosphates of adenine, uracil, cytosine and thymine and GDP.   (1)

Inhibitors

source	inhibitor	type	$K_i(M)$	conditions	
E. coli	GTP	C(dGTP)	1.0×10^{-4}	pH 8.5, glycine, 37°	(1)

References

1. Kornberg, S. R., Lehman, I. R., Bessman, M. J., Simms, E. S. & Kornberg, A. (1958) JBC, 233, 159.

ARYLSULPHATASE

(Aryl-sulphate sulphohydrolase)

A phenol sulphate + H_2O = a phenol + sulphate

Ref.

Molecular weight

source	value		conditions	
Ox liver (sulphatase A)[a]	411,000	[16]	pH 5.0	(2,3,4)
	107,000	[4]	pH 7.5	(2,3,4)
Aerobacter aerogenes	41,000		pH 7.5	(7)

[a]There are three sulphatases in ox liver (sulphatases A, B and C) which can be differentiated by their kinetic properties. Only sulphatase A has been purified (6,8).

Specific activity

Ox liver (sulphatase A; 7000 x) 140 NCS (pH 5.6, 37°) (4)
A. aerogenes   73[a] NPS (pH 7.1, Tris, 38°) (7)

[a]A maximum figure of 125 was obtained.

Specificity and kinetic constants

Arylsulphatase hydrolyzes a variety of simple arylsulphates.

source		substrate	relative velocity	$K_m(M)$	conditions	
Ox liver	A	NCS	1.00	8×10^{-4}	pH 4.9, ace-	(5)
		NPS	0.05	4×10^{-2}	tate, 37°	
	B	NCS	1	7×10^{-2}	pH 5.7, ace-	(6)
		NPS	<0.002	2.5×10^{-2}	tate, 37°	
	C	NCS	1.00	8×10^{-3}	pH 8.0,	(8)
		NPS	2.00	2×10^{-3}	Tris, 37°	
Aspergillus oryzae		NCS	1.00	3.5×10^{-4}	pH 6.0, ace-	(10)
		NPS	2.00	1.7×10^{-4}	tate, 37°	
Alcaligenes metalcaligenes		NCS	1.00	2.2×10^{-4}	pH 8.8, gly-	(9)
		NPS	5.00	4.7×10^{-4}	cine, 37.5°	

Inhibitors   Ref.

source	inhibitor	type	K_i (M)	conditions	
Ox liver A	sulphate sulphite	}	7×10^{-4} 2×10^{-6} }	pH 4.9, ace- tate, 37°	(5)
B	sulphate sulphite	} C(NCS)	7×10^{-2} 5×10^{-4} }	pH 5.7, ace- tate, 37°	(6)
C	sulphate sulphite	}	∞ 1×10^{-4} }	pH 8.0, Tris, 37°	(8)

The enzymes from A. oryzae and A. metalcaligenes are not inhibited by sulphate.   (8,9,10)

Light absorption data

NP[a] ε, (420 mμ) = 6,750 $M^{-1}cm^{-1}$ (pH 7.1)   (4)

_____

[a] One of the products of the hydrolysis of NPS.

Abbreviations

NPS   p-nitrophenyl sulphate
NCS   2-hydroxy-5-nitrophenyl sulphate
NP   p-nitrophenol

References

1. Gregory, J. D. & Robbins, P. W.   (1960) Ann. Rev. Biochem., 29, 357.
2. Nichol, L. W. & Roy, A. B.   (1965) B, 4, 386.
3. Nichol, L. W. & Roy, A. B.   (1966) B, 5, 1379.
4. Nichol, L. W. & Roy, A. B.   (1964) J. Biochem. (Tokyo), 55, 643.
5. Roy, A. B.   (1953) BJ, 55, 653.
6. Roy, A. B.   (1954) BJ, 57, 465.
7. Fowler, L. R. & Rammler, D. H.   (1964) B, 3, 230.
8. Roy, A. B.   (1956) BJ, 64, 651.
9. Dodgson, K. S., Spencer, B. & Williams, K.   (1955) BJ, 61, 374.
10. Robinson, D., Smith, J. N., Spencer, B. & Williams, R. T.   (1952) BJ, 51, 202.

STEROL SULPHATASE

(Sterol-sulphate sulphohydrolase)

Dehydro<u>epi</u>androsterone 3-sulphate + H_2O =

dehydro<u>epi</u>androsterone + sulphate

Ref.

Specificity

Sterol sulphatase from ox liver, rat liver or <u>Patella</u> <u>vulgata</u> (common limpet) catalyzes the hydrolysis of the 3β-sulphates of the 5α- or Δ^5-series of steroids, the latter compounds being hydrolyzed more rapidly. Thus, the enzyme from ox liver was inactive with the following compounds: cortisone-21-sulphate or the sulphates of 3α-hydroxy-5α-androstan-17-one, 3α-hydroxy-5β-androstan-17-one, 3β-hydroxy-5β-androstan-17-one, 17α-hydroxyandrost-4-en-3-one, 17β-hydroxyandrost-4-en-3-one, 3α-hydroxy-5α-pregnan-20-one, 3α-hydroxy-5β-pregnan-20-one, 20α-hydroxypregnane and 20β-hydroxypregnane.   (1,2)

Michaelis constants

source	substrate	$K_m(M)$	conditions	
<u>Patella</u> <u>vulgata</u>	dehydroepiandrosterone 3-sulphate	4×10^{-5}	pH 4.5 acetate, 37°	(1)
Ox liver	dehydroepiandrosterone 3-sulphate	4×10^{-5}	pH 7.8, Tris, 37°	(2)
Rat liver Rat testis Guinea-pig testis	7α-H^3-dehydroiso-androsterone sulphate	$\begin{cases} 1 \times 10^{-5} \\ 1.2 \times 10^{-5} \\ 1.6 \times 10^{-5} \end{cases}$	pH 7.2, Tris, 37°	(3)

Inhibitors

The enzyme (rat testis) was inhibited by P_i.   (3)

References

1. Roy, A. B. (1956) <u>BJ</u>, <u>62</u>, 41.
2. Roy, A. B. (1957) <u>BJ</u>, <u>66</u>, 700.
3. Burstein, S. & Dorfman, R. I. (1963) <u>JBC</u>, <u>238</u>, 1656.

GLYCOSULPHATASE

(Sugar-sulphate sulphohydrolase)

D-Glucose 6-sulphate + H_2O = D-glucose + sulphate

Ref.

Specificity

The enzyme from a number of sources exhibits broad specificity properties. Thus that from Littorina littorea is active towards D-glucose 6-sulphate, D-glucose 3-sulphate, D-galactose 6-sulphate and N-acetyl-D-galactosamine sulphate (in order of decreasing activity), but it is inactive towards a number of polysaccharide sulphates (e.g. chondroitin 4-sulphate, chondroitin 6-sulphate, heparin sulphate, heparin or porphyran) and simple alkyl sulphates.

(1)

Michaelis constants

source	substrate	relative velocity	$K_m(M)$	conditions	
L. littorea (large periwinkle)	D-glucose 6-sulphate	1.00	1.7×10^{-2}	pH 5.5, Tris-acetate, 37°	
	D-glucose 3-sulphate	0.10	3.0×10^{-2}		(1,2)
	D-galactose 6-sulphate	0.21	7.2×10^{-2}		

References

1. Lloyd, A. G. (1966) Methods in Enzymology, 8, 670.

2. Dodgson, K. S. (1961) BJ, 78, 324.

α-AMYLASE

(α-1,4-Glucan 4-glucanohydrolase)

Hydrolyzes α-1,4-glucan links in polysaccharides
containing three or more α-1,4-linked D-glucose units

Ref.

Molecular weight

source	value	conditions	
Bacillus subtilis	96,900 [2]	pH 8.55	(1,2)
Aspergillus oryzae	51,000	pH 4.5	(3)
Hog pancreas	45,000	pH 8.5	(4)
Bacillus stearothermophilus	15,500	various	(8)

Specific activity

B. subtilis	2240	μmoles	pH 5.9, glycero-	(5)
A. oryzae	438	maltose formed	phosphate, 25°	
Hog pancreas	1360	from soluble starch	pH 6.9, glycero-	
Human saliva	1945	min^{-1} mg^{-1} enzyme protein	phosphate, 25°	(5)

Specificity

α-Amylase hydrolyzes in a random fashion the α-1,4-glucan link
in polysaccharides of three or more α-1,4-linked D-glucose units.
The α-1,6-bond is not hydrolyzed. Starch or glycogen - the "natural"
substrates - can be replaced to a limited extent by low molecular
weight compounds. These include oligomers containing five, six,
seven or eight glucose residues or α-p-nitrophenolmaltosides. Synthetic
substrates, however, tend to have a limited affinity for the
enzyme.   (1)

The importance of Ca^{2+} in the mechanism of action of α-amylase is

Specificity contd.

discussed in references (1) and (5).

Michaelis constants

source	substrate	K_m (g ml^{-1})	conditions	
B. stearothermo-philus	starch	1.0×10^{-3}	pH 4.6, acetate, 65°	(6)
B. amylolique-faciens	starch	$2.2-3.4 \times 10^{-3}$ [a]	pH 5.9, Pi, 25°	(9)
P. saccharophilia	starch	6×10^{-4}	pH 5.9, glycerophosphate, 25°	(7)
Swine pancreas	starch	6×10^{-4}	-	(7)
Human saliva	starch	6×10^{-4}	-	(7)

[a]The value obtained depended on the strain of B. amyloliquefaciens.

References

1. Fischer, E. H. & Stein, E. A. (1960) The Enzymes, 4, 313.

2. Menzi, R., Stein, E. A. & Fischer, E. H. (1957) Helv. Chim. Acta., 40, 534.

3. Isemuri, T. & Fujita, S. (1957) J. Biochem. (Tokyo), 44, 443.

4. Danielsson, C. E. (1947) Nature, 160, 899.

5. Hsiu, J., Fischer, E. H. & Stein, E. A. (1964) B, 3, 61.

6. Manning, G. B. & Campbell, L. L. (1961) JBC, 236, 2952.

7. Markovitz, A., Klein, H. P. & Fischer, E. H. (1956) BBA, 19, 267.

8. Manning, G. B., Campbell, L. L. & Foster, R. J. (1961) JBC, 236, 2958.

9. Welker, N. E. & Campbell, L. L. (1967) B, 6, 3681.

β-AMYLASE

(α-1,4-Glucan maltohydrolase)

Hydrolyzes α-1,4-glucan links in polysaccharides
so as to remove successive maltose units from
the non-reducing ends of the chains

Molecular weight

source	value	conditions	
Sweet potato	152,000	pH 6.0	(2,3)
	215,000 [4]	-	(8)

Specific activity

Sweet potato	1640[a]	(pH 4.8, acetate, 30°)	(2,4)
Wheat	680[a]	(pH 5.2, acetate, 20°)	(5)
Malt	805[a]	(pH 5.2, acetate, 20°)	(6)

[a] μ moles maltose liberated min^{-1} mg^{-1} enzyme protein with starch as
the substrate.

Specificity

β-Amylase hydrolyzes α-1,4-glucan links in polysaccharides so as
to remove successive maltose units from the non-reducing ends of the
chains. α-1,6-Glucan links are not hydrolyzed and act as barriers
to the enzyme action. The smallest molecule readily attacked by β-
amylase is maltotetraose. The following compounds are cleaved at
very low rates by the enzyme from sweet potato: maltotriose (1.0),
methyl-α-maltotriose (9.0) and maltose (0.008). Methyl-α-maltotriose
yields maltose and methyl-α-glucoside on hydrolysis. Cyclohexaamylose
is not hydrolyzed by β-amylase. (1,9)

Michaelis constants

source	substrate	$K_m(M)$	conditions	
Sweet potato	44 unit amylose	7.3×10^{-5}	pH 4.8, acetate, 35°	(7)

Inhibitors

source	inhibitor	$K_i(M)$	conditions	
Sweet potato	cyclohexaamylose	1.7×10^{-4}	pH 4.8, acetate, 3°, 10°, 20°	(8)
	methyl-α-glucoside	4.0×10^{-2}	pH 4.8, acetate.	(9)

References

1. French, D. (1960) The Enzymes, 4, 345.

2. Englard, S., Sorof, S. & Singer, T. P. (1951) JBC, 189, 217.

3. Englard, S. & Singer, T. P. (1950) JBC, 187, 213.

4. Balls, A. K., Walden, M. K. & Thompson, R. R. (1948) JBC, 173, 9.

5. Meyer, K. H., Spahr, P. F. & Fischer, E. H. (1953) Helv. Chim. Acta, 36, 1924.

6. Meyer, K. H. Fischer, E. H. & Piguet, A. (1951) Helv. Chim. Acta, 34, 316.

7. Bailey, J. M. & French, D. (1957) JBC, 226, 1.

8. Thoma, J. A., Koshland, D. E. Jr., Ruscica, J. & Baldwin, R. (1963) BBRC, 12, 184.

9. Thoma, J. A. & Koshland, D. E. Jr. (1960) JBC, 235, 2511.

GLUCOAMYLASE

(α-1,4-Glucan glucohydrolase)

Hydrolyzes α-1,4-glucan links in polysaccharides
so as to remove successive glucose units from
the non-reducing ends of the chains

Ref.

Molecular weight

source	value	conditions	
Coniophora cerebella	48,000	Biogel P-100, pH 5.8	(2)

Specificity and Michaelis constants

The enzyme hydrolyzes α-1,4-glucan links in polysaccharides removing successive glucose units from the non-reducing ends of the chains. Thus, maltose is completely and amylopectin and amylose almost completely converted to glucose by the enzyme. The α-1,6-glucan link is also hydrolyzed by glucoamylase. (1,2)

source	substrate	relative velocity	K_m	conditions	
C. cerebella	amylopectin	-	2.2×10^{-7}	pH 4.0, acetate, 40°	(2)
	amylose	-	3.2×10^{-5}		
	maltose	-	1.85×10^{-2}		
Rhizopus delemar	amylopectin	2.0	4.1×10^{-7}	pH 4.5, acetate, 40°	(3)
	amylose	1.0	4.4×10^{-5}		
	maltose	0.5	6.6×10^{-3}		

References

1. Larner, J. (1960) The Enzymes, 4, 370.

2. King, N. J. (1967) BJ, 105, 577.

3. Phillips, L. L. & Caldwell, M. L. (1951) JACS, 73, 3563.

CELLULASE

(β-1,4-Glucan glucanohydrolase)

Hydrolyzes β-1,4-glucan links in cellulose

Ref.

Molecular weight

source	value	conditions	
Myrothecium verrucaria	63,000	–	(3)
component I[a]	55,000		
component II	30,000	Sephadex G75, pH 6.5	(5)
component III	5,300		
Trichoderma viride	61,000	Sephadex G75, pH 6.3	(6)
	52,000	–	(7)
Polyporus versicolor[b]	11,000	pH 5.0	(8)
	51,000	pH 5.0	(9)

[a] Culture filtrates of M. verrucaria possess three major cellulolytic components (I, II and III). Component II constitutes 90% of the total activity.

[b] At least four cellulotytic enzymes are present in this organism.

Specific activity

    M. verrucaria   6.4 cellotetraose (pH 5.0, 35°)   (2)

Specificity and Michaelis constants

    The enzyme (M. verrucaria) hydrolyzes lichinine (β-1,3, β-1,4), xylan (β-1,4), glucomannan (β-1,4), crown gall polysaccharide (β-1,2), lutean (β-1,6), laminarin (β-1,3), methyl β-cellobioside, carboxymethyl cellulose, and sorbityl β-cellobioside but not yeast glucan or methyl β-glucoside. The hydrolysis of oligosaccharides increases in rate and becomes more random with increase in chain length. Cellotriose is hydrolyzed five times as rapidly at its non-reducing linkage as it is at its reducing linkage.

(1)

    The enzyme from Cellvibrio gilvus attacks cellulose oligosaccharides and chemically reduced cellulose oligosaccharides at the second and third glucosyl bond from the non-reducing end of the polysaccharide chain. The primary initial reaction product during the hydrolysis of cellotetraose is α-cellobiose. Unlike the enzyme from M. verrucaria, this enzyme does not appear to possess transferase activity.

(4)

Specificity and Michaelis constants contd.

source	substrate	relative velocity	$K_m(M)$	conditions	
M. verrucaria	cellobiose	0.012 - 0.015	-		
	cellotriose	0.50	-		
	cellotetraose	1.00	-	pH 5.0, 35°	(2)
	cellopentaose	>1.13	-		
	cellohexaose	>1.13	-		
T. viride	cellobiose	-	1.9×10^{-2}		
	cellotriose	-	3.1×10^{-3}		
	cellotetraose	-	2.8×10^{-3}	pH 4.8, 40°	(7)
	cellopentaose	-	7.0×10^{-4}		
	cellohexaose	-	1.0×10^{-4}		

Inhibitors

The enzyme from Irpex lacteus is inhibited by glucose, cellobiose and phenyl β-glucoside. (10)

References

1. Larner, J. (1960) The Enzymes, 4, 371.

2. Whitaker, D. R. (1954) ABB, 53, 439.

3. Whitaker, D. R., Colvin, J. R. & Cook, W. H. (1954) ABB, 49, 257.

4. Storvick, W. O., Cole, F. E. & King, K. W. (1963) B, 2, 1106.

5. Selby, K. & Maitland, C. C. (1965) BJ, 94, 578.

6. Selby, K. & Maitland, C. C. (1967) BJ, 104, 716.

7. Li, L. H., Flora, R. M. & King, K. W. (1965) ABB, 111, 439.

8. Petterson, G., Cowling, E. B. & Porath, J. (1963) BBA, 67, 1.

9. Petterson, G. & Porath, J. (1963) BBA, 67, 9.

10. Nisizawa, K. (1955) J. Biochem. (Tokyo), 42, 825.

LAMINARINASE

(β-1,3(4)-Glucan glucanohydrolase)

Hydrolyzes either β-1,3- or β-1,4-links adjacent to a -1,3-link

Molecular weight

source	value	conditions	
Bacillus circulans	S_{20}, w = 3.3	pH 6.5	(2)

Specific activity

Laminarinase from B. circulans hydrolyzed laminaritriose; laminaritetraose; laminaripentoase and laminarin but not laminaribiose; xylan β-1,4 and β-1,3; starch; CM-cellulose; inulin; cellodextrin; agar-agar; trehalose; kojibiose; nigerose; maltose; cellobiose; isomaltose; gentiobiose; sucrose; lactose; melibiose; raffinose; maltotriose; cellotriose; panose; maltotetraose or cellotetraose.

(2)

References

1. Bull, A. T. & Chesters, C. G. C. (1966) Advances in Enzymology, 28, 341.
2. Horikoshi, K., Koffler, H. & Arima, K. (1963) BBA, 73, 267.

INULASE

(β-1,2-Fructan fructanohydrolase)

Hydrolyses β-1,2-fructan links in inulin.

Specificity

The enzyme purified from Saccharomyces fragalis hydrolyses inulin by an endwise action. The action commences at the D-fructose end of the polymer and yields fructose until the last linkage is broken which yields one D-glucose molecule per molecule of inulin. (1)

The enzyme (Jerusalem artichoke tuber) is specific for straight-chain oligosaccharides and polyfructosides of the inulin series. Methyl-β-fructofuranoside, 6-fructosylglucose, 1-fructosylhexitol, sucrose, raffinose and melezitose are hydrolyzed to a negligible extent and levan and irisin not at all. (2)

Michaelis constants

source	substrate	$K_m(M)$	conditions	
Jerusalem artichoke tuber	inulin (molecular weight = 5000)	3.3×10^{-2}	pH 5.0, acetate, 25°	(2)
	1^F-fructosylsucrose	3.3×10^{-2}		
	inulopentaose	2.2×10^{-2}		

Inhibitors

source	inhibitor	type	$K_i(M)$	conditions	
Jerusalem artichoke tuber	sucrose	NC (inulin)	2×10^{-3}	pH 5, acetate, 25°	(2)

Other inhibitors are 1-fructosylhexitol, inulobiose, melezitose and raffinose. (2)

References

1. Snyder, H. E. & Phaff, H. J. (1962) JBC, 237, 2438.

2. Avigad, G. & Bauer, S. (1966) Methods in Enzymology, 8, 621.

DEXTRANASE

(α-1,6-Glucan 6-glucanohydrolase)

Hydrolyses α-1,6-glucan links

Molecular weight

source	value	conditions	
Cytophaga sp.	60,000	-	(1)

Specificity

The enzyme (Cytophaga sp.) attacks dextrans to produce oligo-saccharides of various lengths and the end product of the reaction appears to be isomaltose with trace amounts of glucose. Sephadex G100, G150 and G200 are completely solubilized by this enzyme.   (1)

References

1. Janson, J.-C. & Porath, J. (1966) Methods in Enzymology, 8, 615.

CHITINASE

(Poly-β-1,4-(2-acetamido-2-deoxy)-D-glucoside glycanohydrolase)

Hydrolyses α-1,4-acetamido-2-deoxy-D-glucoside links in chitin and chitodextrin.

Ref.

Molecular weight

source	value	conditions	
Streptomyces antibioticus	~30,000	-	(1)

Specific activity

The enzyme isolated from S. antibioticus has been shown to be homogeneous. (1)

Specificity

The enzyme is specific for linear polymers of N-acetyl-D-glucosamine; chitosan, carboxymethylchitin, glycolchitin and chitin sulphates are hydrolysed in addition to chitin. The following are not attacked: chitin nitrates, cellulose, mucin, hyaluronate and alginate. (1)

Michaelis constants

source	substrate	K_m (mg ml^{-1})	conditions	
S. antibioticus	chitin	0.1	pH 5.1, citrate P_i, 37°	(1)

References

1. Jeuniaux, C. (1966) Methods in Enzymology 8, 644.

POLYGALACTURONASE

(Poly-α-1,4-galacturonide glycanohydrolase)

Hydrolyzes α-1,4-D-galacturonide links in
pectate and other polygalacturonides

Ref.

Molecular weight

source	value	conditions	
Pectinol K	10-30,000	pH 7.0	(2)
Saccharomyces fragalis	$S_{20,w} = 4.1$	-	(5)

Specificity and kinetic properties

Polygalacturonase hydrolyzes α-1,4-D-galacturonide links in pectate
and other polygalacturonides. Oligogalacturonides are attacked preferentially at the first glycosidic bond adjacent to the reducing group. (1,3)

The enzyme isolated from tomato juice catalyzed the hydrolysis of
pectate (1.00); tetragalacturonate (0.07); trigalacturonate (0.015)
and digalacturonate (0.01). The preferred attack on tetragalacturonate
was a cleavage into galacturonate and trigalacturonate. (3,4)

References

1. Fischer, E. H. & Stein, E. A. (1960) The Enzymes, 4, 307.

2. Purr, A., Hottenroth, B., Döring, M. & Schneider, F. (1957)
   BZ, 329, 261.

3. Patel, D. S. & Phaff, H. J. (1958) Food Research, 23, 693.

4. Luh, B. S., Leonard, S. J. & Phaff, H. J. (1956) Food Research,
   21, 448.

5. Phaff, H. J. & Demain, A. L. (1956) JBC, 218, 875.

LYSOZYME

Hydrolyzes β-1,4-links between N-acetyl-muramic acid (or 2-acetamido-2-deoxy-D-glucose) and 2-acetamido-2-deoxy-D-glucose residues in a mucopolysaccharide, mucopolypeptide or in chitin.

Ref.

Molecular weight

source	value	conditions	
Hens egg white	14,388	sequence studies	(2)
Various	15,000	various	(1,2)

Specificity and kinetic constants[*]

Lysozyme catalyzes the hydrolysis of the cell walls of numerous Gram-positive bacteria. Of these the cell wall of Micrococcus lysodeikticus is the most sensitive. The cell walls of certain Gram-negative bacteria (e.g., Escherichia coli and Salmonella typhosa), chitin (a polymer of N-acetyl glucosamine) and oligomers of N-acetyl glucosamine are also attacked by the enzyme. The enzymic hydrolysis of glycosides proceeds through cleavage of the bond between the 1-carbon and bridge-oxygen. The enzyme also acts as a transferase.

(1,2)

substrate	relative rate	K_s(M)	conditions
N-acetyl glucosamine	0	$4\text{-}6 \times 10^{-2}$	
di-N-acetyl glucosamine	0.003	1.75×10^{-4}	
tri-N-acetyl glucosamine	1	6.58×10^{-6} [(a)]	pH 5.5,
tetra-N-acetyl glucosamine	8	9.45×10^{-6} [(a)]	P_i, (1,3,4)
penta-N-acetylglucosamine	4,000	9.35×10^{-6} [(b)]	25°
hexa-N-acetylglucosamine	30,000	6.15×10^{-6} [(b)]	
p-nitrophenyl-β-D-chitobioside	5×10^{-6} [(c)]	4.0×10^{-3} [(d)]	pH 5-5.2,
o-nitrophenyl-β-D-chitobioside	3.8×10^{-6} [(c)]	4.0×10^{-3} [(d)]	35° (1)

Specificity and kinetic constants[*](contd.)

(a)$K_m >> K_s$

(b)$K_m \sim K_s$

(c)$k_0(sec^{-1})$

(d)These are Michaelis constants.

Inhibitors[*]

The inhibition of lysozyme by imidazole and indole derivatives
is discussed in reference (5).

[*]The data given are those of the enzyme isolated from hens egg white.

References

1. A Discussion on the Structure and Function of Lysozyme (1967)
    Proc. Royal Soc. 167(B), 348-451.

2. Jollès, P. (1964) Angew. Chem. internat. Edit, 3, 28.

3. Dahlqvist, F. W., Jao, L. & Raftery, M. (1966) PNAS, 56, 26.

4. Rupley, J. A., Butler, L., Gerring, M., Hartdegen, F. J. & Pecoraro,
    P. (1967) PNAS, 57, 1088.

5. Shinitzky, M., Katchalski, E., Grisaro, V. & Sharon, N. (1966)
    ABB, 116, 332.

NEURAMINIDASE

(Mucopolysaccharide N-acetylneuraminylhydrolase)

Probably hydrolyzes terminal α-2,6-links between
N-acetylneuraminic acid and 2-acetamido-2-deoxy-D-galactose
residues in various mucopolysaccharides

Ref.

Molecular weight

source	value	conditions	
Vibrio cholerae	10–20,000	pH 8.5	(2)
	90,000	pH 5.7	(3)
Chick allantoic membrane	$S_{20,w} = 3.3$	pH 7.8	(4)
Influenza virus	$S_{20,w} = 4.2$	-	(8)

Specific activity

Clostridium perfringens (17,900 x)	500 μmoles N-acetyl-neuraminate produced min^{-1} with bovine sialyllactose as substrate (pH 4.5, acetate, 37°)	(5)
V. cholerae (5500 x)	21 μmoles N-acetyl-neuraminate produced min^{-1} with bovine sialyllactose as substrate (pH 4.5, acetate, 37°)	(6)
Influenza virus (300 x)	23.4 μmoles N-acetyl-neuraminate produced min^{-1} with N-acetyl neuraminyllactose as substrate (pH 6.5, Tris-maleate, 37°)	(8)

Specificity and Michaelis constants

The enzymes from V. cholerae and C. perfringens have similar
properties. The rate of hydrolysis of a particular substrate is influenced by the position of the sialic acid linkage to the penultimate
sugar in the carbohydrate chain. Prolonged incubation with either
enzyme results in the liberation of essentially all of the sialic acid
from a variety of substrates. The enzyme from V. cholerae requires
Ca^{2+} for activity but that from C. perfringens does not. (5)

The mammalian enzymes are somewhat less efficient in that they only
release 20 - 30% of the sialic acid from most substrates. (9)

The viral enzyme cleaves the 2→3 bond in N-acetylneuraminyl-(2→3)-β
-D-galactopyranosyl-(1→4)-D-glucopyranose and the 2→6 bond in 6-O-
(N-acetylneuraminyl)-N-acetylgalactosamine and in N-acetylneuraminyl-
(2 6)-β-D-galactopyranosyl-(1→4)-D-glucopyranose. (8)

Specificity and Michaelis constants contd.   Ref.

source	substrate	$\frac{V}{\text{(relative)}}$	$K_m(M)$	conditions	
Chick allantoic membrane	sialyllactose	1.000	6.4×10^{-4}	pH 5.8, Tris-maleate, 37°	(4)
	fetuin[a]	2.400	1.7×10^{-3}		
	ovine submaxillary-gland mucin	0.026	1.8×10^{-3}		
V. cholerae	sialyllactose[b]	-	1.2×10^{-3}	pH 4.5, acetate, 37°	(6)
Diplococcus pneumoniae	N-acetylneuraminyl-lactose	1.00	1.8×10^{-3}	pH 6.5, P_i-citrate 37°	(7)
	α_1-acid glyco-protein[c]	0.33	3.5×10^{-4}		
C. perfringens	sialyllactose[b]	-	2.4×10^{-3}	pH 4.5, acetate, 37°	(5)
Influenza virus	N-acetyl neuraminyllactose	-	5.0×10^{-5}	pH 6.5, Tris-maleate, 37°	(8)

[a] Isolated from calf serum
[b] Bovine
[c] Human plasma

References

1. Gottschalk, A. (1960) The Enzymes, 4, 461.
2. Schramm, G. & Mohr, E. (1959) Nature, 183, 1677.
3. Laver, W. G., Pye, J. & Ada, G. L. (1964) BBA, 81, 177.
4. Ada, G. L. (1963) BBA, 73, 276.
5. Cassidy, J. T., Jourdian, G. W. & Roseman, S. (1965) JBC, 240, 3501.
6. Ada, G. L., French, E. L. & Lind, P. E. (1961) J. Gen. Microbiol., 24, 409.
7. Hughes, R. C. & Jeanloz, R. W. (1964) B, 3, 1535.
8. Rafelson, M. E. Jr., Gold, S. & Priede, I. (1966) Methods in Enzymology, 8, 677.
9. Mahadevan, S., Nduaguba, J. C. & Tappel, A. L. (1967) JBC, 242, 4409.
10. Cassidy, J. T., Jourdian, G. W. & Roseman, S. (1966) Methods in Enzymology, 8, 680.

α-GLUCOSIDASE

(α-D-Glucoside glucohydrolase)

An α-D-glucoside + H_2O = an alcohol + D-glucose

Ref.

Equilibrium constant

The reversibility of the reaction has been demonstrated. The forward reaction is strongly favoured. (3)

Molecular weight

source	value	conditions	
Saccharomyces italicus	85,000 ($\pm$30,000)	-	(3,4)
S. cerevisiae	68,500	pH 7.2	(7)

Specific activity

S. cerevisiae (237 x)   95   PNPG   (pH 7.2, P_i.)   (7)

Specificity and Michaelis constants

α-Glucosidase catalyzes the hydrolysis of a variety of α-D-glucopyranosides. Thus the enzyme from S. italicus hydrolyzed the following compounds with decreasing rates: phenyl-α-D-glucoside, turanose, sucrose, β-methyl maltoside, PNPG, maltose, butyl-α-D-glucoside, methyl-α-D-glucoside and ethyl-α-D-glucoside. (3)

S. cerevisiae possesses two α-glucosidases: a maltase catalyzing the hydrolysis of maltose (1.00) and sucrose (0.67) but not of iso-maltose or α-methyl glucoside; and an α-methyl glucosidase catalyzing the hydrolysis of α-methyl glucoside (1.00), isomaltose (1.40) and sucrose (0.73) but not of maltose. (5,7)

α-Glucosidase possesses transglucosidase activity. Thus with the enzyme from S. italicus fructose competes with water for the α-glucosyl unit and the primary product of the process is isomaltulose. (3)

Specificity and Michaelis constants contd.   Ref.

source	substrate	V (relative)	$K_m(M)$	conditions	
S. italicus	PNPG	-	2.0×10^{-4}	pH 6.8, P_i, 30°	(3)
Barley	maltose	1.00	1.8×10^{-3}	pH 6.85, P_i, 37°	(6)
	maltose	8.60	9.1×10^{-3}	pH 3.15, P_i, 37°	(6)
Dog liver[a] (acid α-glucosidase)	maltose	1.00	$4-5 \times 10^{-3}$		
	nigarose	1.20	6.6×10^{-3}		
	α-phenylglucoside	0.24	1.0×10^{-2}		
	glycogen	0.17	1.6×10^{-2}	pH 5.0, acetate, 37°	(8)
	kojibiose	0.38	-		
(neutral α-glucosidase)	maltose	1.00	$0.8-1.4 \times 10^{-3}$		
	nigarose	0.65	1.25×10^{-2}		
	kojibiose	0.32	9.5×10^{-3}		
	glycogen	0.04	2.5×10^{-2}		

[a] Dog liver contains two α-glucosidases: an acid α-glucosidase with a pH optimum 3-6 and a neutral α-glucosidase with a pH optimum 4-7.5.

Inhibitors

source	inhibitor	type	$K_i(M)$	conditions	
Barley	Tris cation	C(maltose)	3.2×10^{-4}	pH 6.85, P_i, 37°	(6)
	erythritol	C(maltose)	8.55×10^{-2}		
S. italicus	maltose		3.5×10^{-2}	pH 6.8, P_i, 30°	(3)
	sucrose	C(PNPG)	3.7×10^{-2}		
	turanose		1.1×10^{-2}		
	α-phenylglucoside		4×10^{-4}		

Light absorption data

p-Nitrophenol[a] ϵ, (400 mμ) = 9,600 (pH 6.8)   (3)

[a] One of the products of the hydrolysis of PNPG

Abbreviations

PNPG   p-nitrophenol-α-D-glucopyranoside

References

1. Gottschalk, A. (1950) The Enzymes, 1, (1), 557.
2. Baumann, H. & Pigman, W. (1957) in The Carbohydrates (ed. Pigmann, W.). Academic Press: New York, p562.
3. Halvorson, H. (1966) Methods in Enzymology, 8, 559.
4. Halvorson, H. & Ellias, L. (1958) BBA, 30, 28.
5. Gorman, J. & Halvorson, H. (1966) Methods in Enzymology, 8, 562.
6. Jorgensen, B. B. & Jorgensen, O. B. (1967) BBA, 146, 167.
7. Khan, N. A. & Eaton, N. R. (1967) BBA, 146, 173.
8. Torres, H. N. & Olavarria, J. M. (1964) JBC, 239, 2427.

β-GLUCOSIDASE

(β-D-Glucoside glucohydrolase)

A β-D-glucoside + H_2O = an alcohol + D-glucose

Ref.

Molecular weight

source	value	conditions	
Trichoderma viride	76,000	-	(3)
Saccharomyces cerevisiae (yeast)	300,000	-	(4)
Rat kidney	40-50,000	Sephadex G200, pH 7.6	(7)

Specific activity

S. cerevisiae   38   NPG   (pH 6.8, P_i, 30°)   (4)

Specificity

The enzyme has high glycone specificity but low aglycone specificity. Aryl glycosides are in general better substrates than alkyl glycosides (1,2,4). The enzyme isolated from T. viride has a broad specificity and hydrolyzes β(1→2), β(1→3), β(1→4) and β(1→6) dissacharides of glucose, celluhexaose and carboxymethylcellulose (3). In extracts of almond emulsin there appears to be a single enzyme that hydrolyzes β-glucosides, β-galactosides and β-D-fucosides. Preparations from limpets and barley, however, each contain a clearly distinguishable β-glucosidase and β-galactosidase. β-D-Fucosides were hydrolyzed by the β-glucosidase component (5). The influence of structure on the hydrolysis of substituted phenyl β-D-glucosides by emulsin is discussed in reference (6).

Michaelis constants

source	substrate	relative velocity	$K_m(M)$	conditions	
S. cerevisiae	NPG	-	8.05×10^{-5}	pH 6.8, P_i, 30°	(4)
	phenyl glucoside	-	2.7×10^{-5}		
Limpet	p-nitrophenyl β-D-fucoside	-	6.0×10^{-4}		
	o-nitrophenyl β-glucoside	-	8.9×10^{-4}		
Almond emulsin	p-nitrophenyl β-D-fucoside	-	1.8×10^{-3}	pH 4.5, P_i-citrate, 37°	(5)
	o-nitrophenyl β-glucoside	-	6.0×10^{-3}		
Barley	p-nitrophenyl β-D-fucoside	-	1.5×10^{-3}		
	o-nitrophenyl β-glucoside	-	2.9×10^{-3}		

Michaelis constants contd.

source	substrate	relative velocity	$K_m(M)$	conditions	
T. viride	cellobiose	1.00	2.2×10^{-3}		
	cellotriose	1.70	1.8×10^{-4}		
	cellotetraose	-	6.5×10^{-5}		
	cellopentaose	-	6.0×10^{-5}	pH 5.0, P_i, 39°	(3)
	cellohexaose	-	1.6×10^{-4}		
	NPG	3.34	-		
	carboxymethylcellulose	0.76	-		

Inhibitors

source	inhibitor[a]	$K_i(M)$	conditions	
Limpet	gluconolactone	1.5×10^{-5}		
	fuconolactone	3.9×10^{-6}		
Almond emulsin	gluconolactone	3.6×10^{-5}	pH 4.5, P_i-citrate, 37°	(5)
	fuconolactone	1.2×10^{-5}		
Barley	gluconolactone	7.6×10^{-6}		
	fuconolactone	2.4×10^{-5}		
S. cerevisiae	D-glucose	8.5×10^{-3}	pH 6.8, P_i, 30°	(4)

[a] C(o-nitrophenyl β-glucoside or p-nitrophenyl β-D-fucoside).

Abbreviations

NPG   p-nitrophenyl-β-D-glucopyranoside

References

1. Baumann, H. & Pigman, W. (1957) in The Carbohydrates (ed. Pigman, W.) Academic Press: New York, p562.
2. Veibel, S. (1950) The Enzymes, 1(1), 583.
3. Li, L. H., Flora, R. M. & King, K. W. (1965) ABB, 111, 439.
4. Duerksen, J. D. & Halvorson, H. (1958) JBC, 233, 1113.
5. Conchie, J., Gelman, A. L. & Levvy, G. A. (1967) BJ, 103, 609.
6. Nath, R. L. & Rydon, H. N. (1954) BJ, 57, 1.
7. Robinson, D., Price, R. G. & Dance, N. (1967) BJ, 102, 525.

α-GALACTOSIDASE

(α-D-Galactoside galactohydrolase)

An α-D-galactoside + H_2O = an alcohol + D-galactose

Ref.

Specificity and Michaelis constants

The coffee bean contains two α-galactosidases (enzymes I and II) which have been separated. They have different pH optima (pH 5.3, and 6.3, respectively) but their specificity properties are identical. Thus, they catalyze the hydrolysis of a wide variety of α-D-galacto-pyranosidic linkages:

a) glycosides of methanol, phenol and p-nitrophenol,

b) disaccharides and derivatives (melibiose, epimelibiose, planteobiose, melibionate)

c) trisaccharides (manninotriose, umbelliferose, raffinose, planteose)

d) oligosaccharides and polysaccharides (lychnose series, isolychnose series)

source	enzyme	substrate	$K_m(M)$ [a]	
Coffee	α-galactosidase I	α-phenylgalactoside	2×10^{-3}	
bean	α-galactosidase II	α-phenylgalactoside	1×10^{-3}	(1)

[a] Conditions = pH 5.3, P_i-citrate, $37°$

Inhibitors

Both enzymes are strongly inhibited by galactose (C(α-phenyl-galactoside)). (1)

References

1. Courtois, J. E. & Petek, F. (1966) Methods in Enzymology, 8, 565.

β-GALACTOSIDASE

(β-D-Galactoside galactohydrolase)

A β-D-galactoside + H_2O = an alcohol + D-galactose

Ref.

Molecular weight

source	value	conditions	
Eschericia coli	540,000 [4]	pH 7.5	(3)
	518,000 [12-16]	pH 7.6	(4,5)
Rat liver	127,000	pH 7.0	Sephadex
Beef liver	85,000	pH 4.5	G100 (6)
	43,000	pH 6.0	

Specific activity

E. coli		340 ONPG	(pH 7.0, P_i, 28°)	(3)
Diplococcus pneumoniae	(500 x)	3.9 ONPG	(pH 6.3, P_i, 37°)	(7)

Specificity and Michaelis constants

source	substrate	$\dfrac{V}{(relative)}$	$K_m(M)$	conditions
E. coli	ONPG	1.00	9.5×10^{-4}	
	phenyl-β-D-galactoside	0.05	3.23×10^{-3}	pH 7.6,
	lactose	0.06	3.85×10^{-3}	(1,2)
	p-nitrophenyl-β-D-galactoside	0.14	4.45×10^{-4}	Tris, 20°
Diplococcus pneumonia	ONPG	1.00	4.5×10^{-3}	pH 6.3,
	lactose	0.10	1.0×10^{-3}	
	2-acetamido-2-deoxy-4-0(β-D-galactopyranosyl)-D-glucose	0.62	4.4×10^{-3}	P_i, (7)
	p-nitrophenyl-β-D-galactopyranoside	0.41	1.9×10^{-3}	37°

Specificity and Michaelis constants contd.

source	substrate	$\frac{V}{\text{(relative)}}$	$K_m(M)$	conditions	
Diplococcus pneumonia	p-nitrophenyl-β-D-fucopyranoside	0.003	8.3×10^{-3}	pH 6.3, P_i, 37°	(7)

Abbreviations

ONPG   o-nitrophenyl-β-D-galactopyranoside

References

1. Wallenfels, K. & Malhotra, O. P. (1960) The Enzymes, 4, 409.

2. Wallenfels, K. (1962) Methods in Enzymology, 5, 212.

3. Craven, G. R., Steers, E. & Anfinsen, C. B. (1965) JBC, 240, 2468, 2478.

4. Sund, H. & Weber, K. (1963) BZ, 337, 24.

5. Weber, K., Sund, H. & Wallenfels, K. (1964) BZ, 339, 498.

6. Chytil, F. (1965) BBRC, 19, 630.

7. Hugh, R. C. & Jeanloz, R. W. (1964) B, 3, 1535.

α-MANNOSIDASE

(α-D-Mannoside mannohydrolase)

An α-D-mannoside + H_2O = an alcohol + D-mannose

Ref.

Specific activity

Jack bean meal (525 x) 105 p-nitrophenyl-α-D-mannoside (pH 4.5, citrate, 25°) (1)

Specificity

The enzyme from jack bean meal hydrolyzes the following compounds: methyl-, benzyl- and p-nitrophenyl-α-D-mannosides; O- α-D-manno-pyranosyl-(1→2)-O-D-mannopyranose; O-α-D-mannopyranosyl-(1→6)-O-D-mannopyranose; O-α-D-mannopyranosyl-(1→2)-O-D-mannopyranosyl-(1→2)-O-D-mannopyranose; O-α-D-mannopyranosyl-(1→3)-O-α-D-mannopyranosyl-(1→2)-O-α-D-mannopyranosyl-(1→2)-O-D-mannopyranose and mannosyl-rhamnose. The enzyme liberates mannose from ovalbumin, ovomucoid and orosomucoid. It also possesses glycosyltransferase activity. The following compounds were not hydrolyzed: phenyl-β-D-mannoside and O-β-D-mannopyranosyl-(1→4)-O-D-mannopyranose. (1)

Michaelis constants

source	substrate	$K_m(M)$	conditions	
Jack bean meal	p-nitrophenyl-α-D-mannoside	2.5×10^{-3}	pH 4.5, citrate, 25°	(1)
	benzyl-α-D-mannoside	3.1×10^{-2}		
	methyl-α-D-mannoside	1.2×10^{-1}		
Rat epididymis	p-nitrophenyl-α-D-mannoside	1.3×10^{-2}	pH 5.0, acetate, 37°	(2)
	phenyl-α-D-mannoside	5.7×10^{-2}		

Inhibitors

source	inhibitor	type	$K_i(M)$	conditions	
Jack bean meal	mannono-(1→4)-lactone	C(p-nitro-phenyl-α-D-mannoside)	1.0×10^{-2}	pH 4.5, citrate, 25°	(1)
	mannono-(1→5)-lactone		1.2×10^{-4}		
Rat epididymis	mannono-(1→4)-lactone		1.1×10^{-2}	pH 5.0, acetate, 37°	(2)

References

1. Li, Y-T. (1967) JBC, 242, 5475.
2. Conchie, J. & Hay, A. J. (1959) BJ, 73, 327.

β-FRUCTOFURANOSIDASE

(β-D-Fructofuranoside fructohydrolase)

A β-D-fructofuranoside + H_2O = an alcohol + D-fructose

Molecular weight

source	value	conditions	
Yeast [a]	270,000	pH 5.4	(3)
Neurospora crassa [b]	$S_{20,w} = 10.3$	pH 7.5	(4)
	$S_{20,w} = 5.2$	pH 7.5	(4)

[a]
    This enzyme is a glycoprotein containing about 50% carbohydrate.

[b]
N. crassa contains two active forms of invertase that are inter-convertible.

Specific activity

Yeast (113 x) 3000 sucrose (pH 5.0, acetate, 30°)   (3)
N. crassa, heavy component (105 x) 1900 sucrose (pH 5.0, acetate 38°)   (6)

Specificity and Michaelis constants

    The enzyme (yeast) catalyzes the hydrolysis of sugars possessing a terminal unsubstituted β-D-fructofuranosyl residue. The following types of compound are not attacked: α-fructofuranosides, fructo-pyranosides, β-L-sorbofuranosides, β-D-xyloketofuranosides and sugars with substitutions in the β-fructofuranosyl residue (e.g. planteose, lychnose and melezitose). The enzyme is much less specific so far as the "afructose" moiety is concerned. It also possesses transferase activity.   (1)

    Helianthus tuberosus (Jerusalem artichoke) has at least three enzymes that catalyze the hydrolysis of β-fructofuranosides: an invertase (present in small amounts) and two enzymes that act on straight chain oligo- and polysaccharides containing β-(2 1') linked fructosyl residues but not on sucrose.   (5)

    The enzyme from Bacillus subtilis has been crystallized; its properties are described in reference (7).

Specificity and Michaelis constants contd. Ref.

source	substrate	V(relative)	$K_m(M)$	conditions	
Yeast	sucrose	-	9.1×10^{-3}	pH 4.6, maleate	(5)
H. tuberosus (invertase)	sucrose	1.00	-	pH 5.0, acetate, 25°	(5)
	raffinose	0.27	-		
	melezitose	0.01	-		
N. crassa	sucrose	1.00	6.1×10^{-3}	pH 5.0, acetate, 38°	(6)
	raffinose	0.22	6.5×10^{-3}		
	β-methyl fructoside	0.30	3.3×10^{-2}		

Inhibitors

The enzyme from H. tuberosus is inhibited by ethanol (NC(sucrose)). (5)

References

1. Myrbäck, K. (1960) The Enzymes, 4, 379.

2. Edelman, J. (1956) Advances in Enzymology, 17, 189.

3. Neumann, N. P. & Lampen, J. O. (1967) B, 6, 468.

4. Metzenberg, R. L. (1964) BBA, 89, 291.

5. Tracey, M. V. (1963) BBA, 77, 147.

6. Metzenberg, R. L. (1963) ABB, 100, 503.

7. Negoro, H. (1957) Nippon Nôgei-Kagaku Kaishi, 31, 253.

TREHALASE

(α,α'-Glucoside 1-glucohydrolase)

Trehalose + H_2O = 2 D-glucose

Specificity

The Galleria mellonella (wax moth) enzyme does not hydrolyze methyl α- or β-glucoside, phenyl α- or β-glucoside, glucose 1-phosphate, sucrose, turanose, maltose, cellobiose, lactose, raffinose, melezitose, starch or glycogen. (1)

The enzyme isolated from Phormia regina (blow fly) is specific for trehalose: maltose, sucrose, melibiose, lactose, raffinose and turanose are not attacked (2). That isolated from hog intestine is similarly specific and sucrose, maltose, isomaltose, phenyl α-D-glucopyranoside, ββ-trehalose and αβ-trehalose were not hydrolyzed by this enzyme. No trans-glycosylase activity has been demonstrated for the enzyme. (3)

Michaelis constants

source	substrate	$K_m(M)$	conditions	
G. mellonella	trehalose	1.3×10^{-4}	pH 5.5, acetate, $30°$	(1)
P. regina	trehalose	6.7×10^{-4}	pH 5.6, citrate, $32°$	(2)
Hog small intestine	trehalose	3.0×10^{-3}	pH 6, maleate, $37°$	(3)

References

1. Kalf, G. F. & Rieder, S. V. (1958) JBC, 230, 691.
2. Friedman, S. (1966) Methods in Enzymology, 8, 600.
3. Dahlqvist, A. (1960) Acta Chem. scand., 14, 9.

CHITOBIASE

Chitobiose acetamidodeoxyglucohydrolase

Chitobiose + H_2O = 2 2-acetamido-2-deoxy-D-glucose

Ref.

Specificity and kinetic constants

The enzyme is inactive with phenyl α-N-acetyl-D-glucosaminide. (1,2)

source	substrate[a]	$\dfrac{V}{(relative)}$	$K_m(M)$	conditions	
Beef liver	trisaccharide	1.00	1.54×10^{-2}	pH 4.3, citrate, 37°	(1)
	p-nitrophenyl glycoside	36.7	1.02×10^{-3}		
	phenyl glycoside	25.0	3.0×10^{-3}		
Pig epididymis	phenyl glycoside	-	2.1×10^{-3}	pH 4.25, citrate, 37°	(2)
	p-nitrophenyl glycoside	-	3.1×10^{-3}		

[a] See Abbreviations

Inhibitors

source	inhibitor	type	$K_i(M)$	conditions	
Bovine liver	acetamide	C(trisaccharide)	1.09×10^{-2}	pH 4.3, citrate, 37°	(1)
		C(p-nitrophenyl glycoside)	7.1×10^{-3}		
	N-acetylglucosaminonolactone	C(trisaccharide)	4×10^{-6}		
		C(p-nitrophenyl glycoside)	7×10^{-7}		
	trisaccharide	C(p-nitrophenyl glycoside)	4.5×10^{-3}		
		C(phenyl glycoside)	5.7×10^{-3}		
Pig epididymis	N-acetylglucosaminonolactone	C(phenyl glycoside)	5.0×10^{-7}	pH 4.25, citrate, 37°	(2)
	N-acetylgalactosaminonolactone		1.4×10^{-6}		

Abbreviations

phenyl glycoside	phenyl β-N-acetyl-D-glucosaminide
p-nitrophenyl glycoside	p-nitrophenyl β-N-acetyl-D-glucosaminide
trisaccharide	β-D-Glc p NAc-(1→4)- β-D-Glc p A-(1→3)- D-Glc p N Ac

References

1. Weissmann, B., Hadjiioannou, S. & Tornheim, J. (1964) JBC, 239, 59.
2. Findlay, J. & Levvy, G. A. (1960) BJ, 77, 170.

β-ACETYLGLUCOSAMINIDASE

(β-2-Acetamido-2-deoxy-D-glucoside
acetamidodeoxyglucohydrolase)

β-Phenyl-2-acetamido-2-deoxy-D-glucoside + H_2O =
phenol + 2-acetamido-2-deoxy-D-glucose

Ref.

Molecular weight

source	value	conditions	
Rat kidney	150 - 160,000	Sephadex G200, pH 7.6	(1)

Specificity

The enzyme attacks both N-acetyl-β-glucosaminides and N-acetyl-β-galactosaminides. It hydrolyzes the terminal glucosaminidic bonds of odd-numbered oligosaccharides to yield N-acetylglucosamine and the next lower even-numbered oligosaccharide. (2,5)

Michaelis constants

source	substrate	$K_m(M)$	conditions	
Diplococcus pneumonia	PNPGNAc	2.2×10^{-4}	pH 5.3, P_i-citrate, 37°	(3)
Rat epididymis	phenyl-N-acetyl-β-glucosaminide	7.1×10^{-4}	pH 4.3, citrate, 38°	(5)
	PNPGNAc	4.0×10^{-4}		
Limpet	phenyl-N-acetyl-β-glucosaminide -	6.4×10^{-3}		
	PNPGNAc	3.8×10^{-3}		
Rat kidney	phenyl-N-acetyl-β-glucosaminide	1.78×10^{-3}	pH 4.3, citrate, 37°	(4)

Inhibitors

source	inhibitor	type	$K_i(M)$	conditions	
Rat epididymis	N-acetylglucos-aminonolactone	$c^{(a)}$	7.2×10^{-7}	pH 4.3, citrate, 38°	(5)
	N-acetylgalactos-aminonolactone		4.0×10^{-7}		
Rat kidney	acetamide	$c^{(a)}$	1.02×10^{-2}	pH 4.3, citrate, 37°	(4)
	acetate		1.7×10^{-2}		
	N-acetylglucosamine		4.4×10^{-3}		

(a) With respect to phenyl N-acetyl-β-glucosaminide as substrate.

Abbreviations

PNPGNAc p-nitrophenyl 2-acetamido-2-deoxy-β-D-glucopyranoside

References

1. Robinson, D., Price, R. G. & Dance, N. (1967) BJ, 102, 525.

2. Linker, A., Meyer, K. & Weissmann, B. (1955) JBC, 213, 237.

3. Hughes, R. C. & Jeanloz, R. W. (1964) B, 3, 1543.

4. Pugh, D., Leaback, D. H. & Walker, P. G. (1957) BJ, 65, 464.

5. Findlay, J., Levvy, G. A. & Marsh, C. A. (1958) BJ, 69, 467.

β-GLUCURONIDASE

(β-D-Glucuronide glucuronohydrolase)

A β-D-glucuronide + H_2O = an alcohol + D-glucuronate

Ref.

Molecular weight

source	value	conditions	
Human liver	218,000	pH 9.1	(2)
Rat kidney	210,000	Sephadex G200, pH 7.3	(3)

Specific activity[a]

Bovine liver	(18,000)	12	phenolphthalein β-glucuronide (pH 5.0, acetate, 37°)	(4)
Human liver	(2,900 x)	3	phenolphthalein β-glucuronide (pH 4.3, acetate, 37°)	(2)

---

[a]In the literature specific activities are expressed in terms of Fishman units. One Fishman unit, which is the amount of enzyme required to liberate 1×10^{-6}g of phenolphthalein from phenolphthalein β-glucuronide per hour at 37°, is the equivalent to 5.2×10^{-5} international units.

Specificity

The enzyme attacks all the natural β-D-glucosiduronates whether glycoside- or acylal-linked, aliphatic or aromatic. It is without activity on α-glucuronides or β-glucosides. (1)

Michaelis constants[a]

source	substrate	$K_m(M)$	conditions	Ref.
Human liver	phenolphthalein β-glucuronide	4×10^{-4}	pH 4.3, acetate, 37°	(2)
Female rat preputial gland	phenolphthalein β-glucuronide	5.7×10^{-5}	pH 4.5, acetate, 38°	(5)
	phenyl β-glucuronide	5.1×10^{-4}		
	phenyl β-galacturonide	6.5×10^{-3}		
	o-nitrophenyl β-galacturonide	8.4×10^{-4}		

(a)

These depend to a large extent on the purity of the enzyme under investigation. (6)

Inhibitors

source	inhibitor	type	$K_i(M)$	conditions	Ref.
Female rat preputial gland	saccharo-1,4-lactone	C(phenolphthalein-β-glucuronide)	1.1×10^{-7}	pH 4.5, acetate, 38°	(5)
	glucuronate	C(β-phenyl glucuronide)	1.5×10^{-3}		
	galacturonate	C(β-phenyl glucuronide)	4.3×10^{-3}		

The enzyme from human liver is subject to inhibition by excess substrate. (2)

References

1. Levvy, G. A. & Marsh, C. A. (1960) The Enzymes, 4, 397.
2. Musa, B. U., Doe, R. P. & Seal, U. S. (1965) JBC, 240, 2811.
3. Robinson, D., Price, R. G. & Dance, N. (1967) BJ, 102, 525.
4. Plapp, B. V., Hopkins, T. R. & Cole, R. D. (1963) JBC, 238, 3315.
5. Levvy, G. A., McAllan, A. & Marsh, C. A. (1958) BJ, 69, 22.
6. Marsh, C. A. (1961) Biochemist's Handbook, p227.
7. Marsh, C. A. & Levvy, G. A. (1958) BJ, 68, 610.

DEXTRIN-1,6-GLUCOSIDASE

(Dextrin 6-glucanohydrolase)

Hydrolyses a-1,6-glucan links in dextrins containing
short 1,6-linked side-chains.

Ref.

Molecular weight

source	value	conditions	
Rabbit muscle	267,000–279,000	various	(1)

Specificity

The rabbit muscle enzyme has a second enzymic activity: oligo-
$1,4 \rightarrow 1,4$-glucantransferase. (The two activities have not been
separated). The specificity of the enzyme is discussed in reference (1).

Michaelis constants

source	activity	substrate	$\frac{V}{(\text{relative})}$	$K_m(M)$	conditions
Rabbit muscle	dextrin-1,6-glucosidase	limit dextrin (end group = 12.9%)	–	7.4×10^{-4} [a]	pH 6, citrate, (1) 30°
	1,4-glucantransferase	branched heptasaccharide	1.0	5.6×10^{-3}	pH 6.6, citrate, (1) 30°
		branched pentasaccharide	5.5	1.8×10^{-3}	

[a] Expressed as total polymeric glucose.

References

1. Brown, D. H. & Illingworth Brown, B. (1966) Methods in Enzymology, 8, 515.

HYALURONIDASE

(Hyaluronate glycanohydrolase)

Hydrolyzes links between 2-acetamido-2-deoxy-D-glucose

and D-glucuronate residues in hyaluronate

Molecular weight

Ref.

source	value	conditions	
Rat liver	89,000	pH 7.4	(2)
Bovine testis	43,200	pH 7.5	(3)

Specific activity

Rat liver (1300 x) 1.29 N-acetylglucosamine released from   (2)
hyaluronate[a] (pH 3.5, acetate, 37°)

[a] Isolated from human umbilical cord

Specificity

   Hyaluronidase catalyzes the hydrolyses of links between 2-aceta-
mido-2-deoxy-D-glucose and D-glucuronate residues in hyaluronate. In
addition, the enzyme attacks chondroitin and mucoitin sulphate. It
also exhibits transglycosylation activity.   (1)

   Hexasaccharide is the lowest molecular weight substrate for the
testicular enzyme while octasaccharide is the minimum size substrate
for the rat liver enzyme.   (2)

Michaelis constants

source	substrate	$K_m(\text{mgml}^{-1})$	conditions	
Rat liver	hyaluronate[a]	8×10^{-2}	pH 3.5, acetate, 37°	(2)

[a] Isolated from human umbilical cord

Inhibitors

   The enzyme (rat liver) is inhibited by chondroitin sulphate B
(C(hyaluronate); $K_i = 3.8 \times 10^{-4}\text{mgml}^{-1}$), desulphated chondroitin
sulphate B, heparitin sulphate, keratosulphate and heparin. High
concentrations of hyaluronate are also inhibitory. The inhibition
by these compounds is reversed by NaCl or protamine sulphate.   (2)

References

1. Meyer, K., Hoffman, P. & Linker, A. (1960) The Enzymes, 4, 447.

2. Aronson, N. N., Jr. & Davidson, E. A. (1967) JBC, 242, 437, 441.

3. Brunish, R. & Högberg, B. (1960) Compt. Rend. Trav. Lab.

    Carlsberg 32, 35.

β-D-FUCOSIDASE

(β-D-Fucoside fucohydrolase)

A β-D-fucoside + H_2O = an alcohol + D-fucose

Kinetic constants

source	substrate or inhibitor	$K_m(M)$	$K_i(M)$	conditions
Patella vulgata [a]	p-nitrophenyl-β-D-fucoside	6.3×10^{-4}	-	
	galactonolactone	-	1.9×10^{-3} [b]	pH 3.7, citrate-P_i, $37°$ (1)
	fuconolactone	-	1.2×10^{-5} [b]	

---

[a] Limpet

[b] C(p-nitrophenyl-β-D-fucoside)

The enzyme is inactive towards o-nitrophenyl-β-D galactoside.   (1)

References

1. Levvy, G. A. & McAllan, A. (1963) BJ, 87, 206.

NUCLEOSIDASE

(N-Ribosyl-purine ribohydrolase)

An N-ribosyl-purine + H_2O = a purine + D-ribose

Specificity

substrate	Relative velocity		
	Lactobacillus delbrueckii[a]	Baker's yeast[b]	Ophiodon elongatus[c]
inosine	1.00	1.00	1.00
adenosine	1.03	0.94	1.07
guanosine	0.90	0.42	1.36
cytidine	0.54	0	0.28
uridine	0.07	0	0
thymine riboside	0.04	-	-
nicotinamide riboside	1.50	-	-
xanthosine	-	-	0.28

[a]From reference (1). The conditions were: pH 6.0, citrate, room temperature.

[b]From reference (2). The conditions were: pH 7.4, glycylglycine, 37°.

[c](Ling cod) From reference (3). The conditions were: pH 5.5, acetate, 37°.

The effectiveness of various synthetic compounds as substrates is discussed in references (1) and (2).

Michaelis constants

source	substrate	$K_m(M)$	conditions	
L. delbrueckii	inosine	3.1×10^{-4}	pH 6.0, ci-trate, room temperature	(1)
	cytidine	1.45×10^{-3}		
	uridine	2.51×10^{-3}		

References

1. Takagi, Y. & Horecker, B. L. (1957) JBC, 225, 77.
2. Heppel, L. A. & Hilmoe, R. J. (1952) JBC, 198, 683.
3. Tarr, H. L. A. (1955) BJ, 59, 386.

URIDINE NUCLEOSIDASE

(Uridine ribohydrolase)

Uridine + H_2O = uracil + D-ribose

Ref.

Specificity

The enzyme is highly specific. Thus, that from Phasedus radiatus (Mung bean) did not hydrolyze deoxyuridine, thymidine, cytidine, deoxycytidine, adenosine, guanosine, inosine or uridylate (2) and that from yeast was without activity on adenosine, guanosine, inosine, cytidine or thymidine (3).

Michaelis constants

source	substrate	$K_m(M)$	conditions	
P. radiatus	uridine	1×10^{-3}	pH 7.5, P_i, 30°	(2)

Light absorption data

Δ_ε (uridine-uracil) at 280 mμ = 2100 M^{-1} cm^{-1} (pH 7.0)   (1)

References

1. Wang, T. P. (1955) Methods in Enzymology, 2, 461.

2. Achar, B. S. & Vaidyanathan, C. S. (1967) ABB, 119, 356.

3. Carter, C. E. (1951) JACS, 73, 1508.

AMP NUCLEOSIDASE

(AMP phosphoribohydrolase)

AMP + H_2O = adenine + D-ribose 5-phosphate

Specificity

AMP nucleosidase from <u>Azotobacter</u> <u>vinelandii</u> is highly specific for AMP which could not be replaced by the following compounds: adenosine, inosine, adenosine 3-phosphate, deoxyadenosine, deoxyuridine, deoxycytidylate, thymidylate, deoxyguanosine, deoxyadenylate, GMP, IMP, CMP, UMP, AMP polymer, 5'-phosphoadenosine 3'-adenosine 5'-phosphate and 3'-phosphouridine 5'-adenosine 3'-phosphate. (1,2)

The enzyme requires ATP for activity. The following compounds could not replace ATP: GTP, ITP, CTP, UTP, 5-phospho-α-D-ribosyl-pyrophosphate and ribose triphosphate. The following compounds could partially or completely replace ATP: PP_i, tripolyphosphate and adenosine tetraphosphate. (1,2)

Michaelis constants

source	substrate	V (relative)	K_m(M)	conditions
A. vinelandii	AMP	-	6×10^{-4}	
	ATP	1.0	1×10^{-4}	
	adenosine tetraphosphate	1.0	5×10^{-4}	pH 7.95, Tris, 37.5° (1,2)
	tripolyphosphate	0.50	1×10^{-3}	
	Mg^{2+}(a)	-	1.1×10^{-4}	

(a)Mg^{2+} could be replaced by Ca^{2+}, Mn^{2+} or Co^{2+} but Fe^{2+} and Zn^{2+} were inactive.

Inhibitors

The following compounds inhibited the enzyme from A. vinelandii: P_i, arsenate and IMP (but not UMP). (1,2)

References

1. Hurwitz, J., Heppel, L. A. & Horecker, B. L. (1957) JBC, 226, 525.
2. Heppel, L. A. (1963) Methods in Enzymology, 6, 117.

NAD NUCLEOSIDASE

(NAD glycohydrolase)

$$NAD + H_2O = nicotinamide + R$$
$$(R\text{-nicotinamide} = NAD)$$

Ref.

Molecular weight

source	value	conditions	
Mouse Ehrlich ascites cells	60,000	pH 7.0	(1)

Specificity and Michaelis constants

The enzyme (Mycobacterium tuberculosis) cleaved NAD and NADP at equal rates but the following were not attacked: NMN, acetylpyridine-adenine dinucleotide, acetylpyridine-hypoxanthine dinucleotide and the reduced forms of NAD and NADP (2). The enzymes isolated from other sources exhibit similar specificity properties (1,3,4,6). The enzyme isolated from mouse Ehrlich ascites cells also exhibits trans-glycosidase activity (6).

source	substrate	relative velocity	K_m(M)	conditions	
M. tuberculosis	NAD	1.00	3.3×10^{-4}	pH 6.5, P_i,	(2)
	NADP	1.00	3.1×10^{-4}	$37°$	
Bull semen	NAD	1.00	8.7×10^{-4}	pH 8.15, Tris,	(3)
	NADP	0.88	9.9×10^{-4}	$38°$	
Aspergillus niger	NAD	1.00	7.7×10^{-6}	pH 7.5, P_i,	(4)
	NADP	1.05	-	$37°$	
Neurospora crassa	NAD	-	5.0×10^{-4}	pH 7.2, P_i,	(5)
				$37°$	
Mouse Ehrlich ascites cells	NAD	1.00	6.0×10^{-5}	pH 7.2,	
	NADP	0.43	-		
	thionicotin-amide-adenine dinucleotide	0.60	-	P_i,	(1,6)
	nicotinamide - inosine dinucleotide	0.25	-	$37°$	

References

1. Green, S. & Bodansky, O. (1965) JBC, 240, 2574.
2. Gopinathan, K. P., Sirsi, M. & Vaidyanathan, C. S. (1964) BJ, 91, 277.
3. Abdel-Latif, A. A. & Alivisatos, S. G. A. (1962) JBC, 237, 500.
4. Sarma, D. S. R., Rajalakshmi, S. & Sarma, P. S. (1964) BBA, 81, 311.
5. Kaplan, N. O. (1955) Methods in Enzymology, 2, 660, 664.
6. Green, S. & Bodansky, O. (1964) JBC, 239, 2613.

NAD(P) NUCLEOSIDASE

(NAD(P) glycohydrolase)

$$NAD(P) + H_2O = \text{nicotinamide} + P(R)$$
R-nicotinamide represents NAD

Ref.

Specificity and Michaelis constants

source	substrate	relative velocity	$K_m(M)$	conditions	
Pig spleen	NADP	1.00	6.0×10^{-6}	pH 7.2, Tris, 37°	(1)
	NAD	0.85	2.3×10^{-5}		
	acetyl pyridine-NADP	0.65	-		
	desamino-NAD	0.43	-		
	acetyl pyridine-NAD	0.09	-		

Isonicotinate hydrazide-NAD, nicotinate-NAD and pyridine 3-aldehyde-NAD are slowly hydrolyzed but NMN, nicocinamide riboside and α-NAD are inactive (1). The transglycosidase activity of the enzyme is discussed in reference (1).

Inhibitors

The enzyme (pig spleen) is inhibited by nicotinamide (NC(NAD)). (1)

References

1. Dickerman, H. W., San Pietro, A. & Kaplan, N. O. (1962) BBA, 62, 230.

ADENOSINE NUCLEOSIDASE

(Adenosine ribohydrolase)

$$\text{Adenosine} + H_2O = \text{adenine} + D\text{-ribose}$$

Ref.

Specificity

The enzyme (<u>Brassica</u> <u>oleracea</u>) is highly specific for **adenosine;** only adeninosine was hydrolyzed among the naturally occurring nucleosides. Adenosine N-oxide (0.86) and purine riboside (0.11) were also hydrolysed. (1)

Michaelis constants

source	substrate	$K_m(M)$	conditions	
B. oleracea (Brussels sprouts)	adenosine	2.4×10^{-3}	pH 4.0, ace-tate, room temperature	(1)

Inhibitors

Adenine, one of the products of the reaction, is a potent inhibitor. (1)

References

1. Mazelis, M. & Creveling, R. K. (1963) JBC, 238, 3358.

ADENOSYLHOMOCYSTEINASE

(S-Adenosyl-L-homocysteine hydrolase)

S-Adenosyl-L-homocysteine + H_2O =

adenosine + L-homocysteine

Equilibrium constant

$$\frac{[\text{adenosine}]\,[\text{L-homocysteine}]}{[\text{S-adenosyl-L-homocysteine}]} = 1.4 \times 10^{-6} \quad (\text{pH } 6.3,\ \text{succinate},\ 37°)\ (1,2)$$

Specificity

Adenosylhomocysteinase from rat liver is highly specific for both of its substrates in the reverse reaction. Thus, L-homocysteine could not be replaced by the following compounds: D-homocysteine, L-cysteine, glutathione, CoA, 3-mercaptoethylamine, 3-mercapto-ethanol or thioglycollate and adenosine could not be replaced by inosine, 2-deoxyadenosine, guanosine, 2-deoxyguanosine, xanthosine, cytidine, 2-deoxycytidine, uridine, thymidine, 2'-, 3'-, or 5'-adenylate, ribose or serine. (1,2)

References

1. de la Haba, G. & Cantoni, G. L. (1959) JBC, 234, 603.

2. de la Haba, G. (1962) Methods in Enzymology, 5, 752.

LEUCINE AMINOPEPTIDASE

(L-Leucyl-peptide hydrolase)

An L-leucyl-peptide + H_2O = L-leucine + a peptide

Ref.

Molecular weight

source	value	conditions	
Swine kidney	300,000	pH 8.5	(2)

Specific activity

Swine kidney   ~600   L-leucine amide   (pH 8.5, N-ethylmorpholine, (3) 25°)

Specificity and Michaelis constants

source	substrate	$\frac{V}{(relative)}$	$K_m(M)$	conditions	
Swine kidney (Mg^{2+} activated enzyme)	L-leucine amide	1.00	5.21×10^{-3}		
	L-leucylglycine	0.70	1.00×10^{-3}		
	L-leucylvaline	0.73	5.1×10^{-4}	pH 8.4, N-ethyl-	
	L-leucylalanine	0.66	7.9×10^{-4}	morpho-	(3)
	L-leucine benzyl ester	0.35	1.56×10^{-3}	line,	
(Mn^{2+} activated enzyme)	L-leucine amide	4.45	1.57×10^{-2}	25°	
	L-leucylglycine	2.02	8.1×10^{-4}		
	L-leucylvaline	3.08	1.04×10^{-3}		
	L-leucylalanine	2.02	6.5×10^{-4}		
	L-leucine benzyl ester	0.55	1.1×10^{-3}		

A large number of peptides and amino acid amides of the L-configuration are hydrolyzed (1,4). The enzyme has esterase activity (1,3).

Inhibitors

The enzyme is inhibited by glycerol and n-butanol (3) and compounds containing large aliphatic side chains compete with the substrate for the hydrophobic region of the active site. (1)

References

1. Smith, E. L. & Hill, R. L. (1960) The Enzymes, 4, 37.

2. Spackman, D. H., Smith, E. L. & Brown, D. M. (1955) JBC, 212, 255.

3. Bryce, G. F. & Rabin, B. R. (1964) BJ, 90, 509.

4. Smith, E. L. & Polglase, W. J. (1949) JBC, 180, 1209.

AMINOPEPTIDASE

(Amino-acyl-oligopeptide hydrolase)

An amino-acyl-oligopeptide + H_2O =
an amino acid + an oligopeptide

Ref.

Molecular weight

source	value	conditions	
Pig kidney	280,000	Sephadex G200, pH 7.2	(1)

Specific activity

Pig kidney (210 x) 37.3 L-leucine-p-nitroanilide   (1)
(pH 7.0, P_i, 37°)

Specificity and kinetic constants

Aminopeptidase splits off the N-terminal residue from di- and tri-peptides. Only derivatives of α-amino acids are attacked, derivatives of secondary amino groups (e.g. proline amide) are not hydrolyzed.   (1)

source	substrate	$\frac{V}{(relative)}$	$K_m(M)$	conditions	
Pig kidney	L-leucine p-nitroanilide	1.00	2.4×10^{-4}		
	L-alanine p-nitroanilide	1.39	6×10^{-4}		
	glycine p-nitroanilide	0.31	1.75×10^{-3}	pH 7.0, P_i, 37°	(1)
	L-alanine amide	0.011	-		
	L-norvaline amide	0.004	-		
	L-norleucine amide	0.004	-		

Inhibitors

The enzyme from pig kidney is inhibited by several amino acids of which L-norleucine, L-phenylalanine and L-leucine are particularly effective. The inhibition is competitive.   (1)

Light absorption data

p-nitrophenol[a] ε, (405 mμ) = 9620 M^{-1} cm^{-1} (pH 7.0)   (1)

[a]A product of the hydrolysis of L-leucine-p-nitroanilide

References

1. Wachsmuth, E. D., Fritze, I. & Pfleiderer, G. (1966) B, 5, 169, 175.

AMINOPEPTIDASE

(Amino-acyl-dipeptide hydrolase)

An amino-acyl-dipeptide + H_2O = an amino acid + a dipeptide

Specificity and Michaelis constants

Aminopeptidase hydrolyzes a variety of tripeptides at the N-terminal bond. It is without effect on dipeptides, dipeptide amides, acyl tripeptides, tripeptide amides or tetrapeptides.　(1)

substrate	relative velocity		
	Calf thymus[a]	Horse erythrocyte[b]	Human erythrocyte[c]
glycylglycylglycine	1.00	1.00	1.00
L-leucylglycylglycine	0.88	0.80	2.5
D-leucylglycylglycine	0	0	-
L-alanylglycylglycine	1.08	1.75	7
glycylglycyl-L-proline	0.71	0.55	-
L-prolylglycylglycine	-	2.35	-
L-hydroxyprolylglycylglycine	-	0.40	-
glycyl-L-prolylglycine	-	0	-
glycyl-L-leucylglycine	0.98	-	-
glycyl-D-leucylglycine	0	-	-
glycylglycyl-L-leucine	0.40	-	-
glycylglycyl-D-leucine	0.09	-	-

[a] From references (1), (2) and (3). The conditions were: pH 7.9, veronal, 38°.

[b] From references (1) and (4). The conditions were: pH 7.8, Tris.

[c] From reference (5). The conditions were: pH 8.0, P_i. This enzyme has been purified 1000x and has a specific activity of 180 with L-alanylglycylglycine as substrate.

source	substrate	$K_m(M)$	conditions
Human erythrocyte	glycylglycylglycine	5×10^{-2}	pH 8.0, P_i.
	L-alanylglycylglycine	4×10^{-2}	
	L-leucylglycylglycine	4×10^{-2}	

(5)

References

1. Smith, E. L. (1955) Methods in Enzymology, 2, 83.
2. Fruton, J. S., Smith, V. A. & Driscoll, P. E. (1948) JBC, 173, 457.
3. Ellis, D. & Fruton, J. S. (1951) JBC, 191, 153.
4. Adams, E., Davis, N. C. & Smith, E. L. (1952) JBC, 199, 845.
5. Tsuboi, K. K., Penefsky, Z. J. & Hudson, P. B. (1957) ABB, 68, 54.

PROLINE IMINOPEPTIDASE

(L-Prolyl-peptide hydrolase)

An L-prolyl-peptide + H_2O = L-proline + a peptide

Ref.

Specificity

Proline iminopeptidase from Escherichia coli cleaves NH-terminal L-proline residues irrespective of the size of the molecule in which they occur. NH-terminal L-hydroxyproline residues are not cleaved. Thus the enzyme attacked polyproline (1.00), L-prolylglycine (0.40), L-prolylglycylglycine (0.40) and L-prolyl-L-proline but not L-hydroxy-prolylglycine, carbobenzoxy-L-prolyl-L-proline, tosyl-L-prolyl-L-proline, glycyl-L-proline, glycyl-L-prolylglycine, glycylglycyl-L-proline, glycylglycylglycine, L-leucylglycylglycine, glycyl-L-tyrosine, glycyl-L-leucine, L-tyrosylglycine, glycylglycine or L-hydroxyprolylglycine. (1,2)

Proline iminopeptidase requires Mn^{2+} specifically: Mg^{2+}, Li^+, Ca^{2+}, Ce^{2+} or Cr^{3+} were inactive and Cd^{2+}, Co^{2+}, Cu^{2+}, Fe^{2+}, Fe^{3+}, Hg^{2+} or Zn^{2+} were inhibitory. (1,2)

References

1. Sarid, S., Berger, A. & Katchalski, E. (1959) JBC, 234, 1740.
2. Sarid, S., Berger, A. & Katchalski, E. (1962) JBC, 237, 2207.

CARBOXYPEPTIDASE A

(Peptidyl-L-amino-acid hydrolase)

A peptidyl-L-amino acid + H_2O = a peptide + an L-amino acid

Ref.

Molecular weight

source	value	conditions	
Bovine pancreas	32,000 - 34,300	various	(1,5)

Specificity and kinetic constants[*]

The enzyme attacks N-acyl peptides, N-acyl amino acids and O-acyl hydroxy acids when the following conditions are met:

1) the terminal residue (which must be of the L-configuration) possess a free carboxyl group,

2) the amino or hydroxyl group in the terminal residue is in a position α to the carboxyl group,

3) the hydrogen in the susceptible peptide bond is unsubstituted. (1,2,3)

Data on the alteration in enzyme activity and specificity induced by metal ions, anhydrides, iodination or photooxidation are summarized in reference (4).

substrate	$k_o(sec^{-1})$	$K_m(M)$	conditions	
carbobenzoxyglycyl-L-phenyl-alanine(a)	106	5.83×10^{-3}	pH 7.5,	
hippuryl-DL-β-phenyllactate	578	8.8×10^{-5}	Tris, 25°	(6)
hippuryl-L-phenylalanine	118	1.91×10^{-3}		
furylacryloylphenyllactate	47	1.32×10^{-4}	pH 7.5, 25°(7)	

────────────

[a] The kinetic constants for several other carbobenzoxyglycyl-L-amino acids are given in reference (8).

Inhibitors[*]

In general, compounds containing a free carboxyl group and an aromatic or heterocyclic ring are competitive inhibitors. Substrate inhibition phenomena are discussed in reference (9).   (1)

Inhibitors (contd.)

inhibitor[a]	K_i (M)	conditions	
phenylacetate	3.9×10^{-4}		
2-phenylpropionate	6.2×10^{-5}	pH 7.5, P_i, 25°	
3-phenylbutyrate	1.13×10^{-3}		(10,
D-phenylalanine	2.0×10^{-3}	S = carbobenzoxy glycyl-	
D-histidine	2.0×10^{-2}	L-phenylalanine	12)
hydrocinnamate	6.2×10^{-5}		
p-nitrophenylacetate	2.5×10^{-3}		
indoleacetate	7.8×10^{-5}	pH 7.5, veronal, 25°	
2-indolepropionate	5.5×10^{-3}	S = carbobenzoxy glycyl-	(11)
3-indolepropionate	3.3×10^{-3}	L-tryptophan	
2-cyclohexylpropionate	2.0×10^{-3}		

[a]Competitive.

Light absorption data

substrate	$\lambda (m\mu)$	$\Delta \varepsilon$ (substrate-products)	
hippurylphenyllactate	254	592 M^{-1} cm^{-1} (pH 7.5)	(9)
furylacryloylphenyllactate	320	14,400 M^{-1} cm^{-1} (pH 7.5)	(7)

*The data given are those of the enzyme isolated from bovine pancreas.

References

1. Neurath, H. (1960) The Enzymes, 4, 18.
2. Green, N. M. & Neurath, H. (1954) The Proteins, 2(B), 1057.
3. Smith, E. L. (1951) Advances in Enzymology, 12, 191.
4. Cunningham, L. (1965) Comprehensive Biochemistry, 16, 151.
5. Smith, E. L. & Stockell, A. (1954) JBC, 207, 501.
6. Whitaker, J. R., Menger, F. & Bender, M. L. (1966) B, 5, 386.
7. McClure, W. O. & Neurath, H. (1966) B, 5, 1425.
8. Slobin, L. I. & Carpenter, F. H. (1966) B, 5, 499.
9. McClure, W. O., Neurath, H. & Walsh, K. A. (1964) B, 3, 1897.
10. Elkins-Kaufman, E. & Neurath, H. (1948) JBC, 175, 893.
11. Smith, E. L., Lumry, R. & Polglase, W. J. (1951) J. Phys. & Colloid Chem., 55, 125.
12. Elkins-Kaufman, E. & Neurath, H. (1949) JBC, 178, 645.

CARBOXYPEPTIDASE B

(Peptidyl-L-lysine hydrolase)

A peptidyl-L-lysine + H_2O = a peptide + L-lysine

<u>Molecular weight</u>

source	value	conditions	
Porcine pancreas			
Bovine pancreas	34,000 - 35,000	various	(1,3)
Dog fish pancreas			

Specificity and kinetic constants[*]

The enzyme is more specific than carboxypeptidase A (3.4.2.1) in that the carboxyl terminal amino acid residue must be L-lysine, L-arginine or L-ornithine for full activity. The enzyme also hydrolyzes the ester analogs of the specific peptides.   (1)

Data on the alteration in enzyme activity and specificity induced by metal ions are summarized in reference (4).

substrate	$k_o(sec^{-1})$	$K_m(M)$	conditions	
hippuryl-L-lysine	220	7.7×10^{-3}		
hippuryl-L-arginine	105	2.1×10^{-4}	pH 8.0,	
hippuryl-L-ornithine	255	1.25×10^{-2}	Tris,	(2)
hippuryl-L-arginate	238	4.0×10^{-5}		
benzoyl-α-L-glutamyl-L-arginine	87	1.5×10^{-4}	23°	
α-benzoyl-L-lysyl-L-lysine	86	1.8×10^{-4}		

Inhibitors[*]

inhibitor[a]	$K_i(M)$	conditions	
L-arginine	5.0×10^{-4}	pH 8.0, Tris, 23°	
D-arginine	5.0×10^{-4}		(2)
N-acetyl-L-arginine	8.0×10^{-4}	S = hippuryl-L-	
N-acetyl-D-arginine	5.4×10^{-4}	arginine	

Inhibitors*(contd.)

inhibitor[a]	K_i(M)	conditions
N-benzoyl-L-arginine	4.0×10^{-5}	
L-aspartyl-L-arginine	2.2×10^{-4}	
L-arginate	2.5×10^{-4}	pH 8.0, Tris, 23°
L-ornithine	1.5×10^{-2}	
L-lysine	1.3×10^{-2}	S = hippuryl-L-arginine
N-benzoyl-L-lysine	1.1×10^{-3}	
DL-homoarginine	1.6×10^{-3}	

(2)

[a] Competitive.

*The data given are those of the enzyme isolated from bovine pancreas.

References

1. Neurath, H. (1960) The Enzymes, 4, 34.

2. Wolff, E. C., Schirmer, E. W. & Folk, J. E. (1962) JBC, 237, 3094.

3. Prahl, J. W. & Neurath, H. (1966) B, 5, 4137.

4. Folk, J. E., Wolff, E. C. & Schirmer, E. W. (1962) JBC, 237, 3100.

YEAST CARBOXYPEPTIDASE

(Peptidyl-glycine hydrolase)

A peptidyl-glycine + H_2O = a peptide + glycine

Specificity and Michaelis constants[a]

substrate	$\dfrac{V}{(\text{relative})}$	$K_m(M)$
carbobenzoxy-glycyl-L-leucine	1.00	4×10^{-3}
carbobenzoxy-glycylglycine	0.22	2×10^{-3}
DNP-glycylglycine	0.12	1.2×10^{-3}
DNP-glycyl-L-leucine	0.05	5×10^{-4}
hippuryl-DL-phenylalanine	0.05	1×10^{-3}
DNP-glycyl-DL-phenylalanine	0.01	1×10^{-4}

---

[a] The data refer to the enzyme from brewer's yeast. Conditions: pH 6.0, P_i, 37°. (1)

Abbreviations

DNP   2,4-dinitrophenol

References

1. Felix, F. & Labouesse-Mercouroff, J. (1956) BBA, 21, 303.

GLYCYL-GLYCINE DIPEPTIDASE

(Glycyl-glycine hydrolase)

Glycyl-glycine + H_2O = 2 glycine

Specificity and Michaelis constants

source	substrate	relative velocity	$K_m(M)$	conditions	
Rat liver	glycylglycine	1.00	5.5×10^{-2}		
	sarcosylglycine	0.08	-	pH 8.2-8.4,	
	glycylsarcosine	0.04	-	Tris, 35°	
	glycyl-L-proline	0.26	-	No metal	(1)
	glycyl-L-leucine	11.80	-	ion	
	glycyl-DL-phenylalanine	7.63	-		
	glycylglycine	5.22	3.7×10^{-2}		
	sarcosylglycine	0.36	-		
	glycylsarcosine	0.11	-	pH 8.2-8.4,	
	glycyl-L-proline	0.35	-	Tris, 35°	(1)
	glycyl-L-leucine	4.73	-	+ Co^{2+}	
	glycyl-DL-phenylalanine	4.89	-		

The enzyme is affected in different ways by different metal ions. Thus, Co^{2+} and Mn^{2+} activated and Ni^{2+}, Pb^{2+}, Zn^{2+}, Cu^{2+}, Cd^{2+} and Hg^{2+} inhibited the enzyme from rat liver. Mg^{2+} and Fe^{2+} were without effect (1). With the enzyme from rat muscle, the splitting of glycine-glycine was activated by Co^{2+} and to a lesser extent by Mn^{2+} (2).

Glycylglycine dipeptidase is inactive with carbobenzoxyglycylglycine, benzoylglycylglycine (2), N-acetylglycine or carbobenzoxy-glycine (1).

Inhibitors

source	inhibitor	type	$K_i(M)$	metal ion	conditions	
Rat liver	L-leucine	C(L-glycyl-glycine)	6.5×10^{-2}	none		
			8.5×10^{-4}	Co^{2+}(a)	pH 8.2-8.4,	
			2.1×10^{-4}	Co^{2+}(b)	Tris, 35°	(1)
			2.1×10^{-4}	Mn^{2+}(a)		

(a) 2×10^{-4}M
(b) 1×10^{-4}M

L-Isoleucine is also inhibitory (1).

References

1. Wilcox, H. G. & Fried, M. (1963) BJ, 87, 192.
2. Smith, E. L. (1948) JBC, 173, 571.

CARNOSINASE

(Amino-acyl-L-histidine hydrolase)

Amino-acyl-L-histidine + H_2O =

an amino acid + L-histidine

Specificity

Carnosinase isolated from swine kidney is a dipeptidase which acts on dipeptides containing L-histidine and **their amides.** A free amino group is essential for activity. The enzyme attacks the following compounds: β-alanyl-L-histidine (1.00), L-alanyl-L-histidine (1.50), glycyl-L-histidine (1.15), D-alanyl-L-histidine (0.89), glycyl-L-histidinamide (0.19), L-2-aminobutyryl-L-histidine (0.13), β-alanyl-D-histidine (0.01) and β-L-aspartyl-L-histidine (0.01). Carbobenzoxy-L-carnosine and carbobenzoxy-L-histidinamide are not hydrolyzed. (1,2)

The enzyme is activated by Mn^{2+} and Zn^{2+}. Other metals tested had either no effect or were slightly inhibitory. (1,2)

References

1. Hanson, H. T. & Smith, E. L. (1949) JBC, 179, 789.
2. Smith, E. L. (1955) Methods in Enzymology, 2, 93.

IMINODIPEPTIDASE

(L-Prolyl-amino-acid hydrolase)

An L-prolyl-amino acid + H_2O =

L-proline + an amino acid

Ref.

Specificity

Iminodipeptidase is specific for dipeptides and requires NH-terminal imino acids. Prolyl and hydroxyprolyl dipeptides are both attacked by the enzyme the latter being hydrolyzed the more rapidly. (1,2,3)

The enzyme from swine kidney (cortex) hydrolyzed the following compounds: L-hydroxyprolylglycine (1.00), L-prolyl-L-tyrosine (0.89), L-prolylglycine (0.68), L-hydroxyprolyl-L-tyrosine (0.63), L-hydroxyprolyl-L-phenylalanine (0.58), L-hydroxyprolyl-L-alanine (0.44), glycyl-L-proline (0.40), L-hydroxyprolyl-L-leucine (0.21) and L-prolyl-L-hydroxyproline (0.031). The following compounds were not hydrolyzed: tripeptides (e.g. L-prolylglycylglycine), polyproline, the amides of L-proline and L-hydroxyproline, L-prolyl-L-aspartate, L-hydroxyprolyl-L-aspartate and L-hydroxyprolyl-L-glutamate. (1,2,3)

References

1. Sarid, S., Berger, A. & Katchalski, E. (1962) JBC, 237, 2207.
2. Davis, N. C. & Smith, E. L. (1953) JBC, 200, 373.
3. Smith, E. L. (1955) Methods in Enzymology, 2, 97.

PROLIDASE

(Amino-acyl-L-proline hydrolase)

Amino-acyl-L-proline + H_2O = an amino acid + L-proline

Ref.

Molecular weight

source	value	conditions	
Swine kidney	150,000	pH 7.9	(1)

Specific activity

Swine kidney (12,000 x) 3500 glycyl-L-proline (pH 8.0, Tris, 40°)(1)

Specificity

Prolidase is a dipeptidase and catalyzes the hydrolysis of substrates in which the sensitive peptide bond involves the imino nitrogen of proline or hydroxyproline. Only substrates with free α-amino and α-carboxyl groups are attacked. The enzyme from swine kidney hydrolyzes the following compounds: glycyl-L-proline (1.00), glycyl-<u>allo</u>hydroxy-L-proline (0.32), glycylhydroxy-L-proline (0.12), L-phenylalanylhydroxy-L-proline (0.12), glycylsarcosine (0.09), β-alanyl-L-proline (0.002) and glycylmethoxy-L-proline (0.002). The following compounds were inactive: glycylglycyl-L-proline, glycyl-L-prolylglycine, carbobenzoxyglycyl-L-proline, carbobenzoxyglycyl-hydroxy-L-proline and dehydrophenylalanyl-L-proline.   (1)

The properties of the enzyme from equine erythrocytes are discussed in reference (2).

References

1. Davis, N. C. & Smith, E. L. (1957) JBC, 224, 261.

2. Smith, E. L. (1955) Methods in Enzymology, 2, 100.

PEPSIN

(Hydrolyses peptides, including those with bonds adjacent to aromatic or dicar-
boxylic L-amino acid residues)

Ref.

Molecular weight

source	value	conditions	
Porcine gastric juice	36,000	various	(1,2)

Specificity and kinetic constants[*]

The specificity of pepsin may be summarized as follows:

1) only the peptide bond is attacked: esters and amides are
   not hydrolysed,

2) both amino acids participating in the bond must be of the
   L-configuration,

3) acylation of the α-amino group increases the susceptibility
   of dipeptides,

4) a decreased rate of hydrolysis results when glutamate is
   replaced by glutamine.   (1,2,3)

substrate	$k_o(sec^{-1})$	$K_m(M)$	conditions	
acetyl-L-phenylalanyldiiodotyrosine	2×10^{-1}	7.5×10^{-5}	pH 2.0, glycine, 37°	(4)
acetyl-L-phenylalanyl-L-phenyl-alanine	1.19×10^{-2}	4.3×10^{-4}	pH 1.85, citrate, 37°	(6)
carbobenzoxy-L-glutamyl-L-tyrosine	1.08×10^{-3}	1.89×10^{-3}	pH 4.0, 31.6^o	(7)
carbobenzoxy-L-glutamyl-L-tyrosine ethyl ester	1.41×10^{-3}	1.78×10^{-3}		
acetyl-L-phenylalanyl-L-tyrosine	-	2.4×10^{-3}	pH 2.0, 37°	(10)
acetyl-L-tyrosyl-L-tyrosine	-	6.3×10^{-3}		

Inhibitors[*]

A number of alcohols inhibit competitively with binding constants decreasing with increase in chain length (K_i, methanol = 6.08 x 10^{-1}M, n-amylalcohol = 1.4 x 10^{-2} M). The pepsin protein inhibitor (molecular weight = 3242) is discussed in reference (9).   (8)

inhibitor[a]	K_i (M)	conditions	
acetyl-D-phenylalanyl-L-diiodotyrosine	8 x 10^{-5}	pH 2.0, glycine, $37°$	(4)
acetyl-L-diiodotyrosine	8.8 x 10^{-4}		
acetaminocinnamoyl-L-diidotyrosine	9 x 10^{-5}	pH 2.0, $35°$	(5)
acetyl-L-phenylalanyl-D-phenylalanine	1.4 x 10^{-3}	pH 1.85, citrate, $37°$	(6)
acetyl-D-phenylalanyl-L-phenylalanine	4.3 x 10^{-3}		

[a]Competitive.

[*]The data given are those of the enzyme isolated from porcine gastric juice.

References

1. Bovey, F. A. & Yanari, S. S. (1960) The Enzymes, 4, 63.

2. Cunningham, L. (1965) Comprehensive Biochemistry, 16, 173.

3. Green, N. M. & Neurath, H. (1954) The Proteins, 2(B), 1057.

4. Jackson, W. T., Schlamowitz, M. & Shaw, A. (1965) B, 4, 1537.

5. Silver, M. S. (1965) JACS, 87, 1627.

6. Cornish-Bowden, A. J. & Knowles, J. R. (1965) BJ, 96, 71P.

7. Casey, E. J. & Laidler, K. J. (1950) JACS, 72, 2159.

8. Tang, J. (1965) JBC, 240, 3810.

9. Van Vunakis, H. & Herriott, R. M. (1956) BBA, 22, 537.

10. Baker, L. E. (1954) JBC, 211, 701.

RENNIN

(Hydrolyses peptides; specificity may
be similar to that of 3.4.4.1)

Molecular weight

source	value	conditions	
Calf stomach	34,000	pH 2	(1)
	30,700	amino acid composition	(1)

Specificity

Rennin is somewhat more restricted in its action on proteins than pepsin (3.4.4.1). Thus pepsin inactivates ribonuclease (2.7.7.16) by splitting off a tetrapeptide from the C-terminus. Rennin has no effect on ribonuclease (1,3). No difference has been found between rennin and pepsin with synthetic substrates and both enzymes attack benzyloxycarbonylglutamyl-tyrosine, benzyloxycarbonylglutamyl-phenylalanine and poly-L-glutamic acid. (1)

The effect of rennin on κ-casein is discussed in reference (1).

References

1. Foltmann, B. (1966) Comp. Rend. Trav. Lab. Carlsberg, 35, 143.
2. Berridge, N. J. (1954) Advances in Enzymology, 15, 423.
3. Berger, A., Neumann, H. & Sela, M. (1959) BBA, 33, 249.

TRYPSIN

(Hydrolyses peptides, amides, esters, etc. at bonds involving the carboxyl group of L-arginine or L-lysine)

Ref.

Molecular weight

source	value	conditions	
Bovine pancreas	23,281	sequence studies	(4)
Porcine pancreas	23,400	pH 3.2	(5)

Specificity and kinetic constants[*]

substrate	$k_o(sec^{-1})$	$K_m(M)$	conditions
benzoyl-L-arginine ethyl ester	22	5×10^{-5}	pH 7.8-8.0,(1) 25°
benzoyl-L-argininamide	0.18	2.1×10^{-3}	
p-toluenesulphonyl-L-arginine methyl ester	147	5×10^{-5}	
L-lysine-p-nitroanilide	0.003	3.64×10^{-4}	pH 8-8.5, 15° (7)
benzoyl-L-arginine p-nitroanilide	0.611	9.39×10^{-4}	

   The kinetics of the hydrolysis of derivatives of arginine, homoarginine and ornithine are discussed in reference (11). Substrate activation phenomena are discussed in reference (9).

Inhibitors[*]

   The protein inhibitors are discussed in references (1) and (6).

inhibitor[(a)]	$K_i(M)$	conditions	
p-aminobenzamidine	8.25×10^{-6}	pH 8.15, 15°	(9)
benzamidine	1.84×10^{-5}		
acetamidine	3.65×10^{-2}		
phenylacetamidine	1.51×10^{-2}		
ethylamine	6.2×10^{-2}	pH 6.6, 25°	(10)
butylamine	1.7×10^{-3}		

[(a)]Competitive

*The data given are those of the enzyme isolated from bovine pancreas.

Light absorption data

substrate	$\lambda(m\mu)$	Δ_ε (substrate-products)	
benzoyl-L-arginine ethyl ester	255	808 M^{-1} cm^{-1} (pH 5-10)	(12)
p-toluenesulphonyl-L-arginine methyl ester	247	540 M^{-1} cm^{-1} (pH 8.1)	(13)
benzoyl-L-arginine-p-nitroanilide	410	8800 M^{-1} cm^{-1} (pH 8.2)	(7)

References

1. Cunningham, L. (1965) Comprehensive Biochemistry, 16, 85.

2. Desnuelle, P. (1960) The Enzymes, 4, 119.

3. Hill, R. L. (1965) Advances in Protein Chemistry, 20, 64.

4. Hofmann, T. (1964) B, 3, 356.

5. Travis, J. & Liener, I. E. (1965) JBC, 240, 1962.

6. Laskowski, M. & Laskowski, M. Jr. (1954) Advances in Protein Chemistry, 9, 203.

7. Erlanger, B. F., Kokowsky, N. & Cohen, W. (1961) ABB, 95, 271.

8. Trowbridge, C. G., Krehbiel, A. & Laskowski, M. Jr. (1963) B, 2, 843.

9. Mares-Guia, M. & Shaw, E. (1965) JBC, 240, 1579.

10. Inagami, T. & Murachi, T. (1963) JBC, 238, PC 1905.

11. Baines, N. J., Baird, J. B. & Elmore, D. T. (1964) BJ, 90, 470.

12. Kézdy, F. J., Lorand, L. & Miller, K. D. (1965) B, 4, 2302.

13. Hummel, B. C. W. (1959) Can. J. Biochem. Physiol., 37, 1393.

CHYMOTRYPSIN A

(Hydrolyses peptides, amides, esters etc. especially at bonds involving the carboxyl groups of aromatic L-amino acids)

Molecular weight

source	value	conditions	
Bovine pancreas	25,310	sequence studies	(11)
Chicken pancreas	20,000	light scattering,	
Turkey pancreas	22,500	pH 7.88	(9)

Specificity and kinetic constants

source	substrate	$k_o(sec^{-1})$	$K_m(M)$	conditions
Bovine pancreas	acetyl-L-tyrosine ethyl ester	193	7×10^{-4}	
	acetyl-L-tryptophan ethyl ester	46.5	9×10^{-5}	
	acetyl-L-phenylalanine ethyl ester	173*	1.2×10^{-3}	
	acetyl-L-phenylalanine methyl ester	63.1	1.8×10^{-3}	pH 7.8 -
	acetyl-L-tyrosinamide	0.44	3.4×10^{-2}	8.0,
	acetyl-L-tryptophanamide	0.036	5.0×10^{-3}	
	acetyl-L-phenylalaninamide	0.039	3.1×10^{-2}	(1,7,8)
	acetyl-L-leucine ethyl ester	4.61	2.9×10^{-2}	
	acetyl-L-alanine methyl ester	1.29	6.11×10^{-1}	25°
	acetyl-L-valine methyl ester	0.15	1.12×10^{-1}	
	acetyl glycine ethyl ester	0.013	9.6×10^{-2}	
	benzoyl-L-alanine methyl ester	0.26	9.75×10^{-3}	
	carbobenzoxy-L-tyrosine nitrophenyl ester	300	-	
	nitrophenyl acetate	0.0068	4×10^{-5}	
	benzoyl-L-leucine ethyl ester	0.07	1.25×10^{-2}	pH 7.8,
	benzoyl-L-phenylalanine ethyl ester	14.4	2.8×10^{-3}	Tris, 25°
	acetyl-L-tryptophan ethyl ester	15.8	1.3×10^{-3}	(13)
	benzoyl-L-tyrosine ethyl ester	43.0	2.6×10^{-3}	(30% methanol)
	benzoyl-L-methionine ethyl ester	0.97	3.1×10^{-3}	

Specificity and kinetic constants (contd.)

source	substrate	$k_o(\text{sec}^{-1})$	$K_m(M)$	conditions
Por-	benzoyl-L-leucine ethyl ester	1.46	1.1×10^{-2}	pH 7.8,
cine	benzoyl-L-phenylalanine ethyl ester	33.9	5.0×10^{-3}	Tris, 25°
pan-	acetyl-L-tryptophan ethyl ester	6.3	1.33×10^{-2}	(30%) [13]
creas	benzoyl-L-tyrosine ethyl ester	57.0	1.2×10^{-3}	methanol)
	benzoyl-L-methionine ethyl ester	1.12	2.9×10^{-3}	

*A value of 63.1 is reported in reference (4).

The kinetic constants obtained with other substrates are given in reference (1). The specificity of chymotrypsin towards the peptide bond is discussed in reference (6).

Inhibitors

source	inhibitor[a]	$K_i(M)$	conditions
Bovine	acetyl-L-tryptophan	1.75×10^{-2}	
pan-	acetyl-D-tryptophan	4.8×10^{-3}	
creas	acetyl-D-tryptophanamide	2.3×10^{-3}	
	acetyl-D-tryptophan methyl ester	9×10^{-5}	pH 7.8 -
	acetyl-L-tyrosine	1.15×10^{-1}	8.0, [1,7]
	acetyl-D-tyrosinamide	1.2×10^{-2}	Tris,
	acetyl-D-tyrosine ethyl ester	5.0×10^{-3}	25°
	acetyl-D-phenylalaninamide	1.2×10^{-2}	
	acetyl-D-phenylalanine methyl ester	2.5×10^{-3}	
	indole	7.2×10^{-4}	
	protein inhibitor[b] (source: Ascaris lumbricoides)	4.7×10^{-8}	pH 7.2, P_i, 37° [5]

[a]Competitive

[b]Molecular weight = 8600

The binding constants of a number of aromatic compounds are given in ref (10).

Light absorption data

substrate	$\lambda(m\mu)$	Δ_ϵ (substrate-products)
acetyl-L-tryptophan ethyl ester	300	234 M^{-1} cm^{-1} (pH 7) (4)
benzoyl-L-tyrosine ethyl ester	256	964 M^{-1} cm^{-1} (pH 7)(12)
acetyl-L-tyrosine ethyl ester	237	~ 400 M^{-1} cm^{-1} (pH 7)(14)

References
1. Cunningham, L. (1965) Comprehensive Biochemistry, 16, 85.
2. Desnuelle, P. (1960) The Enzymes, 4, 93.
3. Niemann, C. (1964) Science, 143, 1287.
4. Zerner, B., Bond, R.P.M. & Bender, M.L. (1964) JACS, 86, 3674.
5. Rola, F. H. & Pudles, J. (1966) ABB, 113, 134.
6. Hill, R. L. (1965) Advances in Protein Chemistry, 20, 68.
7. Zerner, B. & Bender, M. L. (1964) JACS, 86, 3669.
8. Bender, M. L., Kezdy, F.J. & Gunther, C.R. (1964) JACS, 86, 3714.
9. Ryan, C.A., Clary, J. J. & Tomimatsu, Y. (1965) ABB, 110, 175.
10. Wallace, R.A., Kurtz, A.N. & Niemann, C. (1963) B, 2, 824.
11. Eck, R.V. & Dayhoff, M.O. (1966) Atlas of Protein Sequence and Structure. National Biomedical Research Foundation, Silver Spring, Maryland, p. 64.
12. Hummel, B. C. W. (1959) Can. J. Biochem. Physiol., 37, 1393.
13. Folk, J. E. & Schirmer, E. W. (1965) JBC, 240, 181.
14. Patat, F. & Hirsch, H. (1966) Z. Naturforsch., 21, 36.

CHYMOTRYPSIN B

(Specificity similar to that of 3.4.4.5)

Molecular weight

source	value	conditions	
Bovine pancreas	24,850[a]	pH 3	(3)

[a]The molecular weight of chymotrypsinogen B.

Specificity and kinetic constants

source	substrate	$k_o(sec^{-1})$	$K_m(M)$	conditions	
Bovine pancreas	acetyl-L-tryptophan ethyl ester	0.71	2.1×10^{-3}		
	benzoyl-L-leucine methyl ester	0.11	7.2×10^{-3}	pH 7.8,	
	benzoyl-L-phenylalanine ethyl ester	16.2	2.3×10^{-3}	Tris,	(2)
	benzoyl-L-tyrosine ethyl ester	63.0	1.0×10^{-3}	$25°$	
	benzoyl-L-methionine ethyl ester	1.98	4.0×10^{-3}		

The specificity of the enzyme towards the peptide bonds of glucagon is reported in reference (4).

References

1. Desnuelle, P. (1960) The Enzymes, 4, 93.

2. Folk, J. E. & Schirmer, E. W. (1965) JBC, 240, 189.

3. Smillie, L. B., Enenkel, A. G. & Kay, C. M. (1966) JBC, 241, 2097.

4. Enenkel, A. G. & Smillie, L. B. (1963) B, 2, 1449.

PANCREATOPEPTIDASE E

Hydrolyzes peptides, especially at bonds
adjacent to neutral amino acid residues

Ref.

Molecular weight

source	value	conditions	
Pseudomonas aeruginosa	39,500	pH 10	(1)
Swine pancreas	25,000	pH 10	(2)

Specificity

Elastase (P. aeruginosa) hydrolyzes a number of proteins (e.g. denatured casein, haemoglobin, egg-albumin and fibrin) in addition to elastin. Synthetic substrates such as benzoyl-L-argininamide, acetyl-L-tyrosine ethyl ester, carbobenzoxy-L-glutamyl-L-tyrosine, carbobenzoxy-glycyl-L-phenylalanine and L-leucinamide were not hydrolyzed. (1)

The enzyme isolated from swine pancreas also catalyzed the hydrolysis of a number of proteins (elastin, haemoglobin, fibrin, casein, denatured collagen, albumin and soy bean protein but not hair keratin) and, in addition, of a number of synthetic substrates containing L-tyrosine, L-phenylalanine, L-glutamate or L-aspartate. (3,4)

References

1. Morihara, K., Tsuzuki, H., Oka, T., Inoue, H. & Ebata, M. (1965) JBC, 240, 3295.

2. Lewis, U. J., Williams, D. E. & Brink, N. G. (1956) JBC, 222, 705.

3. Mandl, I. (1962) Methods in Enzymology, 5, 665.

4. Grant, N. H. & Robbins, K. C. (1957) ABB, 66, 396.

CATHEPSIN C

Hydrolyzes peptides, especially at bonds
involving an aromatic amino acid adjacent
to a free α-amino group

Ref.

Molecular weight

source	value	conditions	
Beef spleen	210,000	pH 6.9	(2,5)

Specificity and kinetic constants

Cathepsin C hydrolyzes peptides, especially at bonds involving an aromatic amino acid adjacent to a free α-amino group. It also activates the terminal carbonyl groups of dipeptidyl derivatives (e.g. amides and esters) provided that the dipeptidyl unit has a free α-amino (or α-imino) group and is composed of L-α-amino acid (or glycine) residues. (1,2,3)

In addition to its hydrolytic properties cathepsin C catalyzes the polymerization of dipeptide amides. Thus, the enzyme polymerizes L-alanyl-L-phenylalaninamide to a hexapeptide amide; glycyl-L-phenylalaninamide to an octapeptide amide and glycyl-L-tyrosinamide to an octapeptide amide. (1,2,4)

source	substrate	$k_o(sec^{-1})$	$K_m(M)$	conditions	
Beef spleen[a]	glycyl-β-phenyl-L-lactate[b]	210	1.9×10^{-2}		
	glycyl-L-phenylalanine[b]	61	1.3×10^{-3}		
	glycyl-L-phenylalanine[c]	98	1.5×10^{-3}		
	glycyl-L-tyrosine[c]	90	6.3×10^{-4}	pH 5.0,	(3)
	glycyl-L-tryptophan[b]	293	1.5×10^{-3}	37°	
	glycyl-L-leucine[c]	126	4.0×10^{-3}		
	glycyl-glycine[c]	74	5.3×10^{-3}		
	sarcosyl-L-phenylalanine[c]	157	6.1×10^{-2}		

[a]The enzyme also catalyzed the hydrolysis of glycyl-L-tryptophanamide (1.00), glycyl-L-tyrosinamide (0.90), glycyl-L-phenylalaninamide (0.90), L-histidyl-L-phenylalaninamide (0.48), and L-histidyl-L-tyrosinamide (0.27).
[b]O-methyl ester.
[c]O-ethyl ester.

References

1. Fruton, J. S. (1960) The Enzymes, 4, 237.
2. Planta, R. J. & Gruber, M. (1964) BBA, 89, 503.
3. Voynick, I. M. & Fruton, J. S. (1968) B, 7, 40.
4. Nilsson, K. K. & Fruton, J. S. (1964) B, 3, 1220.
5. Metrione, R. M., Neves, A. G. & Fruton, J. S. (1966) B, 5, 1597.

PAPAIN
(Hydrolyses peptides, amides and esters especially at bonds
involving basic amino acids, or leucine or glycine)

Ref.

Molecular weight

source	value	conditions	
Papaya latex (Carica papaya)	21,000	various	(1,2)

Specificity and kinetic constants[a]

substrate	$k_0(sec^{-1})$	$K_m(M)$	conditions	
benzoyl-L-arginine ethyl ester	12.0	1.89×10^{-3}	pH 6, 38°	(3)
benzoyl-L-argininamide	11.0	3.9×10^{-2}		
hippuryl methyl ester	2.7	2.05×10^{-2}	pH 6.0, 35°	(5)
thionohippuryl methyl ester	0.14	6.3×10^{-3}		
hippurylamide	0.6	1.6×10^{-1}		
hippuryl methyl ester	3.1	2.1×10^{-2}	pH 6, 37 – 40°	(3)
carbobenzoxyhistidine amide	4.0	–		
carbobenzoxyglycylglycine	0.08	2.7×10^{-1}		
carbobenzoxyglycine p-nitrophenyl ester	2.73	9.3×10^{-6}		
carbobenzoxyglycine m-nitrophenyl ester	2.18	1.89×10^{-5}	pH 6.8, P_i, 25°	(6)
carbobenzoxyglycine o-nitrophenyl ester	2.14	1.52×10^{-4}		
carbobenzoxyglycine phenyl ester	2.45	1.07×10^{-4}		
carbobenzoxyglycine ethyl ester	1.96	5.14×10^{-3}		

The range of amino acid amides hydrolysed by papain is wide and includes, in descending order of activity, benzoyl-L-lysinamide, carbobenzoxy-L-glutamate diamide, carbobenzoxy-L-histidinamide, carbobenzoxy-L-leucinamide, L-leucinamide and hippurylamide. (8)

The synthetic activity of the enzyme is described in references (1) and (7).

Inhibitors[a]

Product inhibition phenomena are discussed in reference (3).

[a] The data given are those of the enzyme isolated from papaya latex.

Light absorption data

See trypsin (3.4.4.4).

References

1. Cunningham, L. (1965) Comprehensive Biochemistry, 16, 85.
2. Smith, E. L. & Kimmel, J. R. (1960) The Enzymes, 4, 133.
3. Sluyterman, L. A. E. (1964) BBA, 85, 305, 316.
4. Smith, E. L. & Parker, M. J. (1958) JBC, 233, 1387.
5. Lowe, G. & Williams, A. (1965) BJ, 96, 189.
6. Kirach, J. F. & Igelström, M. (1966) B, 5, 783.
7. Carty, R. P. & Kirschenbaum, D. M. (1964) BBA, 85, 446.
8. Dekker, C. A., Taylor, S. P. & Fruton, J. S. (1949) JBC, 180, 155.

CHYMOPAPAIN

Hydrolyzes peptides, etc.; its specificity is
similar to that of 3.4.4.10

Molecular weight

source	value	conditions	
Papaya latex (powder)	27,000	pH 7.2	(1)

Specific activity

The enzyme has been purified to homogeneity. (1)

Specificity

Chymopapain hydrolyzes a number of synthetic peptides, amides
and esters and its specificity is similar to that of papain (3.4.4.10).
Thus, the enzyme attacks N-benzoyl-L-argininamide and N-benzoyl-L-
arginine ethyl ester but it possesses no activity towards peptides,
amides or esters containing any of the aromatic amino acids. (1)

The enzyme is more active than papain in promoting the synthesis
of hippuryl anilide. (2)

References

1. Ebata, M. & Yasunobu, K. T. (1962) JBC, 237, 1086.
2. Carty, R. P. & Kirschenbaum, D. M. (1964) BBA, 85, 446.

FICIN

(Hydrolyses peptides, amides and esters; its specificity is similar to that of 3.4.4.10)

Ref.

Molecular weight

source	value	conditions	
Fig tree latex	26,000	pH 6.7	(3)

Specificity and kinetic constants[*]

substrate	$k_o(sec^{-1})$	$K_m(M)$	conditions	
benzoyl-L-arginine ethyl ester	1.4	2.5×10^{-2}		
benzoyl-L-arginine amide	1.1	4.8×10^{-2}	pH 6.25, 25°	(3,4)
hippuryl methyl ester	0.59	4.8×10^{-2}		
hippuryl amide	0.03	1.3×10^{-1}		
hippuryl methyl ester	3.5	4.8×10^{-2}	pH 6.0, 35° 30% acetone	(5)
thionohippuryl methyl ester	0.06	7.7×10^{-3}	pH 6.06, 25°	(5)

The synthetic properties of ficin are discussed in reference (6).

Inhibitors[*]

inhibitor[(a)]	$K_i(M)$	conditions	
benzoyl-L-arginine	6.0×10^{-2}	pH 5.5, 25°	(3)
benzoyl-L-arginine amide	5.4×10^{-2}		

[(a)]Competitive

Light absorption data

See trypsin (3.4.4.4)

[*]The data given are those of the enzyme isolated from fig tree latex.

References

1. Cunningham, L. (1965) Comprehensive Biochemistry, 16, 85.
2. Smith, E. L. & Kimmel, J. R. (1960) The Enzymes, 4, 168.
3. Bernhard, S. A. & Gutfreund, H. (1956) BJ, 63, 61.
4. Hammond, B. R. & Gutfreund, H. (1959) BJ, 72, 349.
5. Lowe, G. & Williams, A. (1965) BJ, 96, 189.
6. Murachi, T. (1956) ABB, 61, 468.

THROMBIN

Hydrolyzes peptides, amides and esters of

L-arginine; converts fibrinogen into fibrin

Molecular weight

Thrombin has a tendency to aggregate in solution. The aggregation is dependent on ionic strength, buffer type, pH and temperature. (3)

source	value	conditions	
Bovine blood	40,000	pH 7.0	(8)
Human blood	8,000	various	(3)
	32,600	titration with CTNE or CLNE	(4)

Specificity and kinetic constants

Thrombin converts fibrinogen to fibrin and, in addition, hydrolyzes peptides, amides and esters of L-arginine. Thus the bovine enzyme attacked TAME, BAEE, arginine methyl ester and benzoylargininamide but the following compounds were inactive: lysine ethyl ester, diethylaspartate, asparagine, asparagine methyl ester, acetylnorvaline methyl ester, norleucine methyl ester, valine methyl ester, acetylleucine ethyl ester and acetyltyrosine ethyl ester. (1,2,6)

source	substrate	$k_0(sec^{-1})$ [a]	$K_m(M)$	conditions	
Human blood	CTNE	0.22	7.2×10^{-6}	pH 5.02, acetate, 25°	(4)
	CLNE	0.72	2.1×10^{-5}		
	BAEE	16.5	5.6×10^{-5}	pH 8.75, Tris, 25°	(4)
	TAME	-	4×10^{-3}	pH 8.0, 37°	(6)
	fibrin	-	4.38×10^{-7}	pH 7.2, citrate-P_i, 37°	(5)

[a] The molecular weight of thrombin was assumed to be 32,600 daltons.

Inhibitors

The blood clotting activity of the enzyme was inhibited by TAME or N-toluenesulphonyl-L-argininylglycine. (7)

Ref.

Light absorption data

substrate	$\lambda(m\mu)$	Δ_ε(substrate-products)	pH	
CTNE	340	6220 M^{-1} cm^{-1}	pH 5.0	(4)
CLNE	340	6250 M^{-1} cm^{-1}	pH 5.0	(4)
BAEE	255	808 M^{-1} cm^{-1}	pH 5-10	(4)

Abbreviations

CTNE	N-carbobenzoxy-L-tyrosine p-nitrophenyl ester
CLNE	N-carbobenzoxy-L-lysine p-nitrophenyl ester
BAEE	N-benzoyl-L-arginine ethyl ester
TAME	N-toluenesulphonyl-L-arginine methyl ester

References

1. Waugh, D. F., Baughman, D. J. & Miller, K. D. (1960) The Enzymes, 4, 215.

2. Scheraga, H. A. & Laskowski, M. Jr. (1957) Advances in Protein Chemistry, 12, 1.

3. Laki, K. & Gladner, J. A. (1964) Physiol. Revs. 44, 127.

4. Kezdy, F. J., Lorand, L. & Miller, K. D. (1965) B, 4, 2302.

5. Shinowara, G. Y. (1966) BBA, 113, 359.

6. Sherry, S. & Troll, W. (1954) JBC, 208, 95.

7. Lorand, L. & Yudkin, E. P. (1957) BBA, 25, 437.

8. Winzor, D. J. & Scheraga, H. A. (1964) J. Phys. Chem., 68, 338.

PLASMIN

Hydrolyzes peptides and esters of L-arginine
and L-lysine; converts fibrin into soluble products

Molecular weight

source	value	conditions	
Human plasminogen	83,800	pH 2.8	(1)

Specificity and Michaelis constants

Plasmin hydrolyzes peptides and esters of L-arginine and L-lysine, converts fibrinogen to fibrin and hydrolyzes casein, denatured haemoglobin and gelatin. (2,3)

The use of a protamine-heparin complex as a substrate of plasmin is discussed in reference (2).

source	substrate	relative velocity	$K_m(M)$	conditions	
Human plasmin-ogen[a]	p-toluenesulphonyl-L arginine methyl ester	1.00	4×10^{-3}	pH 9, Tris, 37°	(3)
	L-lysine ethyl ester	0.59	1.7×10^{-2}	pH 6.5, imidazole, 37°	(3)
	benzoyl-L-arginine ethyl ester	0.95	-	pH 9, Tris, 37°	(3)
	L-arginine ethyl ester	0.11	-	pH 7, imidazole, 37°	(3)

[a] The following compounds were inactive: the ethyl esters of glycine, DL-valine, L-leucine, L-isoleucine, DL-methionine, L-tyrosine, DL-tryptophan, acetyl-L-tyrosine, acetyl-DL-tryptophan and acetyl-DL-methionine.

References

1. Davies, M. C. & Englert, M. E. (1960) JBC, 235, 1011.
2. Greig, H. B. W. & Cornelius, E. M. (1963) BBA, 67, 658.
3. Troll, W., Sherry, S. & Wachman, J. (1954) JBC, 208, 85.

SUBTILOPEPTIDASE A

Hydrolyzes peptides; converts ovalbumin into plakalbumin

Ref.

Molecular weight

Strain of Bacillus subtilis	value	conditions	
Carlsberg, Novo, BPN'	26,700	various (including sequence studies)	(2,3,4,6)

Specificity and Michaelis constants

Subtilopeptidase A shows a very wide specificity. Thus, the enzyme isolated from the BPN' strain attacks about a third of the peptide bonds in casein and a quarter of those in gelatin. In addition, the enzyme attacks the ester bond (e.g. in ATEE, BAEE, methyl butyrate and methyl valerate) but the amide bond is more resistant (e.g. in benzoyl-L-argininamide and acetyl-L-tyrosinamide).   (1,2)

The enzyme also catalyzes transesterification reactions between L-tyrosine ethyl ester and a number of aliphatic alcohols.   (5)

Strain of B. subtilis	substrate	$k_0(sec^{-1})$	$K_m(M)$	conditions	
Carlsberg	BAEE	16.1	7×10^{-3}		
	ATEE	1316	9×10^{-2}		
Novo	BAEE	4.6	1.0×10^{-2}	pH 8.0, 37°	(2)
	ATEE	731	7×10^{-2}		
BPN'	BAEE	4.6	1.0×10^{-2}		
	ATEE	658	7×10^{-2}		

Inhibitors   Ref.

Strain of B. subtilis	inhibitor	type	$K_i(M)$	conditions	
Carlsberg[a]	indole	C(ATEE)	5×10^{-2}	pH 7.5, 37°	(2)
	phenol	C(ATEE)	1×10^{-1}	pH 7.4, 37°	(2)
	hydrocinnamate	C(ATEE)	1.4×10^{-1}	pH 8.0, 37°	(2)
	methyl butyrate	C(ATEE)	1.7×10^{-1}	pH 7.0, 37°	(2)

[a]Similar results were obtained with the enzymes from the Novo and BPN' strains.

Light absorption data

   see trypsin (3.4.4.4) and chymotrypsin (3.4.4.5)

Abbreviations

   BAEE   benzoyl-L-arginine ethyl ester
   ATEE   acetyl-L-tyrosine ethyl ester

References

1. Hagihara, B. (1960) The Enzymes, 4, 194.

2. Glazer, A. N. (1967) JBC, 242, 433.

3. Matsubara, H., Kasper, C. B., Brown, D. M. & Smith, E. L. (1965) JBC, 240, 1125.

4. Riggsby, W. S. & Rappaport, M. P. (1965) JBC, 240, 87.

5. Glazer, A. N. (1966) JBC, 241, 635.

6. Smith, E. L., Delange, R. J., Evans, W. H., Landon, M. & Markland, F. S. (1968) JBC, 243, 2184.

ASPERGILLOPEPTIDASE A

Hydrolyzes peptides, especially at bonds involving
the carboxyl groups of arginine or leucine; converts
trypsinogen into trypsin

Ref.

Molecular weight

source	value	conditions	
Aspergillus saitoi[a]	93,-98,000	-	(2)
	35,000	pH 4.1	(4)
Penicillium janthinellum	32,100	pH 4.25	(3)
P. cyaneofulvum	44,-45,000	pH 5.5	(6,7)

[a] Aspergillus acid protease

Specific activity

P. janthinellum (60 x)   13.1 trypsinogen activated (pH 3.4,   (3)
                          citrate, 25°)

Specificity and Michaelis constants

Various strains of Penicillia and Aspergilli possess a variety of
proteolytic enzymes of widely different kinetic and molecular properties. This group of enzymes has been assigned the number 3.4.4.17 by
the Enzyme Commission. They catalyze the hydrolysis of proteins and
peptides, especially at bonds involving the carboxyl groups of L-
arginine, L-leucine or L-glutamate and, further, they convert trypsinogen to trypsin and chymotrypsinogen to chymotrypsin.   (1,3,4)

The enzyme from A. saitoi (Aspergillus alkaline protease) cleaved
the following peptides readily: Cbz.Glu-Tyr[a], Benz.Arg-NH$_2$, Leu-
Gly, Leu-Gly.Gly and Gly-Asp. Ala-Gly.Gly was attacked with less
facility and Gly-Leu and Benz.Gly-NH$_2$ were poor substrates. The following were inactive: Gly.Gly, Leu.NH$_2$, Cbz.Tyr, ClAc.Tyr and Cbz.
Phe.   (2)

Aspergillopeptidase A hydrolyzed extensively the peptide bonds
of the A and B chains of oxidized insulin.   (5,6)

The enzyme from P. janthinellum activated trypsinogen and
hydrolyzed native bovine serum, albumin and native apoferritin. It

Specificity and Michaelis constants contd.

was without effect on a number of dipeptides, tripeptides, esters,
amides, α-amino substituted dipeptides and N-substituted amino acids.
P. janthinellum also possesses a peptidase which hydrolyzed a variety
of peptides and substituted peptides. This peptidase did not activate
trypsinogen.   (3,8)

source	substrate	$K_m(M)$	conditions	
P. janthinellum	trypsinogen	7.6×10^{-6}	pH 4.3, citrate, 0°	(3)

(a) The susceptible bond is indicated thus:-. All the amino acids are
of the L-configuration.

Inhibitors

The enzyme (P. janthinellum) was inhibited by a number of amino
acids and peptides and their derivatives (3). Protein inhibitors are
discussed in reference (1).

Abbreviations

    Cbz   the carbobenzoxy group

References

1. Hagihara, B. (1960) The Enzymes, 4, 207.

2. Yoshida, F. & Nagasawa, M. (1956) Bull. Agr. Chem. Soc. Japan,
    20, 257, 262.

3. Hofmann, T. & Shaw, R. (1964) BBA, 92, 543.

4. Ichishima, E. & Yoshida, F. (1965) BBA, 99, 360.

5. Sanger, F., Thompson, E. O. P. & Kitai, R. (1955) BJ, 59, 509.

6. Martin, S. M., Singh, K., Ankel, H. & Khan, A. H. (1962) Can. J.
    Biochem. Physiol, 40, 237.

7. Singh, K. & Martin, S. M. (1960) Can. J. Biochem. Physiol, 38, 969.

8. Shaw, R. (1964) BBA, 92, 558.

STREPTOCOCCUS PEPTIDASE A

Hydrolyzes peptides and amides; shows wide specificity,

but does not attack bonds close to a glycine residue

Ref.

Molecular weight

source	value	conditions	
Streptococcus sp. (Group A)	32,000	-	(2)

Specificity

The enzyme exhibits wide specificity and catalyzes the hydrolysis of a variety of esters and amides. Bonds close to glycine residues are not attacked. A series of synthetic substrates were hydrolyzed at peptide bonds involving the carboxyl groups of aspartate, glutamate, lysine, histidine and arginine. The following were good substrates: benzoyl-L-argininamide, benzoyl-L-lysinamide, benzoyl-L-histidinamide, carbobenzoxy-L-isoglutamine and carbobenzoxy-L-isoasparagine. The enzyme was inactive towards benzoylglycinamide, benzoylglycyl-L-lysinamide, carbobenzoxyglycyl-L-isoglutamine, L-argininamide, glycyl-L-phenylalaninamide and glycylglycylglycine. (1,3)

References

1. Hagihara, B. (1960) The Enzymes, 4, 203.

2. Liu, T-Y, Neumann, N. P., Elliott, S. D., Moore, S. & Stein, W. H. (1963) JBC, 238, 251.

3. Mycek, M. J., Elliott, S. D. & Fruton, J. S. (1952) JBC, 197, 637.

CLOSTRIDIOPEPTIDASE A
Hydrolyzes peptides containing proline,
including collagen and gelatin

Ref.

Molecular weight

source	value	conditions	
Clostridium histolyticum	109,000	pH 6.9	(5)
Cl. histolyticum			
collagenase I	95,000	pH 7.5	(3)
collagenase II	79,000	pH 7.5	(3)

Specificity and kinetic constants

Collagenase is highly specific for collagen (native or denatured) and is without activity on any other protein. Thus, the enzyme from Cl. histolyticum is without activity on fibrin, elastin, keratin, haemoglobin, casein and the albumins. The enzyme hydrolyzes collagen into peptides of average molecular weight 500-700 and, in the main, possessing glycine as the N-terminal residue and proline, hydroxyproline or alanine as the C-terminal residue. A number of synthetic compounds possessing the sequence -Pro-X-Gly-Pro-Y- are also attacked by collagenase.

(1,2,4)

source	substrate	specific activity[a]	conditions	
Cl. histolyticum				
collagenase I	collagen	1.95		
	Cbz-Gly-Pro-Leu-Gly-Pro	0.32		
	Cbz-Gly-Pro-Gly-Gly-Pro-Ala	0.35		
	azocoll	1.24	pH 7.5,	(3)
collagenase II	collagen	1.35	Tris or	
	Cbz-Gly-Pro-Leu-Gly-Pro	4.7	veronal	
	Gbz-Gly-Pro-Gly-Gly-Pro-Ala	16.2		
	azocoll	0.19		

[a] μmoles min^{-1} mg^{-1} enzyme protein.

Inhibitors

Collagenase is not inhibited by di-isopropyl phosphorofluoridate (DFP).

(2)

Abbreviations

Cbz   carbobenzoxy

References
1. Hagihara, B. (1960) The Enzymes, 4, 205.
2. Mandl, I. (1961) Advances in Enzymology, 23, 163.
3. Yoshida, E. & Noda, H. (1965) BBA, 105, 562.
4. Seifter, S. & Gallop, P. M. (1962) Methods in Enzymology, 5, 659.
5. Seifter, S., Gallop, P. M., Klein, L. & Meilman, E. (1959) JBC, 234, 285.

CLOSTRIDIOPEPTIDASE B

Hydrolyzes peptides at bonds involving arginine residues

<u>Ref</u>.

Specificity

Clostridiopeptidase B, isolated from <u>Clostridium</u> <u>histolyticum</u>, hydrolyzes the following compounds: a-benzoyl-L-argininamide (1.00), a-benzoyl-L-arginine ethyl ester (0.98), a-benzoyl-L-arginine iso-propyl ester (0.98), a-benzoyl-L-arginine benzyl ester (0.96), L-arginine methyl ester (0.80) and L-lysine-methyl ester (0.56). The following compounds were inactive: DL-phenylalanine methyl ester, N-benzoyl-DL-phenylalanine ethyl ester, N-benzoyl-DL-phenylalanin-amide, L-leucine methyl ester, L-leucinamide, L-leucylglycine, ben-zoylglycinamide, glycylglycine ethyl ester, glycylglycine, L-proline benzyl ester, L-prolinamide and L-leucylglycylglycine. (1)

References

1. Ogle, J. D. & Tytell, A. A. (1953) <u>ABB</u>, <u>42</u>, 327.

CATHEPSIN D

Hydrolyzes peptides; its specificity is somewhat

similar to 3.4.4.1, but more restricted

Ref.

Molecular weight

source	value	conditions	
Bovine spleen	58,000	-	(1)

Specificity

Cathepsin D is inactive with a variety of synthetic peptides including carbobenzoxy-L-glutamyl-L-tyrosine, benzoyl-L-arginine amide, glycyl-L-tyrosine amide, N-acetyl-DL-phenylalanyl-L-di-iodo-tyrosine, L-tyrosyl-L-cysteine and L-cysteinyl-L-tyrosine. The enzyme attacks the B chain of insulin splitting the peptide bond between the following pairs of amino acid residues: GLU (13)-ALA (14); LEU (15)-TYR (16); TYR (16)-LEU (17); PHE (24)-PHE (25) and PHE (25)-TYR (26). Cathepsin D is thus more restricted in its action on the B chain of insulin than pepsin (3.4.4.1). (1)

Cathepsin D has also been purified from rabbit spleen. (2)

References

1. Press, E. M., Porter, R. R. & Cebra, J. (1960) BJ, 74, 501.
2. Lapresle, C. & Webb, T. (1960) BJ, 76, 538.

BROMELAIN

Hydrolyzes peptides, amides and esters; its
specificity is somewhat similar to that of 3.4.4.10

Ref.

Molecular weight

Various species of the family __Bromeliaceae__ contain appreciable
quantities of proteolytic enzymes (bromelains). Of the species, the pine-
apple (__Ananas comosus__) is the most studied and the stem of this plant
possesses five proteolytic components of molecular weights 18,997;
19,650; 17,885; 18,020 and 20,011. A molecular weight of 33,000 has
also been reported for stem bromelain. (1,2,5)

Specificity and kinetic properties

Bromelain hydrolyzes a variety of proteins, peptides, esters and
amides, including the following: BAEE (1.00), BAME (1.32),
TAME (0.503), benzoylglycine ethyl ester (0.405), L-phenylalanine ethyl
ester (0.293), L-tyrosine ethyl ester (0.217), L-leucine ethyl ester
(0.186), glycine ethyl ester (0.184), benzoyl-DL-alanine ethyl ester
(0.135) and L-lysine ethyl ester (0.0956). L-Histidine ethyl ester,
acetyl-L-tyrosine ethyl ester and Cbz-L-Glu-L-Tyr were not attacked. (3,5)

source	substrate	$k_0(\text{sec}^{-1})$	$K_m(M)$	conditions	
Pine-	BAEE	0.50	1.7×10^{-1}	pH 6.0,	(3)
apple	BAA	3.5×10^{-3}	1.2×10^{-3}	$25°$	

Inhibitors

Bromelain is not inhibited by di-isopropyl phosphorofluoridate (DFP). (4)

Light absorption data

See trypsin (3.4.4.4).

Abbreviations

BAEE	N-benzoyl-L-arginine ethyl ester
BAA	N-benzoyl-L-argininamide
BAME	N-benzoyl-L-arginine methyl ester
TAME	p-toluene-sulphonyl-L-arginine methyl ester
Cbz	carbobenzoxy

References

1. Feinstein, G. & Whitaker, J. (1964) __B__, _3_, 1050.
2. Murachi, T., Yasui, M. & Yasuda, Y. (1964) __B__, _3_, 48.
3. Inagami, T. & Murachi, T. (1963) __B__, _2_, 1439.
4. Murachi, T. & Yasui, M. (1965) __B__, _4_, 2275.
5. Murachi, T. & Neurath, H. (1960) JBC, _235_, 99.

KERATINASE

Hydrolyses some peptide bonds in keratin and poly-L-lysine

Molecular weight

source	value	conditions	
Streptomyces fradiae	27,000	pH 3.0	(1)

Specificity

Of a large number of synthetic peptides tested only poly-L-lysine was hydrolysed to produce tetra-, tri-, and di-lysine. Lysine was not produced even after prolonged periods of incubation. The enzyme was about 4.7 times more active towards haemoglobin than trypsin. It attacked native keratin. Free amino acids were not found in protein hydrolysates. (1)

References

1. Nickerson, W. J. & Durand, S. C. (1963) BBA, 77, 87.

UROKINASE

Converts plasminogen to plasmin

Ref.

Molecular weight

source	value	conditions	
Human urine	53,000	pH 6.8	(2)
	31,500	-	(3)

Specific activity

The enzyme (human urine) has been crystallized. (2,3)

Specificity and Michaelis constants

source	substrate	$K_m(M)$	conditions	
Human urine	N-carbobenzoxy-L-tyrosine p-nitrophenyl ester	5×10^{-4}	pH 8.0, Tris, $30°$	(4)

The esterase activity of the enzyme is discussed in references (4) and (5).

Inhibitors

source	inhibitor	type	K_i	conditions	
Human urine	6-aminocaproate	C (N-carbobenzoxy-L-tyrosine-p-nitrophenyl ester)	1×10^{-2}	pH 7.0, Tris, $30°$	(4)

References

1. Ablondi, F. B. & Hagan, J. J. (1960) The Enzymes, 4, 184.
2. Lesuk, A., Terminiello, L. & Traver, J. H. (1965) Science, 147, 880.
3. White, W. F., Barlow, G. H. & Mozen, M. M. (1966) B, 5, 2160.
4. Lorand, L. & Condit, E. V. (1965) B, 4, 265.
5. Kjeldgaard, N. O. & Ploug, J. (1957) BBA, 24, 283.

CHYMOTRYPSIN C

(Hydrolyses peptides, amides, esters, etc., especially at bonds
involving the carboxyl groups of L-leucine and L-
aromatic amino acids)

Ref.

Molecular weight

source	value	conditions	
Swine pancreas	23,800	pH 7.0	(1)

Specificity and Michaelis constants

source	substrate	$k_o(sec^{-1})$	$K_m(M)$	conditions	
Swine pancreas	benzoyl-L-leucine ethyl ester	25.4	2.8×10^{-2}		
	benzoyl-L-phenyl-alanine ethyl ester	1.55	8.5×10^{-4}		
	acetyl-L-tryptophan ethyl ester	0.32	2.1×10^{-3}		
	benzoyl-L-tyrosine ethyl ester	46.0	1.7×10^{-2}	pH 7.8, Tris, 25°	(1)
	benzoyl-L-tyrosine methyl ester	1.7	1.0×10^{-2}		
	carbobenzoxy-L-leucyl-glycine amide	0.013	1.5×10^{-2}		
	acetyl-L-leucine amide	0.0035	-		

The enzyme differs markedly from chymotrypsins A and B in its
hydrolytic action towards glucagon and carboxymethyl ribonuclease, in its
catalytic activity towards several synthetic ester and peptide substrates and in its ability to hydrolyse the pentapeptide L-seryl-
L-histidyl-L-leucyl-L-valyl-L-glutamate which is resistant to the
other chymotrypsins.   (1)
    The specificity of the enzyme towards several polypeptides is
discussed in reference (2).

References

1. Folk, J. E. & Schirmer, E. W. (1965) JBC, 240, 181.

2. Folk, J. E. & Cole, P. W. (1965) JBC, 240, 193.

ASPERGILLOPEPTIDASE B

Molecular weight

source	value	conditions	
Aspergillus oryzae	17,970	pH 5.02	(2)

Specific activity

The enzyme has been purified to homogeneity. (2)

Specificity

There is little information on the specificity of this enzyme. (1,2)

The enzyme showed the same activity towards casein as α-chymo-trypsin and 3-4 times the activity of trypsin. (2)

References

1. Hagihara, B. (1960) The Enzymes, 4, 207.

2. Subramanian, A. R. & Kalnitsky, G. (1964) B, 3, 1861, 1868.

ASPARAGINASE

(L-Asparagine amidohydrolase)

L-Asparagine + H_2O = L-aspartate + NH_3

Ref.

Molecular weight

source	value	conditions	
Guinea-pig serum	138,000	pH 7	(2)
Escherichia coli	106,000	Sephadex G200, pH 8.0	(2)
Pseudomonas sp.	26,300	pH 6.8	(6)

Specific activity

Guinea-pig serum	(1400 x)	350	L-asparagine (pH 7.1, borate, 37°)	(3)
	(900 x)	47	L-asparagine (pH 8.5, borate, 37°)	(2)

Specificity

The L-asparaginases from different sources vary widely with respect to their substrate specificity. Thus, the enzyme from guinea-pig serum is highly specific and is without effect on L-glutamine, D-glutamine, DL-2-methylasparagine, L-homoglutamine, 2-oxosuccinamate and 2-oxoglutaramate. It hydrolyzes D-asparagine at about 3% of the rate observed with the L-isomer and the following compounds are also attacked, albeit at low rates: L-tyrosine amide, L-phenylalanine amide and L-leucine amide. (4,5,8)

The Pseudomonad enzyme has L-glutaminase activity equal to or greater than its L-asparaginase activity (6). Two L-asparaginases have been found in E. coli and these are designated EC-1 and EC-2. EC-1 does not attack L-glutamine but EC-2 hydrolyzes this substance at 2% the rate obtained with L-asparagine. (7)

Michaelis constants

source	substrate	$K_m(M)$	conditions	
Guinea-pig serum	L-asparagine	2.2×10^{-3}	pH 7.5, borate, 37°	(8)
Pseudomonas sp.	L-asparagine	1×10^{-4}	pH 8.2, barbiturate, 37°	(6)
	L-glutamine	8×10^{-3}	pH 6.6, P_i, 37°	(6)

References

1. Varner, A. (1960) The Enzymes, 4, 243.

2. Yellin, T. O. & Wriston, J. C. (1966) B, 5, 1605.

3. Suld, H. & Herbut, P. A. (1965) JBC, 240, 2234.

4. Meister, A. (1955) Methods in Enzymology, 2, 383.

5. Meister, A., Levintow, L., Greenfield, R. E. & Abendschein, P. A. (1955) JBC, 215, 441.

6. Ramadan, M. E. A., El Asmar, E. & Greenberg, D. M. (1964) ABB, 108, 143, 150.

7. Campbell, H. A., Mashburn, L. T., Boyse, E. A. & Old, L. J. (1967) B, 6, 721.

8. Tower, D. B., Peters, E. L. & Curtis, W. C. (1963) JBC, 238, 983.

GLUTAMINASE

(L-Glutamine amidohydrolase)

L-glutamine + H_2O = L-glutamate + NH_3

Ref.

Equilibrium constant

$$\frac{[NH_4^+]\,[L\text{-glutamate}]}{[L\text{-glutamine}]\,[H_2O]} = 320 \quad (pH\ 5.5,\ 25^\circ) \tag{2}$$

Specificity

Glutaminase isolated from dog kidney attacked L-glutamine (1.00), L-isoglutamine (0.34), a-methyl-DL-glutamine (0.24) and a-L-glutamyl hydrazide (0.05) but the following compounds were inactive: L-asparagine, a-methyl-DL-asparagine, a-L-glutamylmethylamide, a-DL-glutamylbutylamide, nicotinamide, acetamide, adenine and L-glutamyl-a-methyl ester. (3)

The enzyme from Escherichia coli hydrolyzed L-glutamine (1.00) and a-methyl-DL-glutamine (0.25) but it was without activity on L-isoglutamine, D- or L-homoglutamine, a-methyl-DL-asparagine, L-isoasparagine, L-leucine amide, DL-proline amide, DL-alanine amide, L-phenylalanine amide, L-tyrosine amide and a large number of fatty acid amides. (5)

Glutaminase is activated by P_i, sulphate, PP_i or arsenate. (4)

Michaelis constants

source	substrate	$K_m(M)$	conditions	
Pig kidney	L-glutamine	5×10^{-3}	pH 8.2, P_i, 37°	(4)
	P_i	5×10^{-2}		
Dog kidney	L-glutamine	5×10^{-3}	pH 8.1, P_i, 37°	(3)

Inhibitors

The enzyme (dog kidney) was inhibited by ammonia (C(glutamine)), glutamate (NC(glutamine), $C(P_i)$) and by a number of phthalein dyes. (3)

Other inhibitors are discussed in reference (1).

References

1. Roberts, E. (1960) The Enzymes, 4, 285.

2. Benzinger, T., Kitzinger, C., Hems, R. & Burton, K. (1959) BJ, 71, 400.

3. Sayre, F. W. & Roberts, E. (1958) JBC, 233, 1128.

4. Klingman, J. D. & Handler, P. (1958), JBC, 232, 369.

5. Meister, A., Levintow, L., Greenfield, R. E. & Abendschein, P. A. (1955) JBC, 215, 441.

AMIDASE

(Acylamide amidohydrolase)

A monocarboxylic acid amide + H_2O = a monocarboxylate + NH_3

Specific activity

Pseudomonas aeruginosa (35 x)   800 propionamide   (pH 7.2, P_i, 37°) (1)

Specificity and Michaelis constants

The enzyme exhibits low specificity and attacks a number of primary amides. The acetyltransferase activity of the enzyme is discussed in references (1) and (2).

source	substrate	relative velocity	K_m(M)	conditions
P. aeruginosa	propionamide	1.00	2×10^{-4}	
	acrylamide	0.69	-	
	glycollamide	0.61	-	
	acetamide	0.36	-	pH 7.2,
	formamide	0.06	-	P_i, 37° (1)
	lactamide	0.04	-	
	glycinamide	0.02	-	
	3-hydroxypropionamide	<0.01	-	
	butyramide	0	-	
	cyanoacetamide	0	-	
P. fluorescens	acetamide	1.00	5×10^{-3}	pH 7.3,
	acrylamide	0.28	7×10^{-3}	Tris, 25° (2)
	propionamide	1.60	3×10^{-2}	

Inhibitors

source	inhibitor	type	K_i(M)	conditions
P. aeruginosa	urea	NC (propionamide)	1.1×10^{-3}	pH 7.2, P_i,(1) 25°
P. fluorescens	urea	NC (acetamide)	5×10^{-4}	pH 7.3, Tris,(2) 25°

References

1. Kelly, M. & Kornberg, H. L. (1964) BJ, 93, 557.
2. Jakoby, W. B. & Fredericks, J. (1964) JBC, 239, 1978.

UREASE

(Urea amidohydrolase)

$$Urea + H_2O = CO_2 + 2 NH_3$$

Molecular weight

source	value	conditions	
Canalia ensiformis (Jack bean)	483,000[6]	pH 7.0	(2)
	473,000	-	(3)

Specific activity[a]

C. ensiformis		2130	urea (pH 6.7, P_i, 25°)	(2,3)
Bacillus pasteurii (66 x)	2430	urea (pH 6.7, P_i, 20°)	(6)

[a]
In the literature specific activities are reported in Sumner units mg^{-1} protein. One Sumner unit, which is the amount of enzyme required to produce $1 \times 10^{-3}g$ NH_3 nitrogen in 5 min at 20°, is equivalent to 14.3 international units.

Specificity

Urease exhibits absolute specificity: of a large number of compounds tested - including substituted ureas - only urea was active.(1,4,7)

Michaelis constants[a]   <u>Ref.</u>

source	substrate	$K_m(M)$	conditions	
<u>C. ensiformis</u>	urea	1.05×10^{-2}	pH 7.0, P_i, 25°	(5)
<u>B. pasteurii</u>	urea	4×10^{-2}	pH 7.7, P_i, 25°	(6)
<u>Corynebacterium renale</u>	urea	3×10^{-2}	pH 7.5, P_i	(7)

(a)

The values obtained depend on the buffer, pH and concentration of

enzyme used.   (6)

Inhibitors

The following act as competitive inhibitors (urea): Suramin (8)

and thiourea (9). Na^+ and K^+ also inhibit but P_i activates (10).

Ammonia, a product of the reaction, is inhibitory (11).

References

1. Varner, J. E. (1960) The Enzymes, 4, 247.
2. Reithel, F. J., Robbins, J. E. & Gorin, G. (1964) ABB, 108, 409.
3. Gorin, G., Fuchs, E., Butler, L. G., Chopra, S. L. & Hersh, R. T. (1962) B, 1, 911.
4. Sumner, J. B. (1951) The Enzymes, 1, 886.
5. Peterson, J., Harmon, K. & Niemann, C. (1948) JBC, 176, 1.
6. Larson, A. D. & Kallio, R. E. (1954) J. Bacteriol, 68, 67.
7. Lister, A. J. (1956) J. Gen. Microbiol., 14, 478.
8. Wills, E. D. & Wormall, A. (1950) BJ, 47, 158.
9. Kistiakowsky, G. B. & Shaw, W. H. R. (1953) JACS, 75, 866.
10. Fasman, G. D. & Niemann, C. (1951) JACS, 73, 1646.
11. Hoare, J. P. & Laidler, K. J. (1950) JACS, 72, 2487.

β-UREIDOPROPIONASE

(N-Carbamoyl-β-alanine amidohydrolase)

$$N\text{-Carbamoyl-}\beta\text{-alanine} + H_2O = \beta\text{-alanine} + CO_2 + NH_3$$

Ref.

Equilibrium constant

The reaction is essentially irreversible[F] .   (3)

Specificity

β-Ureidopropionase from rat liver degrades N-carbamoyl-β-alanine (β-ureidopropionate) and N-carbamoyl-3-aminoisobutyrate (β-ureido-isobutyrate) but not N-carbamoyl-L-alanine, N-carbamoyl-4-aminoiso-butyrate, N-carbamoylglycine, N-carbamoyl-L-glutamate, N-carbamoyl-L-aspartate, N-carbamoyl-L-proline or L-citrulline.   (1)

The enzyme isolated from Clostridium uracilium showed no activity with N-carbamoylalanine, N-carbamoyl-3-aminoisobutyrate, N-carbamoylglycine or N-carbamoylaspartate.   (3)

Michaelis constants

source	substrate	relative velocity	$K_m(M)$	conditions	
Rat liver	N-carbamoyl-β-alanine	1.00	5×10^{-4}	pH 7.0, Tris, 38°	(2)
	N-carbamoyl-3-amino-isobutyrate	0.51	1×10^{-3}		
C. uracilium	N-carbamoyl-β-alanine	-	6.34×10^{-4}	pH 7.5, P_i, 30°	(3)

References

1. Reichard, P. & Skold, O. (1963) Methods in Enzymology, 6, 187.
2. Caravaca, J. & Grisolia, S. (1958) JBC, 231, 357.
3. Campbell, L. L. (1960) JBC, 235, 2375.

UREIDOSUCCINASE

(N-Carbamoyl-L-aspartate amidohydrolase)

N-Carbamoyl-L-aspartate + H_2O = L-aspartate + CO_2 + NH_3

Ref.

Equilibrium constant

The reaction is essentially irreversible[F] . (1)

Specificity

Ureidosuccinase from Zymobacterium oroticum was unable to utilize ornithine, citrulline or N-carbamoyl-L-glutamate in the place of N-carbamoyl-L-aspartate (ureidosuccinate). (2)

The enzyme exhibits an absolute requirement for a metal ion: Mn^{2+} (1.00), Fe^{2+} (0.69) or Cu^{2+} (0.03). MoO_4^{2-}, Zn^{2+}, Al^{3+}, Mg^{2+} and Ca^{2+} were without effect. (2)

Michaelis constants

source	substrate	$K_m(M)$	conditions	
Z. oroticum	N-carbamoyl-L-aspartate	2.8×10^{-3} [a] 1.3×10^{-2} [b]	pH 7.0, P_i, 30°	(2)

[a] In the presence of Fe^{2+} (1×10^{-3}M)
[b] In the presence of Mn^{2+} (5×10^{-4}M)

References

1. Reichard, P. & Sköld, O. (1963) Methods in Enzymology, 6, 177.
2. Lieberman, I. & Kornberg, A. (1955) JBC, 212, 909.

FORMYLASPARTATE DEFORMYLASE

(N-Formyl-L-aspartate amidohydrolase)

N-Formyl-L-aspartate + H_2O = formate + L-aspartate

Ref.

Specificity

Formylaspartate deformylase has been partially purified from β-(imidazolyl-4(5)) acetate-grown cells and histidine-grown cells of Pseudomonas sp. The two kinds of cells yield two different enzymes (enzymes I and II, respectively) the specificity properties of which are compared below. (The numbers represent μmoles of substrate decomposed hr^{-1} mg^{-1} protein at pH 7.2 and 37°).

(1)

enzyme	activator	formyl-aspartate	chloro-acetyl-L-aspartate	formyl glutamate	acetyl-L-glutamate
I	None	32	0	5	0
	Fe^{2+}	100	0	9	0
	Co^{2+}	51	92	8	7
II	None	26	0	340	80
	Fe^{2+}	6	0	350	-
	Co^{2+}	330	250	350	110

Michaelis constants

enzyme	substrate	$K_m(M)$	conditions	
I	formylaspartate	1.32×10^{-3}	pH 7.5,	
II	formylaspartate	1.25×10^{-3}	Tris, 37°	(1)

References

1. Ohmura, E. & Hayaishi, O. (1957) JBC, 227, 181.

FORMAMIDASE

(Aryl-formylamine amidohydrolase)

N-Formyl-L-kynurenine + H_2O = formate + L-kynurenine

Ref.

Specificity and Michaelis constants

source	substrate	$\dfrac{V}{(\text{relative})}$	$K_m (M)$	conditions	
Neurospora crassa [a]	N-formyl-L-kynurenine	1.00	1.1×10^{-4}		
	formylanthranilate	0.24	3.3×10^{-3}		
	formyl-o-aminoacetophenone	0.22	2.8×10^{-3}		
	formyl-o-aminonitrobenzene	0.13	2.5×10^{-3}	pH 7.5, P_i	(1)
	formyl-m-aminobenzoate	0.035	7.7×10^{-3}		
	formyl-o-aminotoluene	~0.01	-		
	acetylanthranilate	~0.001	-		
Rat liver (b)	N-formyl-L-kynurenine	1.00	-		
	formylanthranilate	0.16	-		
	formylorthanilate	0.10	-		
	formylnitroaniline	0.10	-	pH 7.5, P_i, $25°$	(2)
	formyl-m-aminobenzoate	0.037	-		
	formanilide	0.026	-		
	o-formaminophenol	0.026	-		
	formyl-o-toluidine	0.018	-		

[a] The following compounds were inactive: formyl-L-glutamate, formyl-glycine and formyl-L-aspartate.

[b] The following compounds were hydrolyzed at rates less than 1% of that with N-formyl-L-kynurenine: acetylanthranilate, acetanilide, formyl-p-aminobenzoate, acetyl-p-aminobenzoate and acetyl-o-amino-phenol. The following compounds were inactive: N-formyl-L-alanine, N-formylglycine, and N-formyl-L-phenylalanine.

Inhibitors

Anthranilate inhibits the enzyme from rat liver (2) but not that from N. crassa (1).

Light absorption data

N-formyl-L-kynurenine $\varepsilon, (400 \text{ m}\mu) = 630 \text{ M}^{-1} \text{ cm}^{-1}$ pH 7.5   (1)
formylanthranilate $\varepsilon, (330 \text{ m}\mu) = 1500 \text{ M}^{-1} \text{ cm}^{-1}$ pH 7.5   (1)

The light absorption properties of other substrates will be found in references (1) and (2).

References

1. Jakoby, W. B. (1954) JBC, 207, 657.
2. Mehler, A. H. & Knox, W. E. (1950) JBC, 187, 431.

BIOTINIDASE

(Biotin-amide amidohydrolase)

Biotin amide + H_2O = biotin + NH_3

Ref.

Specificity and Michaelis constants

Biotinidase is specific for the biotin moiety of simple biotin
esters and amides. The enzyme liberates biotin from biocytin-con-
taining peptides but not from propionyl-CoA carboxylase (6.4.1.3).
The natural substrate of the enzyme is thought to be biocytin.

(1)

source	substrate	relative velocity	$K_m(M)$	conditions
Strepto-coccus faecalis	biocytin	1	1.4×10^{-5}	
	biotin methyl ester	4	1.4×10^{-5}	
	biotin amide	8	-	
	N-biotinyl-p aminobenzoate	6	-	pH 7.0, P_i, 30° (1)
	N-biotinyl-β-alanine	1	-	
	N-biotinyl-L-aspartate	0.15	-	

References

1. Koivusalo, M., Elorriaga, C., Kaziro, Y. & Ochoa, S. (1963)
    JBC, 238, 1038.

ARYL ACYLAMIDASE

(Aryl-acylamide amidohydrolase)

An N-acyl-anilide + H_2O = a fatty acid ion + aniline

Specificity and Michaelis constants

Aryl acylamidase from chicken kidney attacks a variety of acylanilides. Substitution in the para position of acetanilide generally results in an increase in the rate of deacetylation and a decrease in K_m. Ortho substitution has a marked effect in the opposite direction. (1)

substituent[a]	N-formylanilide		N-acetylanilide		N-chloroacetylanilide	
	v[b]	$K_m(M)$	v[b]	$K_m(M)$	v[b]	$K_m(M)$
H	5.6	7.4×10^{-3}	10	9.1×10^{-4}	32	1.4×10^{-4}
O.CH_3	16	1.2×10^{-3}	18	5.9×10^{-4}	122	6.1×10^{-4}
COOH	17	1.3×10^{-3}	5.4	2.3×10^{-4}	15	1.0×10^{-3}
CH_2.COOH	19	2.6×10^{-3}	18	7.8×10^{-5}	38	1.2×10^{-4}

---

[a] In the para position.

[b] μmoles hr^{-1} mg protein^{-1}.

The conditions were: pH 7.3, P_i, 38°.

References

1. Nimmo-Smith, R. H. (1960) BJ, 75, 284.

AMINOACYLASE

(N-Acylamino-acid amidohydrolase)

An N-acyl-amino acid + H_2O =

a fatty acid ion + an amino acid

Ref.

Specificity

Aminoacylase (hog kidney) hydrolyzes a variety of N-acyl-L-amino acids and dehydropeptides containing dehydroalanyl residues. N-Acyl-D-amino acids and dehydropeptides other than of dehydro-alanine are not attacked.

N-Acyl-L-amino acids possessing the following structural characteristics are hydrolyzed by the enzyme:

$$R^1CH_2 - CO - NH - \overset{\overset{\textstyle R^2}{\textstyle |}}{CH} - COOH$$

where R^1 = Cl, H, NH_2

R^2 = L-amino acid other than L-aspartate

Thus, the following compounds are attacked by aminoacylase: chloroacetyl-L-amino acids, chloroacetyldehydroalanine, glycyl-L-amino acids, glycyldehydroalanine and L-leucinamide.   (1,2)

For further details of the specificity of aminoacylase the reader is referred to references (1-4).

The properties of the aminoacylase from Lactobacillus arabinosus are discussed in reference (5).

References

1. Greenstein, J. P. (1955) Methods in Enzymology, 2, 109.
2. Birnbaum, S. M. (1955) Methods in Enzymology, 2, 115.
3. Fones, W. S. & Lee, M. (1953) JBC, 201, 847.
4. Birnbaum, S. M., Levintow, L., Kingsley, R. B. & Greenstein, J. P. (1952) JBC, 194, 455.
5. Park, R. W. & Fox, S. W. (1960) JBC, 235, 3193.

ACETYLORNITHINE DEACETYLASE

(a-N-Acetyl-L-ornithine amidohydrolase)

a-N-Acetyl-L-ornithine + H_2O = acetate + L-ornithine

Specificity

Acetylornithine deacetylase from Escherichia coli attacked acetyl-L-ornithine (1.0) and acetyl-DL-methionine (1.0) but the following compounds were inactive: acetyl-DL-alanine, acetyl-DL-valine, acetyl-DL-leucine, acetyl-DL-proline, acetyl-DL-glutamate, chloroacetyl-L-tyrosine and benzoyl-L-arginine. (1)

The enzyme was stimulated by Co^{2+} but Mg^{2+}, Ca^{2+}, Mn^{2+} and Fe^{2+} were ineffective as activators and Cu^{2+}, Zn^{2+} and Ni^{2+} were inhibitory. (1)

Michaelis constants

source	substrate	$K_m(M)$	conditions	
E. coli	acetyl-L-ornithine	2.8×10^{-3}	pH 7.0, P_i, $37°$	(1)

References

1. Vogel, H. J. & Bonner, D. M. (1956) JBC, 218, 97.

ACYL-LYSINE DEACYLASE

(ε-N-Acyl-L-lysine amidohydrolase)

ε-N-Acyl-L-lysine + H_2O = a fatty acid ion + L-lysine

Specificity and Michaelis constants

The enzyme from <u>Achromobacter</u> <u>pestifer</u> attacks ε-acyl lysines and ε-peptides of L-lysines. α-Peptides of L-lysine are inactive. With ε-peptides, the rates of hydrolysis decrease in the order ε-phenylalanyl-, glycyl-, alanyl-, leucyl- and aspartyllysine. The ε-acyl derivatives of ε-aminocaproate and the α-peptide bonds in casein and bovine serum albumin were not attacked. (1)

The enzyme from rat liver attacked the following compounds: ε-acetyl-L-lysine (1.00), ε-chloroacetyl-L-lysine (1.61), α,ε-di-chloroacetyl-L-lysine (1.75), ε-carbobenzoxy-L-lysine (0.008) and ε-biotinyl-L-lysine (0.02). ε-Acetyl-D-lysine and δ-chloroacetyl-L-ornithine were inactive. (2)

source	substrate	$\frac{V}{(\text{relative})}$	$K_m(M)$	conditions	
<u>A.</u> <u>pestifer</u>	ε-benzoyllysine	1.000	7.4×10^{-3}	pH 5.8, acetate,	(1)
	ε-phenylalanyllysine	0.525	3.67×10^{-3}	42°	
	ε-glycyllysine	0.250	1.33×10^{-3}		
	ε-benzoyllysine	0.262	1.80×10^{-3}	pH 5.0, ace-tate, 42°	(1)
	ε-phenylalanyllysine	0.094	1.12×10^{-3}		

Inhibitors

Oxalate inhibits both the peptidase and acylase activities of the enzyme (<u>A.</u> <u>pestifer</u>). (1)

References

1. Padayatty, J. D. & Van Kley, H. (1966) <u>B</u>, <u>5</u>, 1394.

2. Paik, W. K., Bloch-Frankenthal, L., Birnbaum, S. M., Winitz, M. & Greenstein, J. P. (1957) <u>ABB</u>, <u>69</u>, 56.

SUCCINYL-DIAMINOPIMELATE DESUCCINYLASE

(N-Succinyl-LL-2,6-diaminopimelate amidohydrolase)

N-Succinyl-L-2,6-diaminopimelate + H_2O =

succinate + L-2,6-diaminopimelate

Ref.

Specificity

The enzyme isolated from Escherichia coli is highly specific and the following compounds were inactive as substrates: N-acetyl-L-diaminopimelate; 2-N-acetyl-6-N-succinyl-diaminopimelate; 2-N-succinyl-6-oxoaminopimelate; 2-N-succinyl-6-N-dinitrophenyl-L-diaminopimelate, carbobenzoxysuccinyl-L-lysine, N-succinyl-L-aspartate and N-succinyl-D-diaminopimelate. (1,2)

Co^{2+} could to a limited extent be replaced by Mn^{2+}, Zn^{2+}, Fe^{3+} or Ni^{2+} but not by Mg^{2+} or Al^{3+}. (1,2)

Michaelis constants

source	substrate	$K_m(M)$	conditions	
E. coli	N-succinyl-L-diaminopimelate Co^{2+}	1.3×10^{-3} 1.5×10^{-5}	pH 8.1, Tris, 37°	(1,2)

References

1. Kindler, S. H. & Gilvarg, C. (1960) JBC, 235, 3532.

2. Kindler, S. H. (1962) Methods in Enzymology, 5, 851.

NICOTINAMIDE DEAMINASE

(Nicotinamide amidohydrolase)

Nicotinamide + H_2O = nicotinate + NH_3

Ref.

Molecular weight

source	value	conditions	
Torula cremoris	~ 100,000	-	(2)

Specific activity

T. cremoris (850 x)   1.7   nicotinamide   (pH 7.0, Tris, 37°) (2)

Specificity

The enzyme (T. cremoris) is highly specific and the following compounds were not hydrolyzed: glutamine, asparagine, NAD, glycinamide, NMN, benzamide, N^1-methylnicotinamide, N^2-ethylnicotinamide, N^2-diethylnicotinamide, 5'-AMP, cytosine or guanosine.   (2)

Michaelis constants

source	substrate	$K_m(M)$	conditions	
T. cremoris	nicotinamide	1.4×10^{-5}	pH 7.0, Tris, 37°	(2)
Rat liver	nicotinamide	7.0×10^{-2}*	pH 8.8, tris-ethanolamine, 37°	(1)
Rabbit liver	nicotinamide	5.0×10^{-2}*		
Pigeon liver	nicotinamide	4.8×10^{-3}*		

*These values were obtained with partially purified preparations. Higher values were obtained with crude liver homogenates.

Inhibitors

source	inhibitor	type	$K_m(M)$	conditions	
T. cremoris	NAD NADP	NC (nicotin- amide)	5.3×10^{-4} 4.65×10^{-4}	pH 7.0, Tris, 37°	(2)
	acetyl py- ridine	C (nicotin- amide)	3.05×10^{-4}	pH 7.0, Tris, 37°	(2)

References
1. Petrack, B., Greengard, P., Craston, A. & Sheppy, F. (1965) JBC, 240, 1725.
2. Joshi, J. G. & Handler, P. (1962) JBC, 237, 929.

BARBITURASE

(Barbiturate amidohydrolase)

Barbiturate + 2 H_2O = malonate + urea

<u>Ref.</u>

Specificity

    Barbiturase isolated from <u>Mycobacterium</u> sp. was highly specific for barbiturate and was inactive with 5-methyl barbiturate, orotate, barbital, pentobarbital, 2-thiobarbiturate or isobarbiturate.   (1,2)

Michaelis constants

source	substrate	$K_m(M)$	conditions	
<u>Mycobacterium</u> sp.	barbiturate	3.37×10^{-3}	pH 8.0, glycyl-glycine	(1,2)

Light absorption properties

5-methyl barbiturate	ε, (269 mμ) = 17,300 (pH 13)		(1)
	ε, (267 mμ) = 19,700 (pH 7.0)		(1)

References

1. Hayaishi, O. & Kornberg, A. (1952) <u>JBC</u>, <u>197</u>, 717.

2. Hayaishi, O. (1955) <u>Methods in Enzymology</u>, <u>2</u>, 492.

DIHYDROPYRIMIDINASE

(4,5-Dihydropyrimidine amidohydrolase)

4,5-Dihydrouracil + H_2O = 3-ureidopropionate

Equilibrium constant

$$\frac{[\text{3-ureidopropionate}]}{[\text{4,5-dihydrouracil}]} = 0.67 \text{ (pH 5.0, acetate, } 38^o) \tag{1}$$

Molecular weight

source	value	conditions	
Calf liver	$S_{20,w} = 6.99$	pH 6.9	(2)

Specific activity

Calf liver (194 x) 43 4,5-dihydrouracil (pH 9.2, Tris, 30°)   (2)

Specificity and Michaelis constants

source	substrate	$\frac{V}{\text{(relative)}}$	$K_m(M)$	conditions	
Calf liver[a]	4,5-dihydrouracil[b]	1.00	1.175×10^{-1}	pH 9.2, Tris, 30°	(2)
	hydantoin[c]	6.30	8.3×10^{-1}		
	dihydrothymine[d]	0.098	2.1×10^{-3}		

[a] The following compounds were inactive: barbiturate, imidazole-4,5-dicarboxylic acid, 5-(carboxymethylidine) hydantoin, orotate, 4,5-aminoimidazolecarboximide, urocanate, 5-(diphenyl) hydantoin and 3-ureidopropionate amide.

[b] Hydrolyzed to carbamoyl-β-alanine (3-ureidopropionate).

[c] Hydrolyzed to carbamoylglycine.

[d] Hydrolyzed to carbamoyl-3-aminoisobutyrate.

References

1. Grisolia, S. & Wallach, D. P. (1955) BBA, 18, 449.

2. Wallach, D. P. & Grisolia, S. (1957) JBC, 226, 277.

DIHYDRO-OROTASE

(L-4,5-Dihydro-orotate amidohydrolase)

L-4,5-Dihydro-orotate + H_2O = N-carbamoyl-L-aspartate

Equilibrium constant

$$\frac{[\text{N-carbamoyl-L-aspartate}]}{[\text{L-4,5-dihydro-orotate}]} = 1.9 \ (\text{pH } 6.1, \ P_i, \ 30^\circ) \tag{1,4}$$

Specificity

Dihydro-orotase is highly specific, and only the L-isomers of N-carbamoylaspartate and 4,5-dihydro-orotate are active as substrates. (1,4)

The enzyme requires Zn^{2+} for maximum activity. (2)

Michaelis constants

source	substrate	$K_m(M)$	conditions	
Z. oroticum	N-carbamoyl-L-aspartate	8×10^{-4}	pH 5.5, P_i, 30°	(2)
Novikoff ascites hepatoma cells (rat)	N-carbamoyl-L-aspartate	1.1×10^{-3}	pH 6.5, P_i, 37°	(3)

Inhibitors

source	inhibitor[a]	$K_i(M)$	conditions	
Novikoff ascites hepatoma cells (rat)	cytidine	1.5×10^{-4}		
	deoxycytidine	1.0×10^{-4}		
	5-methyldeoxycytidine	1.0×10^{-4}		
	CMP	5.2×10^{-5}		
	CDP	1.5×10^{-4}	pH 6.5, P_i, 37°	(3)
	CTP	1.5×10^{-4}		
	dCMP	6.0×10^{-5}		
	uridine	3.0×10^{-4}		
	deoxyuridine	2.7×10^{-4}		

Inhibitors contd.

source	inhibitor[a]	$K_1(M)$	conditions	
Novikoff ascites hepatoma cells (rat)	UMP	2.3×10^{-4}		
	dUMP	2.5×10^{-4}		
	thymidine	7.0×10^{-5}		
	TMP	7.4×10^{-5}		
	adenosine	1.0×10^{-4}		
	deoxyadenosine	4.5×10^{-5}		
	AMP	2.0×10^{-4}		
	dAMP	1.1×10^{-4}		
	ADP	5.8×10^{-5}	pH 6.5, P_i, 37°	(3)
	ATP	6.5×10^{-5}		
	guanosine	1.1×10^{-4}		
	deoxyguanosine	8.5×10^{-5}		
	dGMP	8.0×10^{-5}		
	xanthosine	8.0×10^{-4}		
	inosine	4.1×10^{-4}		
	deoxyinosine	8.0×10^{-4}		
	adenosine-N'-oxide	3.8×10^{-5}		

[a] C(N-carbamoyl-L-aspartate)

Light absorption data

L-4,5-dihydro-orotate ε, (230 mμ) = 11,700 M^{-1}cm^{-1} (pH 5.5)   (2)

References

1. Lieberman, I. & Kornberg, A. (1954) JBC, 207, 911.

2. Sander, E. G., Wright, L. D. & McCormick, D. B. (1965) JBC, 240, 3628.

3. Bresnick, E. & Blatchford, K. (1964) BBA, 81, 150.

4. Reichard, P. & Sköld, O. (1963) Methods in Enzymology, 6, 180.

ALLANTOINASE

(Allantoin amidohydrolase)

Allantoin + H_2O = allantoate

Ref.

Specificity and Michaelis constants

source	(+)-allantoin[a]	relative velocity methylol-allantoin[b]	5-amino hydantoin[b]	$K_m(M)$ (substrate = (±)-allantoin)
Streptococcus allantoicus	1	0.45	0.064	4.9×10^{-3}
Arthrobacter allantoicus	1	0.25	0.04	1.4×10^{-2}
Escherichia coli	1	0.06	0	2.2×10^{-2}
Pseudomonas acidovorans	21.5	0.08	0	4.5×10^{-2}
Pseudomonas fluorescens	6.3	0.30	0	3.5×10^{-2}
Frog liver	4.9	0.30	0.007	6×10^{-3}
Phaseolus hysterinus	13.5	0.375	0.009	4.6×10^{-2}
Glycine hispita	4.4	0.50	0.005	1.4×10^{-2}

[a] (-)-Allantoin = 1.0

[b] (±)-Allantoin = 1.0

The conditions were: pH 7.7, diethanolamine, 30°.

3-Methylallantoin and 1-acetylallantoin were not degraded by the enzyme from any of the above sources.

References

1. Vogels, G. D., Trijbels, F. & Uffink, A. (1966) BBA, 122, 482.

PENICILLINASE

(Penicillin amido-β-lactamhydrolase)

Penicillin + H$_2$O = penicilloate

Molecular weight

source	value	conditions	
Bacillus licheniformis, strains 749 and 6346	23,000	pH 7.0	(2)
B. cereus, strain 5/B[a]	35,200	P$_i$ buffer	(3)
B. cereus, strain 569[b]	31,500	P$_i$ buffer	(3)

[a] Constitutive penicillinase
[b] Induced penicillinase

Specific activity

B. cereus, strain 5/B	4200	benzyl penicillin	
B. cereus, strain 569	5100	(pH 7.0, 30°)	(4)

B. licheniformis - see Specificity and Michaelis constants section.

Specificity and Michaelis constants

Penicillinase attacks only compounds containing the complete fused β-lactam thiazolidine ring.   (1)

source	strain	substrate	v[a]	K$_m$(M)	conditions	
B. licheniformis	749	benzylpenicillin	5420	4.9 x 10^{-5}		
		methicillin	25	-		
		6-aminopenicillanate	270	-		
		cephalosporin C	58.5	<5 x 10^{-5}		
		benzylcephalosporin C	132	<5 x 10^{-5}	pH 7.0, 37°	(2)
	6346	benzylpenicillin	900	9.5 x 10^{-6}		
		methicillin	9	-		
		6-aminopenicillanate	117	-		
		cephalosporin C	135	<5 x 10^{-5}		
		benzylcephalosporin C	379	<5 x 10^{-5}		

[a] μmoles min^{-1} mg^{-1} enzyme protein

Inhibitors

source	strain	inhibitor	type	K$_i$(M)	conditions	
B. licheniformis	749	methicillin	C(benzyl-penicillin)	9.3 x 10^{-7}	pH 7.0, 30°	(2)
	6346			2.3 x 10^{-7}		

References

1. Pollock, M. R. (1960) The Enzymes, 4, 269.
2. Pollock, M. R. (1965) BJ, 94, 666.
3. Hall, J. R. & Ogston, A. G. (1956) BJ, 62, 401.
4. Kogut, M., Pollock, M. R. & Tridgell, E. J. (1956) BJ, 62, 391.

IMIDAZOLONEPROPIONASE

(4-Imidazolone-5-propionate amidohydrolase)

4-Imidazolone-5-propionate + H_2O =

N-formimino-L-glutamate

Equilibrium constant

The reaction is essentially irreversible [F] .   (1)

Michaelis constants

source	substrate	$K_m(M)$	conditions	
Rat liver	4-imidazolone-5-propionate	7×10^{-6}	pH 7.4, P_i, 25°	(1)
Pseudomonas fluorescens	4-imidazolone-5-propionate	2×10^{-4}	pH 7.2, P_i, 30°	(2)

Light absorption data

4-imidazolone-5-propionate, $\varepsilon(260$ mμ$) = 4000$ M^{-1} cm^{-1} (pH 7)   (1)

References

1. Snyder, S. H., Silva, O. L. & Kies, M. W. (1961) JBC, 236, 2996.

2. Rao, D. R. & Greenberg, D. M. (1961) JBC, 236, 1758.

ARGINASE

(L-Arginine amidinohydrolase)

L-Arginine + H_2O = L-ornithine + urea

Molecular weight

source	value	conditions	
Bovine liver	138,000	$3 \times 10^{-2}M$ maleate $+ 3 \times 10^{-2}$ Mn^{2+}	(2)
	$S_{20,w} = 3.84$	P_i buffer, no Mn^{2+}	(3)

Specific activity

Bovine liver	(270 x)	1040	L-arginine (pH 10.2, 25°)	(1,3)
	(47 x)	124	L-arginine (pH 9.0, 30°)	(4)

Specificity

Arginase is specific for substrates of the following structural characteristics:-
a) a free guanidino group and a free carboxyl group.
b) a free amino group is not necessary and can be substituted or even replaced as by a hydroxyl group in arginiate.
c) a three-membered carbon chain between the guanidino group and the -carbon. Thus 4-guanidino-butyrate and 6-guanidino caproate are not attacked. A carbon atom in the carbon chain can, however, be replaced by oxygen since canavanine is hydrolyzed. (1)

Michaelis constants

source	substrate	$K_m(M)$	conditions	
Bovine liver	L-arginine	1.16×10^{-2}	pH 8.4, P_i	(5)

The effect of pH on the kinetics of manganese-activated arginase is discussed in reference (6).

Inhibitors

source	inhibitor	type	$K_i(M)$	conditions	
Bovine liver	L-ornithine	C(L-arginine)	7.7×10^{-3}	pH 8.4,	(5)
	L-lysine	C(L-arginine)	4.8×10^{-3}	P_i	

The following compounds were inhibitory: several amino acids (monoamino acids are NC(L-arginine)), citrate and borate. (1,5)

References

1. Greenberg, D. M. (1960) The Enzymes, 4, 257.
2. Greenberg, D. M., Bagot, A. E. & Roholt, O. A. (1956) ABB, 62, 446.
3. Grassman, W., Hörmann, H. & Janowsky, D. (1958) Z. physiol. Chem., 312, 273.
4. Bach, S. J. & Killip, J. D. (1958) BBA, 29, 273.
5. Hunter, A. & Downs, C. E. (1945) JBC, 157, 427.
6. Roholt, O. A. & Greenberg, D. M. (1956) ABB, 62, 454.

ARGININE DEIMINASE

(L-Arginine iminohydrolase)

L-Arginine + H_2O = L-citrulline + NH_3

Specificity

Arginine deiminase is highly specific for L-arginine. The enzyme from Streptococcus faecalis, for instance, was unable to utilize D-arginine, L-homoarginine, α-carbobenzoxy-L-arginine, nitro-L-arginine, creatine, creatinine, guanidinoacetate or DL-guanidinosuccinate.

(1,2)

Michaelis constants

source	substrate	$K_m(M)$	conditions	
S. faecalis	L-arginine	1.5×10^{-4}	pH 6.8, P_i, 38°	(1)

Inhibitors

The following compounds were inhibitory: creatinine, guanidino-acetate, L-homoarginine, canavanine and long-chain diguanidines. (2)

References

1. Ratner, S. (1954) Advances in Enzymology, 15, 378.

2. Petrack, B., Sullivan, L. & Ratner, S. (1957) ABB, 69, 186.

CYTOSINE DEAMINASE

(Cytosine aminohydrolase)

Cytosine + H_2O = uracil + NH_3

Specificity

The following structural features are required for a pyrimidine compound to serve as a substrate for the enzyme from baker's yeast:

a) an unsubstituted hydroxyl in position 2 is required,

b) a substituent in position 3 produces an inactive substrate,

c) tautomerization to the lactam form produces an inactive substrate,

d) the intactness of the CH group in position 4 is essential,

e) the susceptible amino group must be situated in position 6. (1)

The deaminase also deaminates 5-methylcytosine to thymine. (1)

Michaelis constants

source	substrate	$K_m(M)$	conditions	
Baker's yeast	cytosine	8.3×10^{-4}	pH 6.9, P_i, 37.5°	(1)

Inhibitors

The enzyme (baker's yeast) is inhibited by isocytosine. (1)

References

1. Kream, J. & Chargaff, E. (1952) JACS, 74, 5157.

ADENINE DEAMINASE

(Adenine aminohydrolase)

Adenine + H_2O = hypoxanthine + NH_3

Ref.

Specificity and Michaelis constants

source	substrate[a]	V (relative)	$K_m(M)$	conditions
Candida utilis	adenine	1.00	3.0×10^{-5}	
	2-amino-6-chloropurine	2.11	1.3×10^{-3}	
	7-aminothiazolo[5,4-d] pyrimidine	1.27	3.0×10^{-4}	
	6-chloropurine	0.29	2.5×10^{-3}	
	6-hydrazinopurine	0.19	9.0×10^{-4}	
	2,6-diaminopurine	0.06	3.7×10^{-4}	pH 7.0, P_i, 25° (1)
Azotobacter vinelandii	adenine	1.00	1×10^{-5}	
	2-amino-6-chloropurine	3.00	1.0×10^{-3}	
	7-aminothiazolo[5,4-d] pyrimidine	2.51	1.5×10^{-4}	
	6-chloropurine	0.62	5×10^{-4}	
	6-hydrazinopurine	0.29	3.0×10^{-4}	
	6-iodopurine	0.19	6.0×10^{-4}	
	2,6-diaminopurine	0.12	2.1×10^{-4}	

[a]
   With substituted purines, the action of the enzyme replaced the substituent in the 6 position (NH_2, Cl etc.) by an hydroxyl group.

   The enzyme isolated from yeast was inactive with adenosine 3'- or 5'-phosphate, adenosine, guanine, cytosine, ADP or ATP.   (2)

Inhibitors

source	inhibitor[a]	K_i(M)	conditions
C. utilis[b]	6-methylaminopurine	5.0×10^{-5}	
	7-aminoimidazo [4,5-b] pyridine	7.0×10^{-5}	
	4-aminoimidazo [4,5-d] pyridazine	2.5×10^{-4}	
	purine	2.2×10^{-4}	
	4-amino-5-imidazole-carboxamide	3.2×10^{-4}	pH 7.0, P_i, 25° (1)
	2-fluoro-6-aminopurine	9.0×10^{-4}	
	4-aminoimidazo [4,5-c] pyridine	1×10^{-3}	
	4-amino-5H-pyrrolo [3,2-d] pyrimidine	1.3×10^{-3}	
	guanylurea	2×10^{-3}	

[a] C(adenine)

[b] The enzyme from A. vinelandii is also inhibited by the compounds listed (1).

References

1. Hartenstein, R. C. & Fridovich, I. (1967) JBC, 242, 740.

2. McElroy, W. D. (1963) Methods in Enzymology, 6, 203.

GUANINE DEAMINASE
(Guanine aminohydrolase)

Guanine + H_2O = xanthine + NH_3

Molecular weight

source	value	conditions	
Rabbit liver	170,000[a]	Sephadex G200, pH 7.3	(1)

[a] A minor component of molecular weight 525,000 was also present.

Specificity and Michaelis constants

The nature of the group at position 6 of the purine ring is very important in relation to enzyme activity. Thus, deamination of the 2-amino group occurs with a hydroxyl or thiol in position 6 but not with an amino group. Methylation at position 1 greatly reduces and methylation at position 7 abolishes activity. (1)

source	substrate	relative velocity	$K_m(M)$	conditions		
Rabbit liver[a]	guanine	1.000	1.05×10^{-5}	pH 7.7	PP$_i$-citrate, 37°	
	8-azaguanine	-	1.02×10^{-4}	pH 5.9		
	1-methylguanine	-	2.70×10^{-3}	pH 7.1		(1)
	thioguanine	0.008	-	pH 6.5		
	1-methylthioguanine	0.004	-	pH 6.5		
Rat brain[b]	guanine	1.00	1.95×10^{-5}			
	8-azaguanine	2.50	-	pH 6.6, P$_i$, 37°		(2)
	2-amino-6-mercapto-purine	0.15	-			
	isoguanine	0.06	-			

[a] This enzyme was inactive with 2,6-diaminopurine, thioazaguanine disulphide and hydroxy-6-aminopyrazolo-(3,4d)-pyrimidine.
[b] This enzyme was inactive with guanosine, guanylate, adenine, adenosine, adenylate and 5-aminopurine.

References

1. Currie, R., Bergel, F. & Bray, R. C. (1967) BJ, 104, 634.

2. Mansoor, M., Kalyankar, G. D. & Talwar, G. P. (1963) BBA, 77, 307.

ADENOSINE DEAMINASE

(Adenosine aminohydrolase)

Adenosine + H_2O = inosine + NH_3

Molecular weight

source	value	conditions	
Calf intestinal mucosa	$S_{20},w = 2.15$	pH 7.0	(1)
Aspergillus oryzae	~ 110,000	Sephadex G200	(2)

Specific activity

Calf intestinal mucosa (232 x) 437 adenosine (pH 7.0, P_i, 37°) (1)

Specificity and Michaelis constants

source	substrate	$\frac{V}{(relative)}$	$K_m(M)$	conditions	
A. oryzae	adenosine	1.00	2.5×10^{-4}		
	adenosine 5'-phosphate	1.29[a]	1.0×10^{-4}[a]		
	2'-deoxyadenosine	1.12	9.4×10^{-4}		
	adenosine 3'-phosphate	1.12[a]	2.1×10^{-4}[a]		
	adenosine 3',5'-cyclic phosphate	1.12	4.0×10^{-4}		
	2',3'-dideoxyadenosine	1.06	9.4×10^{-4}	pH 6.5, P_i, 25°	(2)
	2'-deoxyadenosine 5'-phosphate	0.82	1.8×10^{-4}		
	2',5'-dideoxyadenosine	0.76	4.0×10^{-4}		
	3-(β-D-ribofuranosyl) adenine	0.05	5.0×10^{-3}		
	adenine	0.003	6.7×10^{-4}		
Calf intestinal mucosa	adenosine	1.00	3.53×10^{-5}		
	2'-deoxyadenosine	0.96	2.3×10^{-5}		
	3'-deoxyadenosine	0.65	2.25×10^{-5}		
	2,6-diaminopurine riboside	0.29	3.17×10^{-5}	pH 7.4, P_i, 20°	(6)
	5'-AMP, 3'-AMP, 2'-AMP	0	–		

[a]
Value obtained at pH 5.0 (P_i, 25°)

Inhibitors				Ref.
source	inhibitor[a]	$K_i(M)$	conditions	
A. oryzae	adenine	6.7×10^{-4}		
	inosine	7.0×10^{-4}		
	hypoxanthine	7.9×10^{-3}	pH 6.5,	(2)
	9-(β-D-ribofuranosyl)-purine	3.7×10^{-5}	P_i, 25°	
	purine	2.6×10^{-3}		
Calf intestinal mucosa	9-purine ribonucleotide	8.8×10^{-6}	pH 7.0, P_i, 24-26°	(4)
	several 6-substituted-(9-hydroxyalkyl) purines	$3.4\text{-}38 \times 10^{-5}$	pH 7.6, P_i, 25°	(5)

(a)
Competitive (adenosine)

The inhibitory properties of several adenosine analogs are discussed in reference (4).

References

1. Brady, T. G. & O'Connell, W. (1962) BBA, 62, 216.

2. Wolfenden, R., Sharpless, T. K. & Allan, R. (1967) JBC, 242, 977.

3. Kaplan, N. O. (1955) Methods in Enzymology, 2, 473, 475.

4. Cory, J. G. & Suhadolnik, R. J. (1965) B, 4, 1729, 1733.

5. Schaeffer, H. J. & Bharagara, P. S. (1965) B, 4, 71.

6. Coddington, A. (1965) BBA, 99, 442.

CYTIDINE DEAMINASE

(Cytidine aminohydrolase)

$$\text{Cytidine} + H_2O = \text{uridine} + NH_3$$

Ref.

Specificity and Michaelis constants

Cytidine deaminase is highly specific for the cytosine nucleosides. Thus, the enzyme from <u>Escherichia coli</u> was without activity on adenine, adenosine, cytosine, isocytosine, cytidylate, guanine and guanosine. (1)

The enzyme from mouse kidney catalyzed the hydrolysis of a variety of derivatives of cytidine but not of cytosine or several derivatives of cytosine. (2)

source	substrate	relative velocity	$K_m(M)$	conditions	
E. coli	cytidine	(a)	1.74×10^{-4}	pH 7.5, Tris.	(1)
	cytosine deoxyriboside	(a)	8.9×10^{-5}		
Mouse kidney	cytidine	1.00	2.1×10^{-4}	pH 7.4, P_i, 37°	(2)
	5-iododeoxycitidine	0.79	5.5×10^{-4}		

(a) The deamination was faster with cytosine deoxyriboside than with cytidine.

Inhibitors

source	inhibitor	type	$K_i(M)$	conditions	
Mouse kidney	cytidine	C(5-iododeoxycytidine)	3.0×10^{-4}	pH 7.4, P_i, 37°	(1)
	5-bromocytidine	C(5-iododeoxycytidine)	1.8×10^{-4}		

References

1. Wang, T. P. (1955) <u>Methods in Enzymology</u>, <u>2</u>, 478.
2. Creasey, W. A. (1963) <u>JBC</u>, <u>238</u>, 1772.

AMP DEAMINASE

(AMP aminohydrolase)

$$AMP + H_2O = IMP + NH_3$$

Equilibrium constant

The reaction is essentially irreversible[F].   (2)

Molecular weight

source	value	conditions	
Rabbit skeletal muscle	320,000	pH 6.68	(3)
Rat skeletal muscle	$\sim$300,000	pH 7.4	(4)

Specific activity

Rabbit skeletal muscle	(240 x)	92 (pH 6.5, imidazole 30°)	(8)
Rat skeletal muscle		1740 (pH 6.4, succinate, 30°)	(4)

Specificity and kinetic properties

The enzyme (rabbit muscle) is highly specific: 5'-deoxyadenylate is slowly attacked and the following compounds are inactive: 2'AMP, 3'AMP, ADP, ATP, NAD, NADP, 2,6-diaminopurine and adenosine.   (3,5)

The kinetics exhibited by the enzyme isolated from calf brain are complex. Thus, plots of enzyme activity against AMP concentration in the absence of ATP and alkali metal ions yield strongly sigmoidal curves. ATP increases the apparent affinity of the enzyme for AMP without changing the maximum velocity. Lithium ions (and to a lesser extent Na^+ and K^+ but not NH_4^+) have the same effect. The apparent

Specificity and kinetic properties contd.   Ref.

affinity of the enzyme for ATP is increased by increasing the

concentration of AMP or lithium ions.   (7)

The enzyme isolated from rabbit skeletal muscle exhibits normal

Michaelis-Menton kinetics. This enzyme is also activated by alkali

metal ions.   (8)

source	substrate	$K_m(M)$	conditions	
Rabbit muscle	AMP	6×10^{-5}	pH 5.9, succinate, 25°	(6)
Rat muscle	AMP	1.41×10^{-3}	pH 6.4, succinate, 30°	(4)
Calf brain	AMP	2.7×10^{-3}	pH 6.2, Tris-citrate, $22-24^\circ$. ATP $= 2.5 \times 10^{-3}$ LiCl $= 1.5 \times 10^{-1}$	(7)
	ATP	4.4×10^{-4}	pH 6.2, Tris-citrate, $22-24^\circ$. AMP $= 5 \times 10^{-4}$	(7)

Inhibitors

P_i and PP_i are competitive inhibitors (AMP).   (1)

2,3-Diphosphoglycerate inhibits the enzyme from human erythrocytes. (9)

References

1. Lee, Y. P. (1960) The Enzymes, 4, 279.
2. Long, C. (1961) Biochemist's Handbook, 468.
3. Lee, Y. P. (1957) JBC, 227, 987, 993, 999.
4. Currie, R. D. & Webster, H. L. (1962) BBA, 64, 30.
5. Nikiforuk, G. & Colowick, S. P. (1955) Methods in Enzymology, 2, 469.
6. Nikiforuk, G. & Colowick, S. P. (1956) JBC, 219, 119.
7. Setlow, B. & Lowenstein, J. M. (1967) JBC, 242, 607.
8. Smiley, K. L. Jr., Berry, A. J. & Suelter, C. H. (1967) JBC, 242, 2502.
9. Askari, A. & Rao, S. N. (1968) BBA, 151, 198.

AMINOIMIDAZOLASE

(4-Aminoimidazole aminohydrolase)

4-Aminoimidazole + H_2O = unidentified product + NH_3

Ref.

Specificity and kinetic properties

Aminoimidazolase isolated from Clostridium cylindrosporum was without activity on 2-methyl-4-imidazolone, 3-amino-1,2,4-triazole and 4-hydroxy-1,2,3-triazole. 3-Amino-1,2,4-triazole was an active inhibitor of the enzyme. The enzyme required Fe^{2+} (1.00) for activity; Co^{2+} (0.56), Mn^{2+} (0.41) and Ni^{2+} (0.16) were also effective. Cu^{2+}, Al^{3+} and Zn^{2+} were inactive as activators. (1)

source	substrate	$K_m(M)$	conditions	
C. cylindrosporum	4-aminoimidazole	1.8×10^{-3}	pH 7.0, triethanolamine, 37°	(1)

References

1. Rabinowitz, J. C. & Pricer, W. E. Jr. (1956) JBC, 222, 537.

METHENYLTETRAHYDROFOLATE CYCLOHYDROLASE

(5,10-Methenyltetrahydrofolate 5-hydrolase (decyclizing))

5,10-Methenyltetrahydrofolate + H_2O =

10-formyltetrahydrofolate

Ref.

Equilibrium constant

$$\frac{[\text{10-formyltetrahydrofolate}]\ [H^+]}{[\text{5,10-methenyltetrahydrofolate}]\ [H_2O]} = \frac{2.4 \times 10^{-8}}{(\text{pH 5.7, acetate, 25}^\circ)} \qquad (1,2)$$

In neutral and alkaline solutions the reaction catalyzed by the cyclohydrolase proceeds spontaneously. At pH 6.5, P_i and imidazole buffers accelerate the reaction whereas with triethanolamine or maleate buffers the rate is relatively low.   (2)

Michaelis constants

source	substrate	$K_m(M)$	conditions	
Hog liver	5,10-methenyl-tetrahydrofolate	7.4×10^{-5}	pH 6.5, maleate, 25°	(1,2)

Light absorption data

5,10-methenyltetrahydrofolate $\varepsilon,(350\ \text{m}\mu) = 24{,}900\ M^{-1}\ cm^{-1}$ (in acid)   (1)
$\varepsilon,(355\ \text{m}\mu) = 24{,}900\ M^{-1}\ cm^{-1}$ (pH 6.5)   (1,2)

References

1. Greenberg, D. M. (1963) Methods in Enzymology, 6, 386.
2. Tabor, H. & Wyngarden, L. (1959) JBC, 234, 1830.

PTERIN DEAMINASE

(Pterin aminohydrolase)

A pterin + H_2O = a lumazine + NH_3

Equilibrium constant

The reaction is essentially irreversible [F] . (1,2)

Specificity

The following structural features are required for a pteridine compound to serve as a substrate of the enzyme from Alcaligenes metalcaligenes:

(a) Only those pteridines possessing the pterin structure (i.e. the 2-amino and 4-hydroxyl functional groups) are deaminated.

(b) The nature of the substitution at carbon 6 is relatively unimportant. However, a hydroxyl group at this position results in an inactive substrate.

(c) Carbon 7 must be unsubstituted.

(d) An N-5-formylated and reduced pterin is not deaminated. (1,2)

Light absorption data

With pterin carboxylic acid (2-amino-4-hydroxypteridine-6-carboxylic acid) as the substrate, Δ_ε (substrate-product) at 290 mμ = 9,700 M^{-1} cm^{-1} and at 360 mμ = 4,400 M^{-1} cm^{-1} (pH 6.3). (2)

References

1. Levenberg, B. & Hayaishi, O. (1959) JBC, 234, 955.
2. Hayaishi, O. (1963) Methods in Enzymology, 6, 359.

dCMP DEAMINASE

(dCMP aminohydrolase)

$$dCMP + H_2O = dUMP + NH_3$$

Ref.

Equilibrium constant

The reaction is essentially irreversible [F].   (3)

Molecular weight

source	value	conditions	
Donkey spleen	120,000	various	(3)

Specific activity

Donkey spleen (48,000 x) 920 dCMP (pH 7.5, P_i, 38°)   (3)

Specificity and Michaelis constants

source	substrate	$\frac{V}{(relative)}$	$K_m(M)$	conditions	
Hens' egg embryo	dCMP	1.00	6.6×10^{-4}	pH 8, Tris, 37° (+8 $\times 10^{-5}$ M dCTP)	(2)
	5-methyl dCMP	0.96	6.0×10^{-4}		
	5-iodo dCMP	0.72	6.7×10^{-4}		
	5-bromo dCMP	0.82	6.4×10^{-4}		
	5-fluoro dCMP	0.89	1.9×10^{-3}		
Monkey liver	dCMP	1.00	2.15×10^{-3}	pH 7.2, P_i, 23°	(1)
	5-hydroxymethyl dCMP	0.55	1.31×10^{-3}		
	5-methyl dCMP	0.30	2.3×10^{-4}		
Donkey spleen	dCMP	—	3.7×10^{-3}	pH 7.3, P_i, 38°	(3)

The enzyme (monkey liver) was inactive with 3'-dCMP, dCDP, dCTP, 5'-CMP, 2'-CMP, 3'-CMP or deoxycytidine (1). The enzyme isolated from donkey spleen was inactive with deoxycytidine, 3'-dCMP, dCDP, dCTP, CMP, 2',3'-CMP, GMP, dGMP, AMP or dAMP, but dCMP and 5-methyl dCMP were both substrates.   (3)

The enzyme (hen's egg embryo) requires dCTP and Mg^{2+} for activity.   (2)

Inhibitors

source	inhibitor	type	$K_i(M)$	conditions
Hens' egg embryo	TTP (reversed by dCTP)	NC (dCMP) "end product"	$\sim 1 \times 10^{-4}$	pH 8, Tris, $37°$ ($+8 \times 10^{-5}$ M dCTP) (2)
	N-4hydroxy-dCMP	C (dCMP)	1.3×10^{-5}	
Donkey spleen	TMP	C (dCMP)	1.2×10^{-4}	pH 7.3, P_i, $38°$ (3)
	dUMP		7.0×10^{-4}	
	dGMP		1.4×10^{-4}	
	dAMP		2.0×10^{-4}	

dUTP and 5-fluoro-dUTP are potent inhibitors but TDP inhibits to a much less extent. (2)

Light absorption data

5-methyl dCMP, $\varepsilon(295 \text{ m}\mu) = 10,100 \text{ M}^{-1} \text{ cm}^{-1}$
5-bromo dCMP, $\varepsilon(310 \text{ m}\mu) = 7,480 \text{ M}^{-1} \text{ cm}^{-1}$
5-fluoro dCMP, $\varepsilon(300 \text{ m}\mu) = 8,680 \text{ M}^{-1} \text{ cm}^{-1}$ (acid) (2)
5-iodo dCMP, $\varepsilon(320 \text{ m}\mu) = 6,780 \text{ M}^{-1} \text{ cm}^{-1}$

References

1. Scarano, E., Bonaduce, L. & DePetrocellis, B. (1962) JBC, 237, 3742.

2. Maley, G. F. & Maley, F. (1964) JBC, 239, 1168.

3. Geraci, G., Rossi, M. & Scarano, E. (1967) B, 6, 183.

NITRILASE

(Nitrile cyanohydrolase)

A nitrile + H_2O = a carboxylate + NH_3

Specificity and Michaelis constants

The enzyme acts on a wide range of aliphatic and aromatic

nitriles.   (2)

source	substrate	relative velocity	$K_m(M)$	conditions
Hordeum vulgare	3-indoleacetonitrile	1.00	5.1×10^{-5}	
	3-cyanopyridine	8.00	-	
(barley leaves)	p-chlorobenzonitrile	3.19	-	
	7-aza,3-indoleaceto-nitrile	2.80	-	
	4-cyanopyridine	2.67	-	
	p-fluorobenzonitrile	2.04	-	
	p-nitrobenzonitrile	1.72	-	pH 7, P_i, 35° (1,2)
	2-indoleacetonitrile	1.72	-	
	m-nitrobenzonitrile	1.70	-	
	benzonitrile	1.38	-	
	2-cyanopyridine	0.73	-	
	4-imidazoleacetonitrile	0.28	-	
	p-methoxybenzonitrile	0.23	-	
	p-hydroxybenzonitrile	0.21	-	
	p-aminobenzonitrile	0.15	-	
	3-indolenitrile	0.05	-	

The following were not attacked: 4-cyano,3-indoleacetonitrile, ricinine and o-chlorobenzonitrile.   (2)

References
1. Thimann, K. V. & Mahadevan, S. (1964) ABB, 105, 133.
2. Mahadevan, S. V. & Thimann, K. V. (1964) ABB, 107, 62.

RICININE NITRILASE

(Ricinine[*] cyanohydrolase)

Ricinine + H_2O = N-methyl-3-carboxy-4-methoxy-2-pyridone + NH_3

Ref.

Specific activity

Pseudomonad sp. (400 x)   12 ricinine   (pH 7.4, P_i, 37°)   (1)

Specificity

The enzyme (Pseudomonad sp.) hydrolyses the following compounds:
ricinine (1.00), N-ethyl-3-cyano-4-methoxy-2-pyridone (1.18), N-
methyl-3-cyano-2-pyridone (0.38), N-methyl-3-cyano-4-ethoxy-2-
pyridone (0.36), 3-cyano-2-pyridone (0.28), 3-cyano-4-methoxy-2-
pyridone (0.24) and N-ethyl-3-cyano-4-ethoxy-2-pyridone (0.17).
Indoleacetonitrile, norricine, ricinate and N-methyl-3-carboxamide-
4-methoxy-2-pyridone were not hydrolysed by this enzyme.   (2)

Michaelis constants

source	substrate	$K_m(M)$	conditions	
Pseudomonad sp.	ricinine	5×10^{-5}	pH 7.4, P_i, 37°	(1)

Light absorption data

$\Delta\varepsilon$ (ricinine - N-methyl-3-carboxy-4-methoxy-2-pyridone) at
315 mμ = 5700 $M^{-1}cm^{-1}$. (pH 7.4)   (1)

---

[*]ricinine   N-methyl-3-cyano-4-methoxy-2-pyridone

References

1. Hook, R. H. & Robinson, W. G. (1964) JBC, 239, 4263.
2. Hook, R. H. & Robinson, W. G. (1964) JBC, 239, 4257.

RIBOFLAVINASE

(Riboflavin hydrolase)

Riboflavin + H_2O = ribitol + lumichrome

Specificity

The enzyme (spider lily: Crinum longifolium) was specific for
riboflavin: FMN, FAD or isoriboflavin were not hydrolyzed. (1)
The specificity of the enzyme present in the cell debris of
Pseudomonas riboflavina is discussed in reference (2).

Michaelis constants

source	substrate	$K_m(M)$	conditions
C. longifolium	riboflavin	4.7×10^{-5}	pH 7.5, P_i, 37° (1)

Inhibitors

source	inhibitor	type	$K_i(M)$	conditions
C. longifolium	FAD	C (riboflavin)	$\sim 1 \times 10^{-4}$	pH 7.5, (1) P_i, 37°

References

1. Kumar, S. A. & Vaidyanathan, C. S. (1964) BBA, 89, 127.

2. Yanagita, T. & Foster, J. W. (1956) JBC, 221, 593.

INORGANIC PYROPHOSPHATASE

(Pyrophosphate phosphohydrolase)

Pyrophosphate + H_2O = 2 orthophosphate

Ref.

Equilibrium constant

The reversibility of the reaction has been demonstrated. The forward reaction is strongly favoured.

(1,2)

Molecular weight

source	value	conditions	
Yeast	63,000	pH 6.7	(3)

Specific activity

Yeast	(200 x)	1433	PP_i (pH 7.2, veronal, 30°)	(6)
Escherichia coli	(500 x)	1333	PP_i (pH 9.1, 2-amino-2-methyl-1,3-propanediol, 37°)	(2)

Specificity

The enzyme (yeast) in the presence of Mg^{2+} is a specific catalyst for the hydrolysis of PP_i and several organic pyrophosphates such as ATP, ADP or TPP are not attacked (1). Tripolyphosphate is not hydrolyzed by this enzyme (5). In the presence of Zn^{2+}, however, the enzyme catalyzes the hydrolysis of several nucleoside diphosphates and triphosphates.

(4)

The effect of Mg^{2+}, Co^{2+} or Mn^{2+} as cofactor is discussed in reference (1).

The enzyme isolated from E. coli catalyzes the hydrolysis of PP_i, tripolyphosphate and tetrapolyphosphate with relative velocities of 1.000, 0.0160 and 0.007, respectively. No activity was found with a variety of phosphate esters in the presence or absence of Mg^{2+}, Mn^{2+}, Zn^{2+} or Co^{2+}.

(2)

The reader is referred to enzyme 3.1.3.9 for the inorganic pyrophosphatase activity of rat liver and kidney microsomes.

The properties of the enzyme present in Prymnesium parvum are discussed in reference (7).

Michaelis constants

source	substrate	$K_m(M)$	conditions	
E. coli	Mg PP_i^{2-}	5×10^{-6}	pH 9.1, 2-amino-2-methyl-1,3-propanediol, 30°	(2)

The Michaelis constant for PP_i with the enzyme isolated from yeast has not been obtained. (See, for instance, reference (8)).

Inhibitors

source	inhibitor	type	$K_i(M)$	conditions	
E. coli	PP_i	$C(Mg\ PP_i^{2-})$	1×10^{-7}	pH 9.1, 2-amino-2-methyl-1,3-propanediol, 30°	(2)

P_i and ADP (but not AMP or ATP) also inhibit ($C(Mg\ PP_i^{2-})$). (2)

The enzyme isolated from bull seminal plasma is not inhibited by PP_i. (5)

References

1. Kunitz, M. & Robbins, R. W. (1961) The Enzymes, 5, 169.

2. Josse, J. (1966) JBC, 241, 1938, 1948.

3. Schachman, H. K. (1952) J. Gen. Physiol., 35, 451.

4. Schlesinger, M. J. & Coon, M. J. (1960) BBA, 41, 30.

5. Heppel, L. A. & Hilmoe, R. J. (1951) JBC, 192, 87.

6. Heppel, L. A. (1955) Methods in Enzymology, 2, 570.

7. Ricketts, T. R. (1965) ABB, 110, 184.

8. Kunitz, M. (1952) J. Gen. Physiol., 35, 423.

ATPASE

(ATP phosphohydrolase)

ATP + H_2O = ADP + orthophosphate

Molecular weight

source	value		conditions	
Beef heart mitochondria[a]	284,000	[10]	0.1 M KCl, 25°	(4)
Skeletal muscle myosin	620,000	[3]	0.5 M KCl	(6)
Dog heart muscle myosin	758,000	[3-4]	-	(7)
	225,000		pH 6.8	(8)

[a] At 0° the enzyme at once loses its catalytic activity and dissociates into subunits of molecular weight about 30,000. The process is reversible.

Specific activity

Beef heart mitochondria (57 x)	76.5 ATP (pH 7.4, Tris, 30°, no DNP)	(5)
	114 ATP (pH 7.4, Tris, 30° + 5 x 10⁻⁴ M DNP)	(5)
Skeletal muscle myosin	0.24 ATP (pH 8, 0.15 M Tris)	(7)
Dog heart muscle myosin	0.70 ATP (pH 8, 0.15 M Tris)	(7)

Specificity and catalytic properties

ATPase is universally distributed in living material. The activity is in general associated with the intracellular formed elements and it has been found in myosin, actomyosin, mitochondria, microsomes and cell membranes (1). Mitochondrial ATPase is important as a coupling factor in oxidative phosphorylation (4, 5, 12). Its role (as myosin A ATPase) in muscle contraction is discussed in reference (2) and in the transport of Na^+ and K^+ across cell membranes in reference (3).

Mitochondrial ATPase (beef heart) hydrolyzes ATP (1.00), ITP (1.25), GTP (0.75) and UTP (0.02) but not CTP, nucleoside mono- or diphosphates, fructose 6-phosphate, glucose 6-phosphate, glucose 1-phosphate, ribose 5-phosphate, carbamoylphosphate or PP_i. This enzyme requires Mg^{2+} for activity; Ca^{2+} is inhibitory. DNP activates the activity with ATP but not with ITP, GTP or UTP. (5)

Mitochondrial ATPase (rat liver) is activated by Mg^{2+} or Ca^{2+}. (11)

Myosin ATPase - the only fibrous protein with the properties of an enzyme - attacks all nucleotide triphosphates tested so far. In all cases the enzyme removes only the terminal phosphate of the triphosphate and it is without activity on nucleoside mono- or diphosphates or on pyrophosphates. (1,9)

Specificity and catalytic properties contd.   Ref.

The effects of Ca^{2+}, K^+-EDTA or NH_4^+-EDTA on the catalytic properties of myosin ATPase are complex and are summarized below. (The figures
are relative velocities. The conditions were: pH 7.7, 37°; $CaCl_2$ =
5×10^{-3}M and EDTA = 1×10^{-2}M. The data are from references (1) and (9)).

substrate	Ca^{2+}	K^+-EDTA	NH_4^+-EDTA
ATP	1.00	2.90	17.2
GTP	1.82	0.0	0.0
ITP	4.50	0.0	0.92
CTP	0.45	1.09	1.97
UTP	1.59	0.37	2.58
ATPP	1.09	0.0	0.0

The effects of other modifiers (e.g. thiol reagents and organic
solvents) on the catalytic properties of myosin ATPase are discussed
in references (1) and (2).

The properties of ATPase from the membrane ghosts obtained by lysis
of Streptococcus faecalis protoplasts are discussed in reference (10).

source	substrate	$K_m(M)$	conditions	
Dog heart myosin	ATP	1×10^{-4}	pH 8, 0.5 M KCl	(7)
Rat liver mitochondria	ATP	1.7×10^{-4}	pH 8.5 ATP = Ca^{2+}	(11)

Abbreviations

DNP   2,4-dinitrophenol

References

1. Kielley, W. W. (1961) The Enzymes, 5, 149, 159.
2. Gergely, J. (1966) Ann. Rev. Biochem., 35 (2), 694.
3. Albers, R. W. (1967) Ann. Rev. Biochem., 36 (2), 727.
4. Penefsky, H. S. & Warner, R. C. (1965) JBC, 240, 4694.
5. Pullman, M. E., Penefsky, H. S., Datta, A. & Racker, E. (1960)
    JBC, 235, 3322.
6. Kielley, W. W. & Harrington, W. F. (1960) BBA, 41, 401.
7. Brahms, J. & Kay, C. M. (1963) JBC, 238, 198.
8. Ellenbogen, E., Iyengar, R., Stern, H. & Olson, R. E. (1960) JBC,
    235, 2642.
9. Kielley, W. W., Kalckar, H. M. & Bradley, L. B. (1956) JBC, 219, 95.
10. Abrams, A. (1965) JBC, 240, 3675.
11. Ulrich, F. (1965) BBA, 105, 460.
12. Penefsky, H. S., Pullman, M. E., Datta, A. & Racker, E. (1960) JBC,
    235, 3330.

APYRASE

(ATP diphosphohydrolase)

ATP + H_2O = ADP + orthophosphate

Molecular weight

source	value	conditions	
Potato (red skin)	200,000 [4]	sucrose gradient	(1)

Specificity

The potato contains two enzymes with apyrase activity which have been separated. (2)

The locust enzyme hydrolyzed, in order of effectiveness, ATP, ITP, ADP and IDP but PP_i and several organic phosphate and pyrophosphate esters tested were not attacked. (3)

Michaelis constants

source	substrate	$\frac{V}{(relative)}$	$K_m(M)$	conditions	
Potato Enzyme A	ATP	1.00	2.2×10^{-5}	pH 6.7, veronal-acetate, 37° + Ca^{2+}	(2)
	ADP	0.11	5.8×10^{-5}		
Potato Enzyme B	ATP	1.00	1.9×10^{-5}		
	ADP	0.82	2.4×10^{-5}		
Locust (thoracic muscle)	ATP	1.0	8.6×10^{-4}	pH 8.0, borate, 42° + Mg^{2+}	(3)
	ADP	0.1	3.3×10^{-3}		

References

1. Traverso-Cori, A., Chaimovich, H. & Cori, O. (1965) ABB, 109, 173.
2. Molnar, J. & Lorand, L. (1961) ABB, 93, 353.
3. Gilmour, D. (1955) Methods in Enzymology, 2, 595.

NUCLEOSIDEDIPHOSPHATASE

(Nucleosidediphosphate phosphohydrolase)

A nucleoside diphosphate + H_2O =

a nucleotide + orthophosphate

Specificity and Michaelis constants

Nucleosidediphosphatase acts on IDP, GDP, UDP and D-ribose 5-pyrophosphate but does not catalyze the dephosphorylation of ATP, ITP, ribose 5-triphosphate, IMP, AMP, ADP or CDP.　(1,2)

source	substrate	relative velocity	$K_m(M)$	conditions	
Beef liver	IDP	1.0	5×10^{-4}	pH 7.4, Tris, 20°	(1,2)
	UDP	1.7	-		
	GDP	1.6	-		
Calf liver	IDP	1.0	-	pH 7.0, veronal, 37°	(1)
	UDP	0.6	-		
	GDP	0.8	-		
	ribose 5-pyrophosphate	0.6	-		

References

1. Plaut, G. W. E. (1963) Methods in Enzymology, 6, 231.

2. Plaut, G. W. E. (1955) JBC, 217, 235.

ACYLPHOSPHATASE

(Acylphosphate phosphohydrolase)

An acylphosphate + H_2O = an anion + P_i

Ref.

Molecular weight

source	value	conditions	
Calf brain	13,200	pH 5	(2)

Specific activity

Calf brain	(1750 x)	2638	acetylphosphate	(pH 6.0, acetate, 27°)	(2)

Specificity

The enzyme (horse skeletal muscle) does not catalyze the hydrolysis of PP_i, ATP, ADP, AMP, acetyladenylate, acetylcholine, acetyl-CoA or glycerolphosphate. It does not catalyze the transfer of acetate from acetylphosphate to a group of acetyl acceptors or the transfer of phosphate to glucose or creatine or the exchange of radioactive P_i or acetate into acetylphosphate. The enzyme catalyzes the hydrolysis of acetylphosphate, propionylphosphate, butyrylphosphate, succinylphosphate and 1,3-diphosphoglycerate. (4)

Michaelis constants

source	substrate	$K_m(M)$	conditions	
Calf brain	acetylphosphate	1.1×10^{-2}	pH 6.0, acetate	(3)
	carbamoylphosphate	6.4×10^{-3}		

Inhibitors

The enzyme (calf brain) is inhibited by thyroxine and P_i. (3)

References

1. Lipmann, F. (1946) Advances in Enzymology, 6, 251.
2. Raijman, L., Grisolia, S. & Edelhoch, H. (1960) JBC, 235, 2340.
3. Grisolia, S., Caravaca, J. & Joyce, B. K. (1958) BBA, 29, 432.
4. Harary, I. (1957) BBA, 26, 434.

NUCLEOTIDE PYROPHOSPHATASE

(Dinucleotide nucleotidohydrolase)

A dinucleotide + H_2O = 2 mononucleotides

Ref.

Specificity

Nucleotide pyrophosphatase catalyzes the hydrolysis of a variety of dinucleotides. Thus, the enzyme from potato was active with NAD (1.00), FAD (0.67), ATP (0.27), ADP (0.22), thiamine pyrophosphate (0.21), NADP (0.2) and PP$_i$ (0.03). CoA, UDPglucose and adenosine diphosphate ribose were also cleaved by the enzyme. The following compounds exhibited low activities (<0.01): adenosine 5-phosphate, adenosine 3-phosphate, NMN, glucose 6-phosphate and glycerophosphate. (1,2)

The enzyme from <u>Neurospora</u> <u>crassa</u> was active with NAD or NADP. (3)

Michaelis constants

source	substrate	$K_m(M)$	conditions	
Potato	NAD	1.5×10^{-4}	pH 7.0, P$_i$, 38°	(1)
	NADP	3.0×10^{-3}		
	ATP	2.0×10^{-3}	pH 7.4, glycyl-glycine, 38°	(1)
	thiamine-pyrophosphate	2.6×10^{-3}		
<u>N. crassa</u>	NAD	5×10^{-4}	0.1 M KH_2PO_4, 37°	(3)

Inhibitors

source	inhibitor	type	$K_i(M)$	conditions	
Potato	ATP	C(NAD)	2.5×10^{-3}	pH 7.0, P$_i$, 38°	(1)

References

1. Kornberg, A. & Pricer, W. E. Jr. (1950) JBC, 182, 763.
2. Plaut, G. W. E. (1961) Biochemist's Handbook, 265.
3. Kaplan, N. O., Colowick, S. P. & Nason, A. (1951) JBC, 191, 473.

dCTP-ASE

(dCTP nucleotidohydrolase)

dCTP + H$_2$O = dCMP + pyrophosphate

Specificity

The enzyme isolated from bacteriophage T$_2$-infected Escherichia coli is highly specific and is with little or no activity on TTP, dGTP, dATP, 5-hydroxymethyl dCTP, 5-bromo dCTP, 5-bromo dUTP, ATP, GTP, UTP or CTP. The enzyme also hydrolyzes dCDP (to dCMP and P$_i$) although at a much lower rate than dCTP. (1)

Michaelis constants

source	substrate	K_m(M)	conditions	
T$_2$-infected E. coli	dCTP	3.9 x 10^{-6}	pH 9.2, glycine, 37°	(1)
	dCDP	2.4 x 10^{-6}		

Inhibitors

source	inhibitor	type	K_i(M)	conditions	
T$_2$-infected E. coli	dCTP	C(dCDP)	4.2 x 10^{-6}	pH 9.2, glycine, 37°	(1)
	dCMP	C(dCDP)	1.4 x 10^{-4}		
	dCDP	C(dCTP)	2.7 x 10^{-6}		
	dCMP	C(dCTP)	2.0 x 10^{-4}		

References

1. Zimmerman, S. B. (1963) Methods in Enzymology, 6, 258.

FUMARYLACETOACETASE

(4-Fumarylacetoacetate fumarylhydrolase)

4-Fumarylacetoacetate + H_2O = acetoacetate + fumarate

Specificity

Fumarylacetoacetase attacks a variety of 3,5- and 2,4-diketo-acids. The beef liver enzyme for instance hydrolyzed 4-fumaryl-acetoacetate, succinylacetoacetate and triacetate very rapidly; 2,4-dioxovalerate at about 8% the rate with 4-fumarylacetoacetate but not acetylacetone, triacetic ester, triacetic lactone, acetoacetate, 3-oxo-hexanoate, oxaloacetate, 2-oxoglutarate, laevulinate, sorbate or hexanoate.   (1,2,3)

Michaelis constants

source	substrate	$K_m(M)$	conditions	
Beef liver	triacetate[a]	1.38×10^{-3}	pH 6.5, maleate, 30°	(2)

[a] 3,5-diketohexanoate

Light absorption data

4-fumarylacetoacetate ε, (330 mμ) = 13,500 M^{-1} cm^{-1} (pH 7.5)   (1)

References

1. Edwards, S. W. & Knox, W. E. (1955) Methods in Enzymology, 2, 298.
2. Connors, W. M. & Stotz, E. (1949) JBC, 178, 881.
3. Meister, A. & Greenstein, J. P. (1948) JBC, 175, 573.

KYNURENINASE

(L-Kynurenine hydrolase)

L-Kynurenine + H_2O = anthranilate + L-alanine

Ref.

Specificity

Kynureninase exhibits low specificity. Thus the enzyme from
Neurospora crassa hydrolyzed L-kynurenine (to L-alanine and anthranilate), 3-hydroxy-L-kynurenine (to L-alanine and 3-hydroxyanthra-
nilate) and N'-formyl-L-kynurenine (to L-alanine and formylanthranilate) but not N-acetyl-L-kynurenine or D-kynurenine. (2)

Kynureninase isolated from a species of Pseudomonad attacked
L-kynurenine (1.00), 5-hydroxy-L-kynurenine (0.55), 3-hydroxy-L-
kynurenine (0.20), 2-hydroxybenzoyl-L-alanine (0.13) and benzoyl-L-
alanine (0.06). This enzyme was inactive with N'-formyl-L-kynurenine,
3-methoxykynurenine, 3-hydroxybenzoyl-L-alanine, 2-aminobenzoylprop-
ionate and benzoylpropionate. (1)

The enzyme from rat liver hydrolyzed 3-hydroxy L-kynurenine more
rapidly than L-kynurenine but the following compounds were inactive:
D-kynurenine, kynurenate, xanthurenate and N'-acetyl-DL-kynurenine. (4)

The properties of the enzyme from pig liver are discussed in
reference (3).

Michaelis constants

source	substrate	relative velocity	$K_m(M)$	conditions	
N. crassa	L-kynurenine	1.00	6×10^{-6}	pH 8.1,	
	3-hydroxy L-kynurenine	0.62	3×10^{-6}	PP_i,	(2)
	pyridoxal phosphate	-	6×10^{-7}	37°	
Rat liver	L-kynurenine	-	4×10^{-4}	pH 8.0, P_i, 38°	(4)

Inhibitors

The enzyme (N. crassa) was inhibited by its substrates when

present at high concentrations and by a number of amines.   (2)

Light absorption data

compound	$\lambda(m\mu)$	$\varepsilon, (M^{-1}cm^{-1})$		
kynurenine	365	5150		
	330	151		
	310	98		
kynurenate	365	2060	pH 8.0	(4)
	330	8850		
	310	2290		
anthranilate	365	894		
	330	3990		
	310	3280		

References

1. Hayaishi, O. (1955) in Amino Acid Metabolism (eds. McElroy, W. D. & Glass, H. B.) the Johns Hopkins Press: Baltimore p921.
2. Jakoby, W. B. & Bonner, D. M. (1953) JBC, 205, 699, 709.
3. Wiss, O. & Weber, F. (1956) Z. Physiol. Chem., 304, 232.
4. Knox, W. E. (1953) BJ, 53, 379.

FLUOROACETATE FLUOROHYDROLASE

(Fluoroacetate fluorohydrolase)

Fluoroacetate + H_2O = acetate + fluoride

Ref.

Specificity and Michaelis constants

source	substrate	V(relative)	K_m(M)	conditions
Pseudomonad sp.[*]	fluoroacetate	1.00	2.4×10^{-3}	pH 9.1, 2-amino-2-methyl-1,3-propanediol, 30° (1)
	chloroacetate	0.17	2.0×10^{-2}	

[*]Present in Potomac River mud.

The following were not hydrolysed: 2- or 3-fluoropropionate, difluoroacetate, trifluoroacetate or 2-3,- or 4-fluorobenzoate. Iodo-acetate was hydrolysed at a rate of 0.8% that of fluoroacetate.   (1)

Inhibitors

source	inhibitor	type	K_i(M)	conditions
Pseudomonad sp.	glycollate		4.5×10^{-4}	
	difluoroacetate		1.9×10^{-3}	
	trifluoroacetate		2.1×10^{-3}	pH 9.1, 2-
	benzoate		2.7×10^{-3}	amino-2-
	2-fluorobenzoate	C[*]	4.6×10^{-3}	methyl-1,3- (1)
	phenylacetate		1.1×10^{-2}	propanediol,
	chloroacetate		1.7×10^{-2}	30°
	acetate		3.3×10^{-2}	
	glycine		3.3×10^{-2}	
	chloride	NC[*]	3.0×10^{-1}	

[*]With respect to fluoroacetate.

References

1. Goldman, P. (1965) JBC, 240, 3434.

DFPase

(Di-isopropylphosphorofluoridate fluorohydrolase)

Di-isopropyl phosphorofluoridate + H_2O = di-isopropyl phosphate + fluoride

Specificity

The enzyme from a number of sources is active in the splitting of the P-F linkage in a variety of phosphorofluoridates. Thus, the enzyme isolated from rabbit plasma hydrolyses dimethyl phosphorofluoridate (1.00), diethyl phosphorofluoridate (0.67), di-isopropyl phosphorofluoridate (0.13) and ethyl methyl phosphorofluoridate (0.12). (1)

The hog kidney enzyme hydrolyses di-isopropyl phosphorofluoridate, ethyl-methanefluorophosphonate, propyl-1-methanefluorophosphonate, propyl-2-methanefluorophosphonate (sarin), (2,2-dimethylpropyl)-1-methanefluorophosphonate, propyl-2-ethanefluorophosphonate, propyl-2-isopropanefluorophosphonate and ethyl-dimethylamidocyanophosphonate (tabun). (2)

Michaelis constants

source	substrate	$K_m(M)$	conditions	
Hog kidney	di-isopropyl phosphorofluoridate	1.4×10^{-2}	pH 7.4, $NaHCO_3$, 37°	(3)

The effects of various activators (Mn^{2+}, dipyridyl, histidine and cysteine) on V and K_m are discussed in reference (3).

References

1. Mazur, A. (1955) Methods in Enzymology, 1, 651.

2. Cohen, J. A. & Warringa, M. G. P. J. (1957) BBA, 26, 29.

3. Mounter, L. A., Floyd, C. S. & Chanatin, A. (1953) JBC, 204, 221.

PYRUVATE DECARBOXYLASE
(2-Oxoacid carboxy-lyase)
A 2-oxoacid = an aldehyde + CO_2

Equilibrium constant

The reaction is essentially irreversible [F]. (1)

Molecular weight

source	value	conditions	
Brewer's yeast	175,000 [4]	pH 6.8	(2)
Escherichia coli(a)	183,000	pH 7.0	(3)
Wheat germ	1,000,000	pH 6.8	(4)

(a)The E. coli pyruvate dehydrogenase complex has been separated into three enzymes one of which is pyruvate decarboxylase. The complex contains 12 molecules of the decarboxylase (7).

Specific activity

Brewer's yeast (35 x)	52 pyruvate	(pH 6.0, succinate, 30°)	(2)
Wheat germ (2700 x)	54 pyruvate	(pH 6.0, succinate, 30°)	(4)

Specificity

The yeast enzyme decarboxylates higher homologs of pyruvate up to 2-oxocaproate with the reaction decreasing with chain length. Phenylpyruvate, 2-oxoglutarate and acetoacetate are not attacked. 2-Oxoisovalerate is decarboxylated at the same rate as pyruvate (1,6). The enzyme from wheat germ attacks pyruvate (1.00), 2-oxobutyrate (1.00), 2-oxoglutarate (0.10) but not pyruvamide. (4)

The mechanism of acyloin synthesis (from pyruvate and acetaldehyde) is discussed in reference (5).

Michaelis constants

source	substrate	$K_m(M)$	conditions	
Wheat germ	pyruvate	3.6×10^{-3}	pH 6.0, succinate, 30°	(4)
	Mg^{2+}	1×10^{-4}		
	thiaminepyrophosphate	1.35×10^{-6}		
Yeast	pyruvate	3×10^{-2}	pH 6.0, citrate, 30°	(1,6)
	Mg^{2+}	2.5×10^{-5}		
	thiaminepyrophosphate	2.5×10^{-6}		

Inhibitors

The enzyme from wheat germ is inhibited by acetaldehyde and propionaldehyde. (4)

References

1. Utter, M. F. (1961) The Enzymes, 5, 320.
2. Ullrich, J., Wittorf, J. H. & Gubler, C. J. (1966) BBA, 113, 595.
3. Koike, M., Reed, L. J. & Carroll, W. R. (1963) JBC, 238, 30.
4. Singer, T. P. & Pensky, J. (1952) JBC, 196, 375.
5. Singer, T. P. & Pensky, J. (1952) BBA, 9, 316.
6. Green, D. E., Herbert, D. & Subrahmanyan, V. (1941) JBC, 138, 327.
7. Reed, L. J. & Cox, D. J. (1966) Ann. Rev. Biochem., 35, 57.

OXALATE DECARBOXYLASE

(Oxalate carboxy-lyase)

Oxalate = formate + CO_2

Specificity

Oxalate decarboxylase is highly specific for its substrate. Thus, the enzyme from Collyvia veltipes (a wood-destroying fungus) was inactive with the following compounds: pyruvate, malonate, succinate, glycollate, citrate, malate, 2-oxomalonate, oxaloacetate and formate (1). The enzyme from Aspergillus niger could not utilize formate, acetate, propionate, glyoxalate, glycollate, mesoxalate, pyruvate, oxaloacetate, oxalosuccinate, succinate, fumarate, L(-)-malate, L(+)-tartrate, itaconate, citrate, cis-aconitate, 2-oxoglutarate, gluconate, 2-oxoglutarate or any of the common amino acids (2). The enzyme from Myrothecium verrucaria could not utilize pyruvate, oxaloacetate, malate, malonate, maleate, lactate, glycollate, succinate, citrate, formate, fumarate, tartrate or acetate (3).

The decarboxylase requires trace amounts of oxygen for activity. It does not require any cofactor nor does it possess a prosthetic group. (1,2,3)

Michaelis constants

source	substrate	$K_m(M)$	conditions	
C. veltipes	oxalate	2.05×10^{-3}	pH 3.0, P_i, 37°	(1)
A. niger	oxalate	4×10^{-3}	pH 5.2, acetate.	(2)
M. verrucaria	oxalate	1.7×10^{-3}	pH 4.0, P_i-citrate, 30°	(3)

References

1. Shimazono, H. & Hayaishi, O. (1957) JBC, 227, 151.

2. Emiliani, E. & Bekes, P. (1964) ABB, 105, 488.

3. Lillehoj, E. B. & Smith, F. G. (1965) ABB, 109. 216.

OXALOACETATE DECARBOXYLASE

(Oxaloacetate carboxy-lyase)

Oxaloacetate = pyruvate + CO_2

Ref.

Specific activity

Micrococcus lysodeikticus	(5950 x)	890 oxaloacetate	(2)
		(pH 5.4, acetate, 30°)	

Specificity

The enzyme (M. lysodeikticus) is highly specific and does not decarboxylate pyruvate, 2-oxoglutarate, acetoacetate, oxalosuccinate, acetone dicarboxylate, dihydroxymaleate or dihydroxytartrate.　(2)

Michaelis constants

source	substrate	$K_m(M)$	conditions	
M. lysodeikticus	oxaloacetate	2×10^{-3}	pH 5.4, acetate,	(2)
	Mn^{2+}	2×10^{-4}	30°	

Inhibitors

The enzyme (Pseudomonas ovalis) is competitively inhibited by acyl-CoA derivatives. Succinyl-CoA was less effective in this respect than propionyl-CoA or acetyl-CoA. The following did not inhibit: CoA, pyruvate, acetate or the anhydrides of acetic, propionic or succinic acids.　(3)

References

1. Utter, M. F. (1961) The Enzymes, 5, 323.

2. Herbert, D. (1955) Methods in Enzymology, 1, 753.

3. Horton, A. A. & Kornberg, H. L. (1964) BBA, 89, 381.

ACETOACETATE DECARBOXYLASE

(Acetoacetate carboxy-lyase)

Acetoacetate = acetone + CO_2

Molecular weight

source	value	conditions	
Clostridium acetobutylicum	260,000 [8]	various	(2)

Specific activity

C. acetobutylicum	725	acetoacetate	(pH 5.9, 30°)	(3)

Specificity

The enzyme (C. acetobutylicum) is highly specific for aceto-acetate. Thus, the following are inactive: ethyl acetoacetate, pyruvate, acetopyruvate, oxaloacetate, 2-oxoglutarate and acetone dicarboxylic acid.

(4)

Michaelis constants

source	substrate	$K_m(M)$	conditions	
C. acetobutylicum	acetoacetate	8×10^{-3}	pH 5.0, acetate, 37.5°	(5)

Inhibitors

The enzyme (C. acetobutylicum) is inhibited by a number of substrate analogs (e.g., acetopyruvate, oxaloacetate, malonate, ethyl acetoacetate, 2-oxoglutarate, pyruvate and acetone dicar-boxylic acid).

(5)

References

1. Utter, M. F. (1961) The Enzymes, 5, 326.
2. Lederer, F., Coutts, S. M., Laursen, R. A. & Westheimer, F. H. (1966) B, 5, 823.
3. Zerner, B., Coutts, S. M., Lederer, F., Waters, H. H. & Westheimer, F. H. (1966) B, 5, 813.
4. Seeley, H. W. (1955) Methods in Enzymology, 1, 624.
5. Davies, R. (1943) BJ, 37, 230.

BENZOYLFORMATE DECARBOXYLASE

(Benzoylformate carboxy-lyase)

Benzoylformate = benzaldehyde + CO_2

Equilibrium constant

The reaction is essentially irreversible [F].   (1,2)

Specificity

Benzoylformate decarboxylase from Pseudomonas fluorescens is highly specific for its substrate. The following compounds exhibited slight activities: pyruvate, 2-oxobutyrate and 2-oxoglutarate.   (1,2)

Michaelis constants

source	substrate	$K_m(M)$	conditions	
P. fluorescens	benzoylformate	9×10^{-4}	pH 6.0,	(1,2)
	thiamine-pyrophosphate	4×10^{-6}	P_i, 30^0	

References

1. Stanier, R. Y. (1955) Methods in Enzymology, 2, 278.
2. Gunsalus, C. F., Stanier, R. Y. & Gunsalus, I. C. (1953) J. Bacteriol., 66, 548.

AMINOMALONATE DECARBOXYLASE

(Aminomalonate carboxy-lyase)

Aminomalonate = glycine + CO_2

Ref.

Specificity

The enzyme (rat liver) is highly specific and the following compounds are not decarboxylated: carbobenzoxyaminomalonate, glycylaminomalonate, carbobenzoxyglycylaminomalonate, 2-methylaminomalonate, glycine, L-serine, D-serine, L-threonine, L-cysteine, L-glutamate, L-aspartate, 2-aminoisobutyrate, 2-methylmalonate, ketomalonate and hydroxymalonate. (1)

Michaelis constants

source	substrate	$K_m(M)$	conditions	
Silkworm	aminomalonate	6.5×10^{-2}	pH 5.9-6.1	(2)

Inhibitors

The enzyme (rat liver) is inhibited by α-amino acids of which L-cysteine, L-serine and 2-methylaminomalonate are the most effective. The inhibition was competitive (aminomalonate) and K_i values in the range 8×10^{-3} to 1.5×10^{-3}M were obtained. (1)

References

1. Thanassi, J. W. & Fruton, F. S. (1962) B, 1, 975.
2. Shimura, K., Nagayama, H. & Kikuchi, A. (1956) Nature, 177, 935.

ASPARTATE 4-DECARBOXYLASE

(L-Aspartate 4-carboxy-lyase)

L-Aspartate = L-alanine + CO_2

Ref.

Molecular weight

source	value	conditions	
Pseudomonas dacunhae	820,000	-	(1)
	51,000	minimum: pyridoxal-phosphate content	(1)
Achromobacter sp.	760,000	pH 7.0	(2)
	60,000	minimum: pyridoxal-phosphate content	(2)
Alcaligenes faecalis	$S_{20,w} = 18$	-	(4)

Specific activity

P. dacunhae (68 x)	84.5	L-aspartate (pH 5.3, acetate, 30° + pyridoxal-phosphate + 2-oxoglutarate)	(1)
Achromobacter sp.	90	L-aspartate (pH 5.0, acetate, 30° + pyruvate)	(2,3)
A. faecalis	56	L-aspartate (pH 5.0, acetate, 38° + pyruvate)	(4)

Specificity

The enzyme is highly specific for L-aspartate. Thus that from Achromobacter sp. does not decarboxylate the following compounds: fumarate, malonate, L-threonine, L-glutamate, L-serine, L-malate, β-alanine, (+)-tartrate, α-L-alanine, DL-β-methylaspartate, maleate, succinate, DL-erythro-β-hydroxyaspartate and DL-threo-β-hydroxy-aspartate. (2)

Specificity contd. Ref.

The enzyme from *A. faecalis* also catalyzes the following reactions: L-aspartate + pyruvate = L-alanine + oxaloacetate and L-aspartate + 2-oxo-glutarate = L-glutamate + oxaloacetate. The rates observed were about 0.2% that of the decarboxylation reaction. (4)

The enzyme is activated by a number of keto compounds. (1,2)

Michaelis constants

source	substrate	K_m(M)	conditions	
Achromobacter sp.	L-aspartate pyruvate[a]	8.0×10^{-5} 6.25×10^{-6}	pH 5.0, acetate, 30°	(2)

[a] As activator

Inhibitors

source	inhibitor	type	K_i(M)	conditions	
Achromobacter sp.	DL-*threo*-β-hydroxyaspartate	C(L-aspartate)	1.1×10^{-5}	pH 5.0, acetate, 30°	(2)
	DL-*erythro*-β-hydroxyaspartate	C(L-aspartate)	3.2×10^{-4}	pH 5.0, acetate, 30°	(2)

References

1. Chibata, I., Kakimoto, T., Kato, J., Shibatani, T. & Nishimura, N. (1967) BBRC, 26, 662.

2. Wilson, E. M. & Kornberg, H. L. (1963) BJ, 88, 578.

3. Wilson, E. M. (1963) BBA, 67, 345.

4. Novogrodsky, A., Nishimura, J. S. & Meister, A. (1963) JBC, 238, PC 1903.

GLUTAMATE DECARBOXYLASE

(L-Glutamate 1-carboxy-lyase)

L-Glutamate = 4-aminobutyrate + CO_2

Molecular weight

source	value	conditions	
Escherichia coli	300,000	pH 5.4	(4)
Mouse brain	75-100,000	Sephadex G75, G100 and G200, pH 6.5	(1)

Specific activity

E. coli[(a)]	151	L-glutamate (pH 4.6, pyridine, 36°)	(2)
E. coli[(b)]	80	L-glutamate (pH 4.6, pyridine, 36° + pyridoxal phosphate)	(4)

[(a)] Var. communior
[(b)] Strain 26

Specificity

The enzyme is highly specific. Thus, that from Escherichia coli is inactive towards any of the common amino acids except L-glutamate and possibly L-glutamine (3). The following analogs of glutamate are, however, decarboxylated: L-glutamate (1.00), 4-methylene-DL-glutamate (0.30), threo-3-hydroxy-DL-glutamate (0.18), erythro-3-hydroxy-DL-glutamate (0.006), L-glutamine (0.02), threo-4-hydroxy-DL-glutamate (0.02), 4-benzyl-L-glutamate (0.01), 4-methyl-DL-glutamate (0.003) and 4-L-glutamyl methyl ester (0.003). erythro-4-Hydroxy-DL-glutamate was not attacked. (5)

Michaelis constants

source	substrate	$K_m(M)$	conditions	
Mouse brain	L-glutamate	7.9×10^{-3}	pH 7.2, P_i, 37°	(1)
E. coli	L-glutamate	8.2×10^{-4}	pH 4.6, pyridine, 36°	(4)

Inhibitors

P_i inhibits (C(L-glutamate)) the enzyme from mouse brain. (1)

References

1. Susz, J. P., Haber, B. & Roberts, E. (1966) B, 5, 2870.
2. Anderson, J. A. & Chang, H. F. W. (1965) ABB, 110, 346.
3. Lawson, A. & Quinn, A. G. (1967) BJ, 105, 483.
4. Shukuya, R. & Schwert, G. W. (1960) JBC, 235, 1649.
5. Homola, A. D. & Dekker, E. E. (1967) B, 6, 2626.

LYSINE DECARBOXYLASE

(L-Lysine carboxy-lyase)

L-Lysine = cadaverine + CO_2

Ref.

Molecular weight

source	value	conditions	
Escherichia coli	$S_{20,w}$ = 22	-	(4)

Specificity

Lysine decarboxylase is highly specific. Thus, the enzymes from E. coli and Bacterium cadaveris utilize both lysine and hydroxylysine as substrates but the following compounds are inactive: D-lysine, L-arginine, L-glutamate, L-ornithine, L-histidine, DL-alanine, DL-valine, L-leucine, L-phenylalanine, L-tyrosine, L-tryptophan, DL-serine, L-proline, L-aspartate, and the 2-acetyl-,2-methyl, 6-acetyl- and 6-methyl-derivatives of lysine. (2,3)

Michaelis constants

source	substrate	$K_m(M)$	conditions	
Escherichia coli	L-lysine	1.5×10^{-3}	pH 6.0, P_i,	
B. cadaveris	L-lysine	1.5×10^{-3}	30-37°	(1,3)

References

1. Najjar, V. A. (1955) Methods in Enzymology, 2, 188.
2. Linstedt, S. (1951) Acta Chem. Scand., 5, 486.
3. Gale, E. F. & Epps, H. M. R. (1944) BJ, 38, 232.
4. Sher, I. H. & Mallette, M. F. (1954) ABB, 53, 354.

ARGININE DECARBOXYLASE

(L-Arginine carboxy-lyase)

L-Arginine = agmatine + CO_2

Ref.

Molecular weight

source	value	conditions	
Escherichia coli	780,000	pH 5.2	(2)

Specificity

The enzyme is highly specific. Thus, that from E. coli is inactive towards any of the common amino acids except L-arginine. (1)

Michaelis constants

source	substrate	$K_m(M)$	conditions	
E. coli	L-arginine	7.5×10^{-4}	pH 5.25, acetate, 30°	(3)

References

1. Lawson, A. & Quinn, A. G. (1967) BJ, 105, 483.
2. Sher, I. & Mallette, M. F. (1954) ABB, 53, 370.
3. Taylor, E. S. & Gale, E. F. (1945) BJ, 39, 52.

DIAMINOPIMELATE DECARBOXYLASE

(meso-2,6-Diaminopimelate carboxy-lyase)

meso-2,6-Diaminopimelate = L-lysine + CO_2

Ref.

Molecular weight

source	value	conditions	
Escherichia coli	200,000	pH 6.8	(1)

Specific activity

E. coli (200 x)   10   meso-2,6-diaminopimelate (pH 6.8, P_i, 37°)   (1)

Specificity

Diaminopimelate decarboxylase is highly specific for its substrate. Thus, the enzyme from Lemna perpusilla was inactive with L-2,6-diaminopimelate; D-2,6-diaminopimelate; DL-2-aminopimelate; L-2-aminoadipate; L-lysine; D-lysine and L-ornithine (2) and the enzyme from Aerobacter aerogenes could not utilize a large number of structural analogs of meso-2,6-diaminopimelate (3).

Michaelis constants

source	substrate	$K_m(M)$	conditions	
E. coli	meso-2,6-diaminopimelate	1.7×10^{-3}	pH 6.8, P_i, 37°	(1)
L. perpusilla	meso-2,6-diaminopimelate	3.5×10^{-4}	pH 7.0, P_i, 37°	(2)
A. aerogenes	meso-2,6-diaminopimelate	2.8×10^{-3}	pH 6.8, P_i, 37°	(3)

Inhibitors

A number of structural analogs of meso-2,6-diaminopimelate were inhibitors of the enzyme from E. coli. These included cystine, glutamate, diaminopropionate, 2-aminopimelate and lysine.   (1)

References

1. White, P. J. & Kelly, B. (1965) BJ, 96, 75.
2. Shimura, Y. & Vogel, H. J. (1966) BBA, 118, 396.
3. Dewey, D. L., Hoare, D. S. & Work, E. (1954) BJ, 58, 523.

HISTIDINE DECARBOXYLASE
(L-Histidine carboxy-lyase)

L-Histidine = histamine + CO_2

Ref.

Molecular weight

source	value	conditions	
Lactobacillus 30a	195,000	sucrose gradient	(2)

Specific activity

Lactobacillus 30a (200 x) 52.5 L-histidine (pH 4.8, ammonium   (2)
acetate, 37°)

Specificity

The enzyme is highly specific. Thus, that from Escherichia coli is inactive towards any of the naturally occurring amino acids except for L-histidine. The enzyme from Clostridium welchii does not decarboxylate thiol histidine, carnosine, D-histidine or any of the naturally occurring amino acids. The enzyme from Lactobacillus 30a is similarly highly specific.   (1,2,3)

Michaelis constants

source	substrate	$K_m(M)$	conditions	
Clostridium welchii	L-histidine	7.5×10^{-3}	pH 4.5, acetate, 30°	(1)
Lactobacillus 30a	L-histidine	9×10^{-4}	pH 4.8, ammonium acetate, 37°	(2)

Inhibitors

source	inhibitor (C(L-histidine))	$K_i(M)$	conditions	
Lactobacillus 30a	imidazolepropionate	1.8×10^{-3}		
	urocanate	2.1×10^{-3}	pH 4.8, ammonium acetate, 37°	(2)
	imidazoleacetate	1.3×10^{-1}		
	imidazolecarboxylate	9.7×10^{-1}		
	imidazole	3.2×10^{-3}		
	N-methylimidazole	7.2×10^{-3}		

References

1. Epps, H. M. R. (1945) BJ, 39, 42.

2. Rosenthaler, J., Guirard, B. M., Chang, G. W. & Snell, E. E. (1965) PNAS, 54, 152.

3. Lawson, A. & Quinn, A. G. (1967) BJ, 105, 483.

OROTIDINE-5'-PHOSPHATE DECARBOXYLASE

(Orotidine-5'-phosphate carboxy-lyase)

Orotidine 5'-phosphate = UMP + CO_2

Ref.

Equilibrium constant

The reaction is essentially irreversible [F].   (3)

Michaelis constants

source	substrate	$K_m(M)$	conditions	
Calf thymus	orotidine 5'-phosphate	2.0×10^{-6}	pH 7.9, Tris.	(1)
Phaseolus vulgaris (bean)	orotidine 5'-phosphate	1.2×10^{-6}	pH 6.2, P_i, 27°	(2)

Inhibitors

The enzyme from yeast was inhibited by the 5'-monophosphates of uridine ($K_i = 1.5 \times 10^{-4}M$), cytidine, adenosine and guanosine whereas only that of uridine, and, to a lesser extent, of cytidine, was active with liver preparations (3). High substrate concentrations were inhibitory (1).

References

1. Kasbekar, D. K., Nagabhushanam, A. & Greenberg, D. M. (1964) JBC, 239, 4245.
2. Wolcott, J. H. & Ross, C. (1966) BBA, 122, 532.
3. Creasey, W. A. & Handschumacher, R. E. (1961) JBC, 236, 2058.

DOPA DECARBOXYLASE

(3,4-Dihydroxy-L-phenylalanine carboxy-lyase)

3,4-Dihydroxy-L-phenylalanine =
dihydroxyphenylethylamine + CO_2

Ref.

Specificity and Michaelis constants

DOPA decarboxylase from guinea-pig kidney decarboxylates all the
naturally occurring aromatic L-amino acids.   (1)

source	substrate	V(relative)	K_m(M)	conditions
Guinea-pig kidney	DOPA	1.000	4.0×10^{-4}	
	5-hydroxytryptophan	0.156	2×10^{-5}	
	tryptophan	0.034	3.00×10^{-3}	
	p-tyrosine	0.005	1.30×10^{-2}	pH 9.0, Tris, 37° (1)
	phenylalanine	0.016	2.00×10^{-2}	
	histidine	0.002	2.20×10^{-2}	
	a-methyl-DOPA[a]	0.005	5.4×10^{-4}	

[a] A number of other a-methyl aromatic amino acids were also decarboxylated.

Abbreviations

DOPA   3,4-dihydroxy-L-phenylalanine

References

1. Lovenberg, W., Weissbach, H. & Udenfriend, S. (1962) JBC, 237, 89.

CYSTEINESULPHINATE DECARBOXYLASE

(L-Cysteinesulphinate carboxy-lyase)

L-Cysteine sulphinate = hypotaurine + CO_2

Ref.

Specificity

Tissue extracts (rat liver or brain) catalyze the decarboxylation of L-cysteine sulphinate, L-cysteate and L-glutamate. It is not clear whether one or more enzymes is responsible for these activities. (1)

Michaelis constants

source	substrate	relative velocity	K_m(M)	conditions
Rat liver	L-cysteine sulphinate	1.00	1.4×10^{-4}	
	L-cysteate	0.14	4.0×10^{-4}	pH 7.35, P_i, 37° (1)
Rat brain	L-cysteine sulphinate	1.00	2.0×10^{-3}	
	L-cysteate	0.12	4.0×10^{-3}	
	L-glutamate	1.55	2.9×10^{-3}	

Inhibitors

source	inhibitor	type	K_i(M)	conditions
Rat liver	L-cysteate	C(L-cysteine sulphinate)	5.0×10^{-4}	
	L-cysteine sulphinate	C(L-cysteate)	1.4×10^{-4}	
Rat brain	L-cysteate	C(L-cysteine sulphinate)	5.0×10^{-3}	pH 7.35, P_i, 37° (1)
	L-cysteine sulphinate	C(L-cysteate)	2.1×10^{-3}	
	L-glutamate	C(L-cysteine sulphinate)	8.2×10^{-3}	
	L-cysteine sulphinate	C(L-glutamate)	8.0×10^{-3}	

References

1. Jacobsen, J. G., Thomas, L. L. & Smith, L. H. Jr. (1964) BBA, 85, 103.

PHOSPHOPYRUVATE CARBOXYLASE

(Orthophosphate: oxaloacetate carboxy-lyase (phosphorylating))

Orthophosphate + oxaloacetate = H_2O + phospho-enolpyruvate + CO_2

Ref.

Equilibrium constant

The reaction is essentially irreversible[R].   (1,2)

Molecular weight

source	value	conditions	
Germinating peanut[a] cotyledons	350,000	pH 7.5	(2)

[a] *Arachis hypogeae*

Specific activity

Germinating peanut cotyledons (2700 x) 50 PEP (pH 7.9, Tris, 30°)   (2)

Specificity

The enzyme (*Escherichia coli*) is activated by the following compounds: no activator (1.0), acetyl-CoA (22.0), propionyl-CoA (13.7), butyryl-CoA (11.7), acryloyl-CoA (4.3) and crotonyl-CoA (3.5).   (5)

Michaelis constants

source	substrate	$K_m(M)$	conditions	
Germinating peanut cotyledons	PEP HCO_3 Mg^{2+}	$5\text{-}6 \times 10^{-4}$ 3.1×10^{-4} $3\text{-}4 \times 10^{-4}$	pH 7.9, Tris, 30°	(2)

Michaelis constants contd.   Ref.

source	substrate	$K_m(M)$	conditions	
E. coli	PEP	5.5×10^{-3}	pH 8.5, Tris, 20-22°, in the absence of acetyl-CoA[a]	(5)
	acetyl-CoA	1.4×10^{-4}	} pH 8.5, Tris, 20-22°	(5)
	Mg^{2+}	9.8×10^{-4}		

[a] Acetyl-CoA increases the apparent affinity of the enzyme for PEP.

Inhibitors

L-Aspartate is an allosteric inhibitor of the enzyme isolated from E. coli. The inhibition is relieved by acetyl-CoA. The enzyme (Salmonella typhimurium) is also inhibited by L-aspartate and activated by acetyl-CoA, but that isolated from spinach leaf is not affected in this way.   (3,4)

Abbreviations

PEP   phospho-enolpyruvate

References

1. Utter, M. F. (1961) The Enzymes, 5, 331.

2. Maruyama, H., Easterday, R.L., Chang, H-C. & Lane, M. D. (1966) JBC, 241, 2405.

3. Izui, K., Iwatani, A., Nishikido, T., Katsuki, H. & Tanaka, S., (1967) BBA, 139, 188.

4. Maeba, P. & Sanwal, B. D. (1965) BBRC, 21, 503.

5. Canovas, J. L. & Kornberg, H. L. (1966) Proc. Roy. Soc., 165(B), 189.

PHOSPHOPYRUVATE CARBOXYLASE

(GTP: oxaloacetate carboxy-lyase (transphosphorylating))

GTP + oxaloacetate = GDP + phospho-enolpyruvate + CO_2

Ref.

Equilibrium constant

$$\frac{[IDP]\,[PEP]\,[CO_2]}{[ITP]\,[oxaloacetate]} = 0.372 \text{ M} \quad (30^\circ) \tag{1}$$

Molecular weight

source	value	conditions	
Pig liver mitochondria	73,300	pH 7.5	(3)

Specific activity

Pig liver mitochondria (208 x)	9.1[a]	PEP	(pH 7.0, imidazole, 30°)	(3)
	64[b]	oxaloacetate	(pH 7.5, Tris, 30°)	(3)

[a] With IDP (reverse reaction)
[b] With ITP (forward reaction)

Specificity

Phosphopyruvate carboxylase utilizes GTP or ITP in the forward reaction and GDP or IDP in the reverse reaction with equal facility. (2,5,6)

The enzyme cannot utilize the polyphosphates of adenosine, cytosine, uridine or xanthosine. (2,5)

Michaelis constants

source	substrate	K_m(M)	conditions	
Guinea-pig liver (mitochondrial or soluble)	GTP	$0.9\text{-}3.0 \times 10^{-3}$	pH 8.0, Tris, 30°	(4)
	ITP	$0.6\text{-}1.8 \times 10^{-3}$		
	oxaloacetate	1.4×10^{-3}		
	IDP	$0.7\text{-}6.2 \times 10^{-4}$	pH 7.4, Tris, 30°	(4)
	PEP	$1.3\text{-}1.4 \times 10^{-4}$		

Michaelis constants contd.

source	substrate	$K_m(M)$	conditions	
Pig liver (mitochondrial)	PEP[a]	1.25×10^{-5}	pH 7.5, Tris, $30°$	(6)
	IDP	3.3×10^{-5}		
	GDP	6.3×10^{-5}	pH 7.1, imidazole, $30°$	(6)
	KHCO$_3$[a]	2.5×10^{-5}	pH 7.5, Tris, $30°$	(6)
	Mn^{2+}	3.33×10^{-4}		
	oxaloacetate[b]	1.5×10^{-4}		
	ITP	5.8×10^{-4}		
	GTP	1.6×10^{-4}		
	Mn^{2+}	4.3×10^{-4}		

[a]With IDP as the nucleotide substrate
[b]With ITP as the nucleotide substrate

Inhibitors

The enzymes from guinea-pig liver differ in their response towards AMP. Thus, AMP inhibits C(GTP or ITP) the mitochondrial enzyme but is without effect on that from the cytoplasm. ATP is without effect on either of these enzymes. (4)

The enzyme (pig liver) is inhibited by bicarbonate (C(oxaloacetate), $K_i = 4.3 \times 10^{-2}$) and by GDP and GMP (mixed type) in the forward reaction. (6)

Abbreviations

PEP   phosphoenolpyruvate

References

1. Utter, M. F. (1961) The Enzymes, 5, 337.
2. Kurahashi, K., Pennington, R. J. & Utter, M. F. (1957) JBC, 226, 1059.
3. Chang, H-C. & Lane, M. D. (1966) JBC, 241, 2413.
4. Holten, D. D. & Nordlie, R. C. (1965) B, 4, 723.
5. Bandurski, R. S. & Lipmann, F. (1956) JBC, 219, 741.
6. Chang, H-C., Maruyama, H., Miller, R. S. & Lane, M. D. (1966) JBC, 241, 2421.

UDPGLUCURONATE DECARBOXYLASE

(UDPglucuronate carboxy-lyase)

$$UDPglucuronate = UDPxylose + CO_2$$

Ref.

Specificity

The enzyme (wheat germ) cannot utilize pseudo-UDP-D-glucuronate or UDP-D-galacturonate as substrate (1,2) and that isolated from Cryptococcus laurentii cannot utilize pseudo-UDP-D-glucuronate, UDP-D-galacturonate, D-glucuronate 1-phosphate or D-glucuronate (1,3).

Michaelis constants

source	substrate	$K_m(M)$	conditions	
Wheat germ	UDPglucuronate	3×10^{-4}	pH 7, P_i, $37°$	(1,2,3)
C. laurentii	UDPglucuronate	1.1×10^{-3}		
	NAD[(a)]	3×10^{-6}		

[(a)]Activator (absolute requirement)

Inhibitors

source	inhibitor	type	$K_i(M)$	conditions	
C. laurentii	UMP	C(UDPglucuronate)	2×10^{-3}	pH 7.0, P_i, $37°$	(1,3)
	UDPglucose		2×10^{-3}		
	UDP		2×10^{-4}		
	reduced NAD	C(NAD)	2×10^{-6}		
	AMP		2.8×10^{-5}		

The enzyme (wheat germ) is inhibited by several uridine compounds (1,2).

References

1. Ankel, H. & Feingold, D. S. (1966) Methods in Enzymology, 8, 287.
2. Ankel, H. & Feingold, D. S. (1965) B, 4, 2468.
3. Ankel, H. & Feingold, D. S. (1966) B, 5, 182.

PHOSPHOPYRUVATE CARBOXYLASE

(Pyrophosphate: oxaloacetate carboxy-lyase (phosphorylating))

Pyrophosphate + oxaloacetate =

orthophosphate + phospho-enolpyruvate + CO_2

Ref.

Equilibrium constant

The reaction is reversible. (1)

Specificity

The enzyme isolated from **Propionibacterium shermanii** is highly specific. Thus, P_i can be replaced by arsenate but not by PP_i, GDP, hypoxanthine diphosphate, ADP or UDP. Neither pyruvate nor ATP can replace phospho-enolpyruvate. (1)

Michaelis constants

source	substrate	$K_m(M)$	conditions	
P. shermanii	phosphoenol-pyruvate	1.7×10^{-4}		
	$NaHCO_3$	2.9×10^{-4}	pH 7.8,	(1)
	P_i	1.2×10^{-3}	Tris, $25°$	
	Mn^{2+}	1.4×10^{-4}		
	Mg^{2+}	2.1×10^{-3}		

Inhibitors

High levels of P_i or PP_i are inhibitory. (1)

References

1. Siu, P. M. L. & Wood, H. G. (1962) JBC, 237, 3044.

RIBULOSEDIPHOSPHATE CARBOXYLASE

(3-Phospho-D-glycerate carboxy-lyase (dimerizing))

2 3-Phospho-D-glycerate = D-ribulose 1,5-diphosphate + CO_2

Ref.

Equilibrium constant

The reaction is essentially irreversible [R].   (1)

Molecular weight

source	value	conditions	
Spinach leaf (chloroplast)[a]	515,000	pH 7.4	(3)
	557,000 [24]	pH 8.3	(4,5)
	300,000	pH 6.9	(6)

[a] The enzyme is composed of two distinct kinds of polypeptide chains which differ in molecular weight and amino acid composition (5).

Specific activity

Spinach leaf (chloroplast)	(7 x)	2.3	RuDP	(pH 7.9, Tris, 30°)	(4)
	(10 x)	5.2	RuDP	(pH 7.7, Tris, 25°)	(6)

Specificity

The enzyme is highly specific for RuDP which cannot be replaced by ribulose 5-phosphate, ribose 1,5-diphosphate, ribulose 1-phosphate or xylulose 1,5-diphosphate.   (2,6)

Michaelis constants

source	substrate	$K_m(M)$	conditions	
Spinach leaf (chloroplast)	RuDP	1.2×10^{-4}		
	HCO_3^-	2.2×10^{-2}	pH 7.9, Tris, 30°	(4)
	Mg^{2+}	1.1×10^{-3}		
	Mn^{2+}	3.9×10^{-5}		

Inhibitors

source	inhibitor	type	$K_1(M)$	conditions	
Spinach leaf (chloroplast)	P_i	$C(RuDP)$	4.2×10^{-3}		
	ammonium sulphate		8.1×10^{-3}	pH 7.9, Tris, 30°	(4)
	3-phosphoglycerate	$NC(RuDP)$	8.3×10^{-3}		
	3-phosphoglycerate	$C(HCO_3^-)$	9.5×10^{-3}		

RuDP inhibits at concentrations greater than 7×10^{-4}M.　　　　(4)

Abbreviations

RuDP　　　D-ribulose 1,5-diphosphate

References

1. Utter, M. F. (1961) The Enzymes, 5, 332.
2. Racker, E. (1962) Methods in Enzymology, 5, 266.
3. Trown, P. W. (1965) B, 4, 908.
4. Paulsen, J. M. & Lane, M. D. (1966) B, 5, 2350.
5. Rutner, A. C. & Lane, M. D. (1967) BBRC, 28, 531.
6. Weissbach, A., Horecker, B. L. & Hurwitz, J. (1956) JBC, 218, 795.

PHOSPHOPYRUVATE CARBOXYLASE (ATP)

(ATP: oxaloacetate carboxy-lyase (transphosphorylating))

ATP + oxaloacetate = ADP + phospho-enolpyruvate + CO_2

Ref.

Equilibrium constant

The reversibility of the reaction has been demonstrated.   (1)

Specific activity

Yeast   (200 x)   5.5   oxaloacetate   (pH 5.4, borate-   (1)
                      4.31 phosphoenolpyruvate   succinate, $30°$)

Specificity

The enzyme (yeast) is highly specific and will not utilize 2-oxoglutarate, L-malate, tartrate, malonate, maleate or fumarate in the place of oxaloacetate. ATP cannot be replaced by ITP, GTP or CTP. The purified enzyme also catalyzes the pyruvate kinase reaction (2.7.1.40) the velocity of which is 10% of that corresponding to phospho-enolpyruvate carboxylation.   (3)

Michaelis constants

source	substrate	$K_m(M)$	conditions	
Baker's yeast	HCO_3	5×10^{-3}	pH 5.4, borate-	(2)
	CO_2	9.9×10^{-3}	succinate, $30°$	
	oxaloacetate	7.7×10^{-3}	pH 5.4, borate-succinate, $30°$	(3)

Inhibitors

The enzyme (yeast) is inhibited by high concentrations of oxalo-acetate and ATP. 2-Oxoglutarate, fumarate, tartrate and L-malate also inhibit.   (3)

References

1. Cannata, J. J. B. & Stoppani, A. O. M. (1963) JBC, 238, 1196.
2. Cannata, J. J. B. & Stoppani, A. O. M. (1963) JBC, 238, 1208.
3. Cannata, J. J. B. & Stoppani, A. O. M. (1963) JBC, 238, 1919.

GLYOXYLATE CARBOLIGASE

(Glyoxylate carboxy-lyase (dimerizing and reducing))

2 Glyoxylate + $2H^+$ = hydroxymalonate semialdehyde + CO_2

Ref.

Specificity

The enzyme requires FAD, TPP and Mg^{2+} for full activity. (1,2)

The mechanism of the reaction catalyzed by the enzyme from Escherichia coli (4) and Pseudomonas sp. (3) involves the formation of 2-hydroxymethylthiamine pyrophosphate as an intermediate. FAD is not reduced in the course of the reaction. (2)

Michaelis constants

source	substrate	$K_m(M)$	conditions	
E. coli	FAD	2×10^{-7}	pH 7.3, P_i, 30° (argon atmosphere)	(2)

References

1. Gupta, N. K. & Vennesland, B. (1964) JBC, 239, 3787.

2. Gupta, N. K. & Vennesland, B. (1966) Methods in Enzymology, 9, 693.

3. Jaenicke, L. & Koch, J. (1962) BZ, 336, 432.

4. Kohlhaw, G., Deus, B. & Holzer, H. (1965) JBC, 240, 2135.

HYDROXYOXOBUTYRATE ALDOLASE

(4-Hydroxy-2-oxobutyrate formaldehyde-lyase)

4-Hydroxy-2-oxobutyrate = pyruvate + formaldehyde

Ref.

Specificity

The enzyme isolated from beef liver is highly specific for its substrates in the reverse reaction. Thus, pyruvate could be replaced by phenylpyruvate but not by acetaldehyde, benzaldehyde, crotonaldehyde, acetone, folate, acetoacetate, malonate, mesoxalate, 2-oxoisocaproate, 3-oxoisocaproate, 2-oxoglutarate or oxaloacetate and formaldehyde could not be replaced by acetaldehyde, benzaldehyde, crotonaldehyde or by acetone.

(1)

Michaelis constants

source	substrate	$K_m(M)$	conditions	
Beef liver	pyruvate formaldehyde	5.5×10^{-5} 9×10^{-5}	pH 7.5, 37°	(1)

References

1. Hift, H. & Mahler, H. R. (1952) JBC, 198, 901.

KETOTETROSE ALDOLASE

(Erythrulose-1-phosphate formaldehyde-lyase)

Erythrulose 1-phosphate =

dihydroxyacetone phosphate + formaldehyde

Equilibrium constant

$$\frac{[\text{dihydroxyacetone phosphate}]\,[\text{formaldehyde}]}{[\text{erythrulose 1-phosphate}]} = \begin{array}{l} 0.33 \\ (\text{pH } 7.2, \text{ P}_i, 37^\circ) \end{array} \quad (1,2)$$

Specificity

The enzyme from rat liver could not utilize acetaldehyde, glycol-aldehyde or glyceraldehyde in the place of formaldehyde.   (1,2)

References

1. Charalampous, F. C. (1962) Methods in Enzymology, 5, 283.
2. Charalampous, F. C. (1954) JBC, 211, 249.

DEOXYRIBOALDOLASE

(2-Deoxy-D-ribose-5-phosphate acetaldehyde-lyase)

2-Deoxy-D-ribose 5-phosphate = D-glyceraldehyde 3-phosphate + acetaldehyde

Ref.

Equilibrium constant

$$\frac{[\text{D-glyceraldehyde 3-phosphate}]\,[\text{acetaldehyde}]}{[\text{2-deoxy-D-ribose 5-phosphate}]} = 2 \times 10^{-4} \text{ M} \quad (1)$$

(pH 6.3, maleate, 37°)

Molecular weight

source	value	conditions	
Lactobacillus plantarum	60,800	pH 6.3	(2)
Rat liver	253,000	sucrose gradient	(3)

Specific activity

L. plantarum   620 2-deoxy-D-ribose 5-phosphate   (pH 6.3, maleate,   (1,2)
37°)

Specificity

The enzyme (L. plantarum) shows greatest activity with acetaldehyde but will also react with propionaldehyde. D-Glyceraldehyde 3-phosphate can be replaced by L-glyceraldehyde 3-phosphate, D-erythrose 4-phosphate, glycolaldehyde phosphate, D-ribose 5-phosphate, D-glyceraldehyde or by D-erythrose (1). The enzyme isolated from rat liver is inactive with deoxyribose 1-phosphate, deoxyribose, purine deoxyribonucleotides or pyrimidine deoxyribonucleotides (3).

Michaelis constants

source	substrate	K_m(M)	conditions	
Rat liver	deoxyribose 5-phosphate	1.7×10^{-4}		
	acetaldehyde	2.67×10^{-4}		
	D-glyceraldehyde 3-phosphate	2.0×10^{-4}	pH 7.5,	(3)
	citrate*	1×10^{-4}	Tris,	
	succinate*	2×10^{-4}	22°	
	glutarate*	5×10^{-4}		

*These are activators. The enzyme isolated from L. plantarum also requires a carboxylic acid for full activity (1).

References

1. Hoffee, P., Rosen, O. M. & Horecker, B. L. (1966) Methods in Enzymology, 9, 545.

2. Hoffee, P., Rosen, O. M. & Horecker, B. L. (1965) JBC, 240, 1512.

3. Groth, D. P. (1966) Methods in Enzymology, 9, 549.

THREONINE ALDOLASE

(L-Threonine acetaldehyde-lyase)

L-Threonine = glycine + acetaldehyde

Ref.

Equilibrium constant

The reaction is reported to be reversible in reference (1) but later work suggests that it is irreversible [F].　　　　　　　　　　　　(3)

Specificity

Threonine aldolase is highly specific for its substrates. Thus, with the enzyme from beef liver the following compounds could not replace L-threonine: D-threonine, L-serine, L-homoserine, epinephrine, L-alanine, lactate, glycollate or phospho-L-threonine. In the reverse reaction no activity was observed when acetaldehyde was replaced by formaldehyde, propionaldehyde or formate.　　　　　　　　　　　　(1)

The enzyme from Clostridium pasteurianum was also highly specific and could not utilize D-threonine or DL-allothreonine.　　　　　　　　(3)

Michaelis constants

source	substrate	$K_m(M)$	conditions	
Beef liver	L-threonine	4.35×10^{-3}		
	pyridoxal-phosphate[a]	1.11×10^{-4}	pH 7.6, P_i, 37°	(1)
Rat liver	L-threonine	2×10^{-2}	pH 7.4, P_i, 37°	(2)
C. pasteurianum	L-threonine	4.3×10^{-4}	pH 7.0, 30°	(3)

[a] No other vitamin B_6 derivative was active.

References

1. Karasek, M. A. & Greenberg, D. M. (1957) JBC, 227, 191.
2. Malkin, L. I. & Greenberg, D. M. (1964) BBA, 85, 117.
3. Dainty, R. H. (1967) BJ, 104, 46P

ALLOTHREONINE ALDOLASE

(L-Allothreonine acetaldehyde-lyase)

L-Allothreonine = glycine + acetaldehyde

Equilibrium constant

$$\frac{[\text{glycine}][\text{acetaldehyde}]}{[\text{L-allothreonine}]} = 1.78 \times 10^{-2} \quad (\text{pH } 7.6, \text{ P}_i, 37^\circ) \tag{1}$$

Specificity

The enzyme (sheep liver) is highly specific. Thus, D-allothreonine, D-threonine and L-serine were inactive. (2)

Michaelis constants

source	substrate	$K_m(M)$	conditions	
Sheep liver	L-allothreonine	6.9×10^{-2}	pH 7.6, P$_i$, 37°	(1,2)
	pyridoxal-phosphate	1.75×10^{-5}		

References

1. Greenberg, D. M. (1962) Methods in Enzymology, 5, 931.
2. Lin, S-C. C. & Greenberg, D. M. (1954) J. Gen. Physiol., 38, 181.

KETOSE-1-PHOSPHATE ALDOLASE
(Ketose-1-phosphate aldehyde-lyase)

A ketose 1-phosphate = dihydroxyacetone phosphate + an aldehyde

Ref.

Equilibrium constant

$$\frac{\text{[dihydroxyacetone phosphate] [D-glyceraldehyde]}}{\text{[fructose 1-phosphate]}} = 1.7 \times 10^{-6} \text{ M} \qquad (4)$$

Molecular weight

source	value	conditions	
Rabbit liver	154,000 [3]	pH 7.3	(1)

Specific activity

Rabbit liver	(100 x)	1.46 FDP or fructose 1-phosphate	(pH 7.5, glycyl-glycine, 28°)	(1)

Specificity and Michaelis constants

source	substrate	$\underset{\text{(relative)}}{V}$	K_m(M)	conditions	
Rabbit liver (type B enzyme)	FDP	1.0	2.3×10^{-6}	pH 7.5, glycyl-glycine, 28°	(2)
	fructose 1-phosphate	1.0	8.3×10^{-4}		
	dihydroxyacetone phosphate	6.5	3.7×10^{-4}		
	glyceraldehyde 3-phosphate	6.5	3.0×10^{-4}		

The enzyme (rabbit liver) also catalyzes the reversible condensation of formaldehyde with dihydroxyacetone phosphate to erythrulose phosphate (1). The enzyme discussed is "aldolase B of adult rabbit liver" (1). The differences between this enzyme and aldolase A (4.2.1.13) are discussed in references (2) and (3).

Inhibitors

The enzyme (rabbit liver) is inhibited by AMP, ADP (but not ATP) and by a number of aldehydes. (1)

Abbreviations

FDP   fructose 1,6-diphosphate

References

1. Rajkumar, T. V., Woodfin, B. M. & Rutter, W. J. (1966) Methods in Enzymology, 9, 491.
2. Rutter, W. J., Woodfin, B. M. & Blostein, R. E. (1963) Acta Chem. Scand., 17, (Suppl. 1) 226.
3. Blostein, R. & Rutter, W. J. (1963) JBC, 238, 3280.
4. Rutter, W. J. (1961) The Enzymes, 5, 341.

PHOSPHOKETOLASE

(D-Xylulose-5-phosphate D-glyceraldehyde-3-phosphate-
lyase (phosphate-acetylating))

D-Xylulose 5-phosphate + P_i =
    acetylphosphate + D-glyceraldehyde 3-phosphate + H_2O

Ref.

Equilibrium constant

The reaction is essentially irreversible [F].   (1)

Molecular weight

source	value	conditions	
Lactobacillus plantarum	≮ 550,000	pH 6.0	(2)

Specificity activity

Leuconostoc mesenteroides	(35.5 x)	18.5 xylulose 5-phosphate	pH 6.1, succinate, 37°	(4)

Specificity

With the enzyme isolated from Lactobacillus plantarum, P_i can be
replaced by arsenate. The enzyme is highly specific for D-xylulose 5-
phosphate; ribulose 5-phosphate, ribose 5-phosphate, sedoheptulose 7-
phosphate and fructose 6-phosphate are inactive (1), but also see (3).
In the absence of P_i, xylulose 5-phosphate (1.00), hydroxypyruvate (0.56)
and fructose 6-phosphate (0.14) are oxidized with ferricyanide as the
electron acceptor. In the presence of P_i, all three substrates yield
acetyl phosphate with rates equal to those in the presence of ferricyanide (3). The enzyme isolated from Leuconostoc mesenteroides can utilize xylulose 5-phosphate, fructose 6-phosphate, glycolaldehyde and
hydroxypyruvate as substrates and arsenate can replace P_i (4).

Michaelis constants (see next page).

Michaelis constants

source	substrate	$K_m(M)$	second substrate	conditions
L. plantarum	hydroxypyruvate	3.1×10^{-3}	ferricyanide	
		3.0×10^{-3}	P_i	pH 6.0,
	thiamine pyrophosphate	2.0×10^{-5}	ferricyanide	succinate (3)
	D-fructose 6-phosphate	1.3×10^{-3}	ferricyanide	
L. mesenteroides	D-xylulose 5-phosphate	4.7×10^{-3}	P_i	
	D-fructose 6-phosphate	2.9×10^{-2}	P_i	pH 6.1, succinate, (4)
	P_i	5.55×10^{-3}	D-xylulose 5-phosphate	
	Mg^{2+}	3.95×10^{-7}	D-xylulose 5-phosphate	37°
	thiamine pyrophosphate	4.04×10^{-7}	D-xylulose 5-phosphate	

References

1. Horecker, B. L. (1962) Methods in Enzymology, 5, 261.

2. Heath, E. C., Hurwitz, J., Horecker, B. L. & Ginsberg, A. (1958) JBC, 231, 1009.

3. Holzer, H. & Schröter, W. (1962) BBA, 65, 271.

4. Goldberg, M., Fessenden, J. M. & Racker, E. (1966) Methods in Enzymology, 9, 515.

HYDROXYNITRILE LYASE

(p-Hydroxymandelonitrile hydroxybenzaldehyde-lyase)

p-Hydroxymandelonitrile = p-hydroxybenzaldehyde + HCN

Ref.

Specificity

Hydroxynitrile lyase isolated from etiolated sorghum seedlings decomposed the cyanohydrins of p-hydroxymandelate (1.00) and vanillin (0.20). The cyanohydrins of the following aldehydes were inactive: m-hydroxybenzaldehyde, o-hydroxybenzaldehyde and benzaldehyde.

(1)

Michaelis constants

source	substrate	$K_m(M)$	conditions	
Etiolated sorghum seedlings	p-hydroxymandelonitrile	5.5×10^{-4}	pH 5.4, acetate.	(1)

Light absorption data

p-hydroxybenzaldehyde ε, (285 mμ)   14,800 M^{-1} cm^{-1} (pH 5.4)   (1)

References

1. Bove, C. & Conn, E. E. (1961) JBC, 236, 207.

FRUCTOSEDIPHOSPHATE ALDOLASE

(Fructose-1,6-diphosphate D-glyceraldehyde-3-phosphate-lyase

Fructose 1,6-diphosphate =
dihydroxyacetone phosphate + D-glyceraldehyde 3-phosphate

Ref.

Equilibrium constant

$$\frac{[\text{dihydroxyacetone phosphate}]\ [\text{D-glyceraldehyde 3-phosphate}]}{[\text{fructose 1,6-diphosphate}]}$$ (1)

$$= 8.1 \times 10^{-5} \text{ M} \quad (30^\circ)$$

Molecular weight

source		value	conditions	
Class I	(Plants, protozoa, animals, green algae)	$\sim$ 150,000 [3-4]	various	(2,3)
Class II	(Bacteria, yeast, fungi, blue-green algae)	$\sim$ 70,000 [2]	various	(2,3)

Specific activity

Class I	$\sim$ 21	FDP	"under optimum conditions"	(2)
Class II	$\sim$ 83-100			
Yeast (Class II)	179	FDP	pH 7.2, glycylglycine, 30°	(3)

Specificity and Michaelis constants

source	substrate	$\frac{V}{\text{(relative)}}$	K_m(M)	conditions	
Yeast	FDP	1.00	3×10^{-4}		
	DHAP	3.00	2×10^{-3}	pH 7.5, glycyl-	(3)
	glyceraldehyde 3-phosphate	3.00	2×10^{-3}	glycine, 30°	
	glyceraldehyde	0.75	1×10^{-2}		
Rabbit muscle	FDP	-	1.4×10^{-5}	pH 7.1, glycyl-	(4)
	fructose 1-phosphate	-	7.0×10^{-3}	glycine, 25°	
Rabbit liver (type A enzyme)	FDP	1.00	6×10^{-5}		
	fructose 1-phosphate	0.02	1×10^{-2}	conditions	(2)
	DHAP	-	2×10^{-3}	not given	
	glyceraldehyde 3-phosphate	-	1×10^{-3}		

The yeast enzyme is highly specific for FDP; L-sorbose 1,6-diphosphate is cleaved at 30% the rate of FDP and L-sorbose 1-phosphate and

Specificity and Michaelis constants (contd.)

D-fructose 1-phosphate are cleaved very slowly and D-fructose 6-phosphate not at all (3). The enzymes from <u>Clostridium perfringens</u> and Boa constrictor are discussed in references (3) and (5), respectively.

Inhibitors

source	inhibitor	type	K_i(M)	conditions	
Yeast	L-sorbose 1-phosphate		2×10^{-4}		
	D-fructose 1-phosphate	C (FDP)	1×10^{-3}	pH 7.5, glycyl-glycine, 30°	(3)
	L-sorbose 1,6-diphosphate		1.3×10^{-4}		
	D-fructose 6-phosphate		3.8×10^{-3}		

Rabbit muscle aldolase is competitively inhibited by ATP > ADP > AMP, and the liver enzyme is inhibited by AMP >> ADP but not by ATP. Glycolaldehyde, glyoxal, methylglyoxal, fructose 6-phosphate, P_i and PP_i also inhibit these enzymes (4). The inhibition by structural analogs of FDP of the rabbit muscle enzyme is discussed in reference (6).

Abbreviations

FDP	fructose 1,6-diphosphate
DHAP	dihydroxyacetone phosphate

References

1. Rutter, W. J. (1961) The Enzymes, 5, 341.

2. Rutter, W. J. (1964) FP, 23(b), 1248.

3. Rutter, W. J., Hunsley, J. R., Groves, W. E., Calder, J., Rajkumar, T. V. & Woodfin, B. M. (1966) Methods in Enzymology, 9, 479.

4. Spolter, P. D., Adelman, R. C. & Weinhouse, S. (1965) JBC, 240, 1327.

5. Schwartz, E. & Horecker, B. L. (1966) ABB, 115, 407.

6. Hartman, F. C. & Baker, R. (1965) B, 4, 1068.

PHOSPHO-2-KETO-3-DEOXYGLUCONATE ALDOLASE

(6-Phospho-2-keto-3-deoxy-D-gluconate D-glyceraldehyde-
3-phosphate lyase)

6-Phospho-2-keto-3-deoxy-D-gluconate =

pyruvate + D-glyceraldehyde 3-phosphate

Ref.

Equilibrium constant

$$\frac{[\text{pyruvate}]\,[\text{D-glyceraldehyde 3-phosphate}]}{[\text{6-phospho-2-keto-3-deoxy-D-gluconate}]} = 0.62 - 1.87 \times 10^{-3} \text{ M} \quad (1)$$

(pH 8.0, Tris, room
temperature)

Molecular weight

source	value	conditions	
Pseudomonas fluorescens	86,150 [2]	pH 6.0	(1)

Specific activity

P. fluorescens	(500 x)	312 KDPG	(pH 8.0, imidazole, room temperature)	(1)

Specificity

The enzyme (P. fluorescens) is highly specific - pyruvate cannot be replaced by 2-oxobutyrate, D-glyceraldehyde 3-phosphate or glycolaldehyde phosphate, nor KDPG by 2-keto-3-deoxy-gluconate (1), fructose-1,6-diphosphate or deoxyribose 5-phosphate (2).

Michaelis constants

source	substrate	$K_m(M)$	conditions	
P. fluorescens	KDPG	1.1×10^{-3}	pH 7.65, Tris	(2)

Abbreviations

KDPG   6-phospho-2-keto-3-deoxy-D-gluconate

References

1. Meloche, H. P. & Wood, W. A. (1964) JBC, 239, 3511.
2. Kovachevich, R. & Wood, W. A. (1955) JBC, 213, 757.

<u>PHOSPHO-2-KETO-3-DEOXY-HEPTONATE ALDOLASE</u>

(7-Phospho-2-keto-3-deoxy-D-<u>arabino</u>-heptonate

D-erythrose-4-phosphate-lyase (pyruvate-phosphorylating))

7-Phospho-2-keto-3-deoxy-D-<u>arabino</u>heptonate + orthophosphate =

phospho-enolpyruvate + D-erythrose 4-phosphate + H_2O

Ref.

Equilibrium constant

The reaction is essentially irreversible [R].   (1)

Specificity and kinetic properties

The enzyme (<u>Escherichia coli</u>) is highly specific for its substrates. (1)

Extracts prepared from <u>E. coli</u> contain two enzymes which catalyze
the conversion of D-erythrose 4-phosphate and PEP to DAHP. The activity
of one of these (enzyme I) is inhibited by L-phenylalanine and the other
(enzyme II) by L-tyrosine. In both cases the inhibition is non-
competitive with respect to both substrates (2). The ability of a
number of analogs of L-phenylalanine and L-tyrosine to inhibit
enzymes I and II is discussed in reference (3).

source	substrate	K_m(M)	condi-tions	
E. coli				
Enzyme I	PEP	2.7×10^{-4}		
	D-erythrose 4-phosphate	5.1×10^{-4}	pH 6.4,	
Enzyme II	PEP	8.3×10^{-4}	P_i, 37°	(2)
	D-erythrose 4-phosphate	8.8×10^{-4}		
'whole extract'	PEP	3.5×10^{-3}	pH 6.4,	
	D-erythrose 4-phosphate	1.2×10^{-3}	P_i, 37°	(1)

Abbreviations

DAHP 7-phospho-2-keto-3-deoxy-D-<u>arabino</u>heptonate
PEP   phospho-enolpyruvate

References

1. Sprinson, D. B., Srinivasam, R. R. & Katagiri, M. (1962) <u>Methods
    in Enzymology</u>, <u>5</u>, 394.
2. Smith, L. C., Ravel, J. M., Lax, S. R. & Shive, W. (1962) <u>JBC</u>,
    <u>237</u>, 3566.
3. Smith, L. C., Ravel, J. M., Lax, S. R. & Shive, W. (1964) <u>ABB</u>,
    <u>105</u>, 424.

L-FUCULOSEPHOSPHATE ALDOLASE

(L-Fuculose-1-phosphate L-lactaldehyde-lyase)

L-Fuculose 1-phosphate = dihydroxyacetone phosphate + L-lactaldehyde

Ref.

Equilibrium constant

$$\frac{[\text{dihydroxyacetone phosphate}] \; [\text{L-lactaldehyde}]}{[\text{L-fuculose 1-phosphate}]} = 4.6 \times 10^{-4} \; M \qquad (1)$$

$$(\text{pH } 7.2, \text{ Tris, } 37^{\circ})$$

Specificity

The enzyme isolated from Escherichia coli cleaves ketose 1-phosphates with the cis configuration of the hydroxyl groups at C-3 and C-4. Thus, the following sugar phosphates were attacked: L-fuculose 1-phosphate (1.00), D-fructose 1,6-diphosphate (0.04), 6-deoxy-L-sorbose 1-phosphate (0.05), D-fructose 1-phosphate (0.06) and D-ribulose 1,5-diphosphate (0.06). The following aldehydes were active in the reverse direction: L-lactaldehyde (1.00), D-lactaldehyde (0.73), D- and L-glyceraldehyde (0.33) and glycolaldehyde. Little activity was exhibited towards formaldehyde, acetaldehyde or D-glyceraldehyde 3-phosphate. (1)

Michaelis constants

source	substrate	K_m(M)	conditions	
E. coli	L-fuculose 1-phosphate	7.0×10^{-4}	pH 7.2, Tris, 37°	(1)

References

1. Ghalambor, M. A. & Heath, E. C. (1962) JBC, 237, 2427.

2. Ghalambor, M. A. & Heath, E. C. (1966) Methods in Enzymology, 9, 538.

2-KETO-3-DEOXY-D-GLUCARATE ALDOLASE

(2-Keto-3-deoxy-D-glucarate tartronate-semialdehyde-lyase)

2-Keto-3-deoxy-D-glucarate = pyruvate + tartronate semialdehyde

Ref.

Equilibrium constant

The reversibility of the reaction has been demonstrated.   (1)

Specificity

The enzyme (Escherichia coli) is highly specific and the following are inactive as substrates: 2-keto-D-gluconate, 2-keto-3-deoxyoctonate, 6-phospho-2-keto-3-deoxy-D-gluconate, 2-keto-3-deoxyheptonate, 2-keto-3-deoxy-D-gluconate, 2-keto-3-deoxy-D-galactonate, oxaloacetate or fructose 1,6-diphosphate. 5-Keto-4-deoxy-D-glucarate is also cleaved.   (1)

Michaelis constants

source	substrate	K_m(M)	conditions	
E. coli	2-keto-3-deoxy-D-glucarate	2.5×10^{-4}	pH 7.8, P_i, 30°	(1)

Inhibitors

Sugar acids inhibit the E. coli enzyme in the following order of effectiveness: hexaric > hexuronic = pentaric > hexonic = tetraric and the following are competitive inhibitors: 2-keto-D-gluconate, 2-keto-3-deoxyoctonate and 6-phospho-2-keto-3-deoxy-D-gluconate (1).

References

1. Fish, D. C. & Blumenthal, H. J. (1966) Methods in Enzymology, 9, 529.

L-RHAMNULOSE-1-PHOSPHATE ALDOLASE

(L-Rhamnulose 1-phosphate L-lactaldehyde-lyase)

L-Rhamnulose 1-phosphate = dihydroxyacetone phosphate + L-lactaldehyde

Ref.

Equilibrium constant

$$\frac{[\text{dihydroxyacetone phosphate}]\,[\text{L-lactaldehyde}]}{[\text{L-rhamnulose 1-phosphate}]} = 8.3 \times 10^{-2} \text{ M} \quad (2)$$

(pH 7.5, glycyl-
glycine, 37°)

Specificity and Michaelis constants

source	substrate	relative velocity	K_m(M)	conditions
Escherichia coli	L-lactaldehyde	1.00	-	
	D-glyceraldehyde	0.50	-	pH 7.5,
	glycolaldehyde	0.40	-	glycyl-
	acetaldehyde	0.15	-	glycine, 30°
	formaldehyde	0.10	-	second sub-
	D-lactaldehyde	0.10	-	strate = di-
	L-glyceraldehyde	0		hydroxyace-
	D-glyceraldehyde 3-phosphate	0	-	tone phos-
	propionaldehyde	0		phate (2)
	L-rhamnulose 1-phosphate	1.000	6.4×10^{-3}	
	D-fructose 1,6-diphosphate	0.018	-	pH 7.5,
	L-fuculose 1-phosphate	0.017	-	glycyl-
	D-ribulose 1,5-diphosphate	0.013	-	glycine, (2)
	6-deoxy-L-sorbose 1-phosphate	0.008	-	37°
	L-sorbose 1-phosphate	0.003	-	
	L-rhamnulose 1-phosphate	-	1×10^{-2}	pH 9.3, (1,3) glycine, 37°

The following compounds were not cleaved by the E. coli enzyme:
D-fructose 6-phosphate, L-sorbose 6-phosphate, D-fructose 1-phosphate,
L-sorbose 1,6-diphosphate. The enzyme is absolutely specific for
dihydroxyacetone phosphate. (2)

References
1. Sawada, H. & Takagi, Y. (1964) BBA, 92, 26.
2. Chiu, T. H. & Feingold, D. S. (1965) BBRC, 19, 511.
3. Takagi, Y. (1966) Methods in Enzymology, 9, 542.

PHOSPHO-2-KETO-3-DEOXY-GALACTONATE ALDOLASE

(6-Phospho-2-keto-3-deoxy-galactonate D-glyceraldehyde 3-phosphate-lyase)

6-Phospho-2-keto-3-deoxy-galactonate = pyruvate + D-glyceraldehyde 3-phosphate

Ref.

Equilibrium constant

$$\frac{[\text{pyruvate}]\,[\text{D-glyceraldehyde 3-phosphate}]}{[\text{6-phospho-2-keto-3-deoxy-galactonate}]} = 2.7 \times 10^{-2}\ M \qquad (1)$$

(pH 6.8, Tris, 25°)

Molecular weight

source	value	conditions	
Pseudomonas saccharophilia	$S_{20,w} = 3.84$		(1)

Specific activity

P. saccharophilia	132 KDP-Gal	(pH 8, Tris)	(1)

Specificity

The enzyme (P. saccharophilia) did not cleave 6-phospho-2-keto-3-deoxy-D-gluconate, 6-phospho-3-deoxy-galactose, glucometa-saccharinate or keto-3-deoxy-L-arabonate nor were these compounds inhibitors of the reaction. (1)

Michaelis constants

source	substrate	$K_m(M)$	conditions	
P. saccharophilia	KDP-Gal	5×10^{-4}	pH 8, Tris	(1)

Abbreviations

KDP-Gal   6-phospho-2-keto-3-deoxy-galactonate

References

1. Shuster, C. W. (1966) Methods in Enzymology, 9, 524.

3-DEOXYOCTULOSONATE ALDOLASE

(3-Deoxyoctulosonate D-arabinose-lyase)

3-Deoxyoctulosonate = pyruvate + D-arabinose

Equilibrium constant

$$\frac{[\text{pyruvate}]\,[\text{D-arabinose}]}{[\text{3-deoxyoctulosonate}]} = \sim 9 \times 10^{-2}\ M \quad (\text{pH } 7,\ P_i,\ 37^\circ) \tag{1}$$

Specificity

The enzyme (<u>Aerobacter</u> <u>cloacae</u>) is highly specific. Thus, little activity was exhibited towards 3–deoxy-D-<u>arabino</u>-heptulosonate, 3–deoxy-D-<u>erythro</u>-hexulosonate or N-acetylneuraminate. In the direction of condensation, however, the enzyme is somewhat less specific and the following reacted with pyruvate: D-arabinose (1.00) and D-ribose (0.29), and slight activity was exhibited towards D-arabinose 5–phosphate, L-arabinose, D-xylose, D-lyxose or N-acetyl-D-mannosamine. (1)

Michaelis constants

source	substrate	$K_m(M)$	conditions	
E. coli	3-deoxyoctulosonate	6×10^{-3}	pH 7, P_i, 37°	(1)

References

1. Ghalambor, M. A. & Heath, H. C. (1966) Methods in Enzymology, <u>9</u>, 534.

2-OXO-4-HYDROXYGLUTARATE ALDOLASE

(2-Oxo-4-hydroxyglutarate glyoxylate-lyase)

2-Oxo-4-hydroxyglutarate = pyruvate + glyoxylate

Ref.

Equilibrium constant

$$\frac{[\text{pyruvate}][\text{glyoxylate}]}{[\text{2-oxo-4-hydroxyglutarate}]} = \begin{array}{l} 11.8 \text{ M} \quad (\text{pH } 8.4, \text{ Tris}, 37^\circ) \\ 10.4 \text{ M} \quad (\text{pH } 8.4, \text{ Tris}, 37^\circ) \end{array}$$

(1)
(2)

Molecular weight

source	value	conditions	
Rat liver	120,000	Sephadex G200	(2)

Specific activity

Rat liver (425 x) 7.7 2-oxo-4-hydroxyglutarate (pH 8.4, Tris, 37°) (2)

Specificity

The enzyme (rat liver) attacks the following 2-keto-3-deoxyonic acids: L-2-oxo-4-hydroxyglutarate (1.00), D-2-oxo-4-hydroxyglutarate (0.91), 2-oxo-3-deoxyglucarate (0.30), and 2-oxo-4,5-dihydroxyvalerate (0.07), but the following were inactive: 2-oxo-3-deoxygluconate, 2-oxo-4-hydroxy-4-methylglutarate, N-acetylneuraminate, 2-oxo-3-deoxy-heptonate, 2-oxo-gluconate and 2-oxo-3-deoxygalactonate. (1)

Michaelis constants

source	substrate	K_m(M)	conditions	
Rat liver	2-oxo-4-hydroxy-glutarate	1.0×10^{-3}	pH 8.4, Tris, 37°	(1)
	pyruvate	6×10^{-3}	pH 8.4, Tris, 37° (glyoxylate = 3.2×10^{-3}M)	(2)
	glyoxylate	1.0×10^{-2}	pH 8.4, Tris, 37° (pyruvate = 1.6×10^{-2}M)	(2)

Inhibitors

Pyruvate and glyoxylate are mutually competitive. (2)

References

1. Maitra, U. & Dekker, E. E. (1964) JBC, 239, 1485.
2. Rosso, R. G. & Adams, E. (1967) JBC, 242, 5524.

FRUCTOSE 6-PHOSPHATE PHOSPHOKETOLASE

(D-Fructose-6-phosphate D-erythrose-4-phosphate lyase (phosphate-acetylating))

D-Fructose 6-phosphate + P_i =

acetylphosphate + D-erythrose 4-phosphate + H_2O

Ref.

Specificity

The enzyme isolated from Acetobacter xylinum will utilize xylulose 5-phosphate in addition to fructose 6-phosphate but not the following: fructose 1,6-diphosphate, dihydroxyacetone phosphate, sedoheptulose 7-phosphate, glucose 6-phosphate, ribose 5-phosphate, erythrose 4-phosphate, glycolaldehyde 2-phosphate, fructose, xylulose, hydroxypyruvate, pyruvate or glycolaldehyde.   (1,2)

Michaelis constants

source	substrate	$K_m(M)$	conditions	
A. xylinum	D-fructose 6-phosphate	2.5×10^{-3}	pH 5.7, histidine, $30°$	(1,2)
	P_i	8.7×10^{-4}		

References

1. Racker, E. (1962) Methods in Enzymology, 5, 276.
2. Schramm, M., Klybas, V. & Racker, E. (1958) JBC, 233, 1283.

ISOCITRATE LYASE

(threo-D_s-Isocitrate glyoxylate-lyase)

threo-D_s-Isocitrate = succinate + glyoxylate

Equilibrium constant

$$\frac{[\text{succinate}][\text{glyoxylate}]}{[\text{threo-}D_s\text{-isocitrate}]} = \begin{array}{l} 2.89 \times 10^{-2}\text{M (pH 7.6, Tris, 27}^\circ\text{)} \\ 4.34 \times 10^{-2}\text{M}^{(a)}\text{ (pH 8.0, Tris, 28}^\circ\text{)} \end{array}$$

(8)
(2)

---

[a] Calculated from the Haldane equation.

Molecular weight

source	value	conditions	
Pseudomonas indigofera	222,000	pH 7.7 + glutathione	(3)
Chlorella pyrenoidosa	170,000	pH 7.7 + mercaptoethanol	(4)

Specific activity

P. indigofera (17 x) 46 isocitrate (pH 7.7, Tris, 30°) (9)
C. pyrenoidosa (14 x) 35 isocitrate (pH 7.6, triethanolamine, 30°) (4)

Specificity

The enzyme isolated from a number of sources is highly specific. Thus, acetaldehyde and pyruvate do not substitute for glyoxylate and threo-D_s-isocitrate is the only isomer of isocitrate which is cleaved. (1,2)

Michaelis constants

source	substrate	K_m(M)	conditions	
P. aerogenosa	isocitrate glyoxylate succinate	4.5×10^{-4} 1.6×10^{-4} 7.0×10^{-4}	pH 8.0, Tris, 28°	(2)
Yeast	isocitrate Mg^{2+} cysteine[a]	1.2×10^{-3} 1×10^{-4} 4×10^{-5}	pH 6.0, P_i, 28°	(5)
Neurospora crassa	isocitrate	1.18×10^{-3}	pH 6.8, imidazole	(6)
C. pyrenoidosa	isocitrate	2.3×10^{-5}	pH 7.6, triethanolamine, 30°	(4)

---

[a] A thiol compound is required for maximum activity.

The enzyme isolated from Chlorella vulgaris exhibits abnormal Michaelis-Menton kinetics and with this enzyme there is evidence of co-operativity. (7)

Inhibitors

source	inhibitor	type	$K_i(M)$	conditions	
P. aerogenosa	maleate	C(succinate)	3.6×10^{-4}	pH 8.0, Tris, 30°	(2)
	succinate	NC(isocitrate)	7×10^{-3}	pH 7.6, Tris, 30°	(8)
	oxalate	NC(isocitrate)	2×10^{-3}		
P. indigofera	glyoxylate		5.3×10^{-3}		
	2-oxoglutarate	NC(isocitrate)	6.8×10^{-3}	pH 7.7, Tris, 30°	(9)
	L-malate		5.9×10^{-3}		
	succinate		1.4×10^{-3}		

The enzyme from P. indigofera is also inhibited by fumarate, malonate, maleate and glycollate but not by acetate, L-alanine, L-aspartate, butyrate, citrate, L-glutamate or glycine. (9)

Light absorption data

glyoxylate simicarbazone $\varepsilon,\ (252\ m\mu) = 12{,}400\ M^{-1}\ cm^{-1}$ (5)

glyoxylate phenylhydrazone $\varepsilon,\ (324\ m\mu) = 16{,}800\ M^{-1}\ cm^{-1}$ (6)

References

1. Olson, J. A. (1961) The Enzymes, 5, 387.

2. Daron, H. N., Rutter, W. J. & Gunsalus, I. C. (1966) B, 5, 895.

3. Shio, I., Shio, T. & McFadden, B. A. (1965) BBA, 96, 114, 123.

4. John, P. C. L. & Syrett, P. J. (1967) BJ, 105, 409.

5. Olson, J. A. (1959) JBC, 234, 5.

6. Turian, G. & Kobr, M. (1965) BBA, 99, 178.

7. Harrop, L. C. & Kornberg, H. L. (1966) Proc. Roy. Soc. 166(B), 11.

8. Smith, R. A. & Gunsalus, I. C. (1957) JBC, 229, 305.

9. McFadden, B. A. & Howes, W. V. (1963) JBC, 238, 1737.

MALATE SYNTHASE

(L-Malate glyoxylate-lyase (CoA-acetylating)

L-Malate + CoA = acetyl-CoA + H_2O + glyoxylate

Ref.

Equilibrium constant

$$\frac{[\text{acetyl-CoA}]\,[H_2O]\,[\text{glyoxylate}]}{[\text{L-malate}]\,[\text{CoA}]} = 1.59 \times 10^3 \quad \text{(pH 8.5, Tris,} \atop \text{room temperature)}} \qquad (1)$$

Specificity

The enzyme is highly specific. Thus, that from yeast could not utilize the following compounds in the place of glyoxylate: oxalo-acetate, pyruvate, 2-oxoglutarate, glyoxal, glycolaldehyde, formalde-hyde or acetaldehyde. Fluoroacetyl-CoA possessed 25% the activity of acetyl-CoA but butyryl-CoA, S,N-diacetylcysteamine, S-acetylpante-theine, propionyl-CoA and malyl-CoA were all inactive. (2)

The enzyme also catalyzes the enolization of acetyl-CoA (this reaction is stimulated by 2-oxoacids) and the hydrolysis of malyl-CoA. (5)

Michaelis constants

source	substrate	$K_m(M)$	conditions	
Yeast (baker's)	acetyl-CoA	$<1.0 \times 10^{-5}$	pH 8.0, Tris, 25°	(2)
	glyoxylate	9.34×10^{-5}		
	Mg^{2+}	4.8×10^{-4}		
	acetyl-CoA	4.0×10^{-5}	pH 8.0, PP_i.	(5)
Escherichia coli $A\{^a\}$ $G\{^a\}$	glyoxylate	8.2×10^{-5}	pH 8.0, Tris.	(3)
	glyoxylate	4.92×10^{-5}		

Michaelis constants contd.

(a) There are two malate synthases in E. coli which have been separated from each other.

Inhibitors

source	inhibitor	type	$K_i(M)$	conditions	
Yeast[a]	oxalate	C(glyoxylate)	1.9×10^{-5}	pH 8.0, Tris, 25°	(2)
	glycollate	C(glyoxylate)	3.08×10^{-4}		
	fluoroacetate	C(glyoxylate)	2.46×10^{-4}		
	malate	C(acetyl-CoA)	1×10^{-3}	pH 8.1, PP_i.	(5)
E. coli A	oxalate	C(glyoxylate)	1.88×10^{-5}	pH 8.0, Tris.	(3)
	glycollate	C(glyoxylate)	2.54×10^{-5}		
G	oxalate	C(glyoxylate)	1.13×10^{-5}		
	glycollate	C(glyoxylate)	1.99×10^{-5}		

(a) The following compounds were without effect: acetate, glycol-aldehyde and oxaloacetate.

Light absorption data

Acetyl CoA ε, (232 mµ)   =   4,500 $M^{-1}cm^{-1}$ (pH 7.1)   (4,5)

References

1. Goldman, D. S. & Wagner, M. J. (1962) BBA, 65, 297.

2. Dixon, G. H. & Kornberg, H. L. (1962) Methods in Enzymology, 5, 633.

3. Falmagne, P., Vanderwinkel, E. & Wiame, J. M. (1965) BBA, 99, 246.

4. Dixon, G. H. & Kornberg, H. L. (1959) BJ, 72, 3P

5. Eggerer, H. & Klette, A. (1967) European J. Biochem., 1, 447.

N-ACETYLNEURAMINATE LYASE

(N-Acetylneuraminate pyruvate-lyase)

N-Acetylneuraminate = 2-acetamido-2-deoxy-
D-mannose + pyruvate

Ref.

Equilibrium constant

$$\frac{[\text{2-acetamido-2-deoxy-D-mannose}]\,[\text{pyruvate}]}{[\text{N-acetylneuraminate}]} = 9.6 \times 10^{-2}M^{(a)}$$
(pH 7.2, P_i, 37°) (3)

$$\frac{[\text{N-glycolylamido-2-deoxy-D-mannose}]\,[\text{pyruvate}]}{[\text{N-glycolylneuraminate}]} = 9.0 \times 10^{-2}M$$
(pH 7.2, P_i', 37°) (3)

$^{(a)}$A value of 6.4×10^{-2} is reported in reference (1).

Specificity

The enzyme isolated from Clostridium perfringens attacks the
following substances: N-acetylneuraminate (1.00), N-glycolylneuramin-
ate (0.65) and N,O-diacetylneuraminate (0.14). A large number of other
substances tested did not react (1). In the reverse reaction, the
enzyme is active with pyruvate and either N-acetyl-D-mannosamine or
N-glycolyl-D-mannosamine but phospho-enolpyruvate cannot replace pyruvate (2). A large number of hexosamine derivatives were shown to be
inactive (1). The mammalian enzyme has similar properties (3).

Michaelis constants

source	substrate	relative velocity	K_m(M)	conditions	
C. perfringens	N-acetylneuraminate N-glycolylneuraminate	1.00 0.65	} 3.9×10^{-3}	pH 7.2, P_i, 37°	(1)
Hog kidney cortex	N-acetylneuraminate N-glycolylneuraminate	1.00 0.65	} 1.5×10^{-3}	pH 7.2, P_i, 37°	(3)

References

1. Comb, D. G. & Roseman, S. (1962) Methods in Enzymology, 5, 391.

2. Comb, D. G. & Roseman, S. (1960) JACS, 80, 497.

3. Brunetti, P., Jourdian, G. W. & Roseman, S. (1962) JBC, 237, 2447.

HYDROXYMETHYLGLUTARYL-CoA LYASE

(3-Hydroxy-3-methylglutaryl-CoA acetoacetate-lyase)

3-Hydroxy-3-methylglutaryl-CoA =
acetyl-CoA + acetoacetate

Ref.

Equilibrium constant

The reaction is essentially irreversible [F].   (1,2)

Specificity

The enzyme from pig heart is highly specific for 3-hydroxy-3-methylglutaryl-CoA. The following compounds were inactive: 3-hydroxy-3-methylglutarate, 3-hydroxyisovaleryl-CoA and the glutathione, pantetheine, cysteine and N-acetylthioethanolamine thiol esters of 3-hydroxy-3-methylglutarate. The lyase requires Mg^{2+} or Mn^{2+} and a thiol compound (cysteine, glutathione, thioethanolamine or thioglycollate) for activity. The enzyme is active over the pH range 7.4 to 10.5.   (1,2)

References

1. Coon, M. J. (1962) Methods in Enzymology, 5, 900.

2. Bachhawat, B. K., Robinson, W. G. & Coon, M. J. (1955) JBC, 216, 727.

HYDROXYMETHYLGLUTARYL-CoA SYNTHASE
(3-Hydroxy-3-methylglutaryl-CoA
acetoacetyl-CoA-lyase (CoA-acetylating))

3-Hydroxy-3-methylglutaryl-CoA + CoA =
acetyl-CoA + H_2O + acetoacetyl-CoA

Ref.

Equilibrium constant

The reaction is essentially irreversible [R].   (1)

Molecular weight

source	value	conditions	
Yeast	$S_{20,w} = 7.7$	pH 8.2	(1)

Specificity and kinetic properties

Hydroxymethylglutaryl-CoA synthase of yeast is closely associated with acetyl-CoA acetyltransferase (2.3.1.9). The two activities have not been separated.   (1)

With the yeast enzyme, acetyl-CoA (1.00) could be replaced by acetylglutathione (0.29) or acetylpantetheine (0.20) and acetoacetyl-CoA (1.00) by acetoacetylglutathione (0.06) but not by acetoacetyl-pantetheine or acetoacetate. The acetyl and acetoacetyl thiol esters of pantetheine and glutathione were inactive.   (1,2)

The kinetics of the enzyme are difficult to interpret since even at low concentrations acetoacetyl-CoA is inhibitory.   (1)

Light absorption data

acetoacetyl-CoA ε, (300 mμ) = 3600 M^{-1} cm^{-1} (pH 8.2)   (1)

References

1. Stewart, P. R. & Rudney, H. (1966) JBC, 241, 1212.
2. Ferguson, J. J. Jr. & Rudney, H. (1959) JBC, 234, 1072.

CITRATE LYASE

(Citrate oxaloacetate-lyase)

Citrate = acetate + oxaloacetate

Ref.

Equilibrium constant

$$\frac{[\text{acetate}^-]\,[\text{oxaloacetate}_{(\text{keto})}^{2-}]}{[\text{citrate}^{3-}]} = 3.25 \times 10^{-1}M \quad (\text{pH } 8.4,\ 25^\circ,\ Mg^{2+} = 5 \times 10^{-4} - 1 \times 10^{-2}M).$$ (1)

Molecular weight

source	value	conditions	
Aerobacter aerogenes	316,000	pH 7.0	(2)

Specific activity

A. aerogenes (37 x) 46 citrate (pH 7.0, P_i, 37°) (2)

Specificity

Citrate lyase is highly specific. Thus, the enzyme from Escherichia coli is inactive with isocitrate, cis-aconitate, tricarballylate, itaconate and citraconate. (3)

Michaelis constants

source	substrate	$K_m(M)$	conditions	
A. aerogenes	citrate	2.1×10^{-4}		
	Mg^{2+}	3.0×10^{-3}		
E. coli	citrate	1.6×10^{-4}	pH 7.4, Tris, 25°	(3)
	Mg^{2+}	3.0×10^{-3}		
	Mn^{2+}	8.0×10^{-5}		
Streptococcus diacetilactis	citrate	1×10^{-3}	pH 7.0, Tris, 30°	(4)
	Mg^{2+}	9.9×10^{-4}		
	Mn^{2+}	9.4×10^{-5}		

Inhibitors

source	inhibitor	type	$K_i(M)$	conditions	
S. diacetilactis	Mg^{2+}	C(citrate-Mg)	2.5×10^{-2}	pH 7.0, Tris, 30°	(4)
	Ca^{2+}	C(Mg^{2+})	1.68×10^{-4}		

The enzyme (A. aerogenes) is inhibited by oxaloacetate. (1)

References

1. Tata, S. S. & Datta, S. P. (1965) BJ, 94, 470.
2. Bowen, T. J. & Rogers, L. J. (1963) BBA, 77, 685.
3. Daron, H. H. & Gunsalus, I. C. (1962) Methods in Enzymology, 5, 622.
4. Harvey, R. J. & Collins, E. B. (1963) JBC, 238, 2648.

CITRATE SYNTHASE

(Citrate oxaloacetate-lyase (CoA-acetylating))

Citrate + CoA = acetyl–CoA + H_2O + oxaloacetate

Ref.

Equilibrium constant

$$\frac{[\text{acetyl-CoA}] [H_2O] [\text{oxaloacetate}]}{[\text{citrate}] [\text{CoA}]} = 1.2 \times 10^{-4} \text{ M} \quad (P_i, 22°) \tag{2}$$

Molecular weight

source	value	conditions	
Pig heart	86,000	pH 8.2	(3)

Specific activity

Pig heart	(100 x)	78 citrate	(pH 8, Tris, 25°)	(4)

Specificity

The only substrates of the pig heart enzyme (in addition to citrate and CoA) are fluoroacetate (5), citroyl-CoA (6), S-maloyl-CoA (7) and fluoroacetyl-CoA (8). Propionyl-CoA exhibits only 0.1% of the activity of acetyl-CoA and buturyl-CoA is inactive (1).

Michaelis constants

source	substrate	$K_m(M)$	conditions	
Pig heart	CoA	2.8×10^{-5}	pH 6.1, imidazole-	(9)
	citrate	2.5×10^{-4}	acetate, 22°	

The Michaelis constants of acetyl-CoA and oxaloacetate are discussed in reference (9) - these depend on the pH and the concentration of the substrate at constant concentration.

Inhibitors

source	inhibitor	type	$K_i(M)$	conditions
Pig heart	fluoroacetyl-CoA	C (acetyl-CoA)	1.3×10^{-6}	pH 7.0, (10) triethanol-amine, $23°$

Palmitoyl-CoA inhibits the enzymes from a number of sources (11). Citroyl-CoA inhibits the pig heart enzyme and competes with acetyl-CoA and oxaloacetate (6).

References

1. Stern, J. R. (1961) The Enzymes, 5, 367.

2. Stern, J. R., Ochoa, S. & Lynen, F. (1952) JBC, 198, 313.

3. Srere, P. A. (1966) JBC, 241, 2157.

4. Srere, P. A. & Kosicki, G. W. (1961) JBC, 236, 2557.

5. Fanshier, D. W., Gottwald, L. K. & Kun, E. (1962) JBC, 237, 3588.

6. Srere, P. A. (1963) BBA, 77, 693.

7. Eggerer, H., Remberger, U. & Grunwalder, C. (1964) BZ, 339, 436.

8. Marcus, A. & Elliott, W. B. (1956) JBC, 218, 823.

9. Kosicki, G. W. & Srere, P. A. (1961) JBC, 236, 2560.

10. Brady, R. O. (1955) JBC, 217, 213.

11. Srere, P. A. (1965) BBA, 106, 445.

ATP CITRATE LYASE

(ATP: citrate oxaloacetate-lyase (CoA-acetylating and
ATP-dephosphorylating))

ATP + citrate + CoA = ADP + orthophosphate +
acetyl-CoA + oxaloacetate

Ref.

Equilibrium constant

$$\frac{[ADP]\ [P_i]\ [acetyl\text{-}CoA]\ [oxaloacetate]}{[ATP]\ [citrate]\ [CoA]} = 1.0\text{-}1.5\ M\ (pH\ 7.4,\ Tris,\ 25^\circ)\quad (1)$$

Molecular weight

source	value	conditions	
Rat liver	500,000	pH 7.4	(2)
Chicken liver	1,000,000	-	(3)

Specific activity

Rat liver	(70 x)	1.60[a]	citrate	(pH 7.4, Tris, 25°)	(1)
		0.21[a]	oxaloacetate	(pH 7.4, Tris, 25°)	(1)
	(58 x)	5.94	citrate	(pH 8.4, Tris, 37°)	(2)

[a] A maximum figure.

Specificity

The enzyme is highly specific for its substrates. Thus, the enzyme from pigeon liver is inactive with succinate, malate, aconitate or isocitroyl-CoA (3), and that from rat liver is inactive with cis-aconitate, isocitrate, tricarballylate, CTP, GTP or UTP (2). The enzyme from chicken liver is equally active with citrate or citroyl-CoA (4). That from rat liver possesses ATP-ADP exchange activity (1).

Michaelis constants

source	substrate	$K_m(M)$	conditions	
Rat liver	Mg–ATP	2.84×10^{-4}		
	Mg citrate	1.62×10^{-6}		
	CoA	7.08×10^{-5}	pH 7.4, Tris, 25°	(1)
	Mg–ADP	4.1×10^{-6}		
	P_i	1.49×10^{-3}		
	acetyl–CoA	9.8×10^{-6}		
	oxaloacetate	1.77×10^{-4}		
	citrate	5.8×10^{-4}	pH 8.4, Tris, 37°	(2)
	ATP	1.72×10^{-4}		
Chicken liver	citroyl–CoA	2.86×10^{-5}	pH 7.4, Tris, room temperature	(4)

Inhibitors

source	inhibitor	type	$K_i(M)$	conditions	
Rat liver	ADP	C(ATP)	1.71×10^{-4}	pH 8.4, Tris, 37°	(2)

The enzyme from rat liver is also inhibited by P_i but not by (2)
acetyl–CoA or oxaloacetate.

References

1. Plowman, K. M. & Cleland, W. W. (1967) JBC, 242, 4239.

2. Inoue, H., Suzuki, F., Fukunishi, K., Adachi, K. & Takeda, Y.
   (1966) J. Biochem. (Tokyo), 60, 543.

3. Srere, P. A. (1959) JBC, 234, 2544.

4. Srere, P. A. & Bhaduri, A. (1964) JBC, 239, 714.

N-ACYLNEURAMINATE-9-PHOSPHATE SYNTHASE

(N-Acylneuraminate-9-phosphate phosphoenolpyruvate-lyase
(pyruvate phosphorylating))

N-Acylneuraminate-9-phosphate + P$_i$ =

2-acetamido-2-deoxy-D-mannose 6-phosphate + phosphoenolpyruvate

Ref.

Equilibrium constant

The reverse reaction is strongly favoured. (1)

Specificity

The enzyme (pig submaxillary gland) is highly specific, and
the following were inactive as substrates: erythrose 4-phosphate,
arabinose 5-phosphate, ribose 5-phosphate, glucose 6-phosphate,
mannose 6-phosphate, glucose 1-phosphate, fructose 6-phosphate,
galactose 1-phosphate, glucosamine 6-phosphate, N-acetylglucosamine
6-phosphate, mannosamine 6-phosphate, galactosamine 6-phosphate, N-
acetylmannosamine, or N-glycolylmannosamine. Phosphoenolpyruvate
could not be replaced by pyruvate or oxaloacetate. (1)

Michaelis constants

source	substrate	K$_m$(M)	conditions
Pig submaxillary gland	N-acetylmannosa-mine 6-phosphate	6.9×10^{-4}	pH 7.8, Tris, 37° (1)
	N-glycolylmanno-samine 6-phos-phate	1.6×10^{-3}	

References

1. Watson, D., Jourdian, G. W. & Roseman, S. (1966) Methods in
   Enzymology, 8, 201.

N-ACETYLNEURAMINATE LYASE

(N-Acetylneuraminate phosphoenolpyruvate-lyase (pyruvate phosphorylating))

N-Acetylneuraminate + P_i = 2-acetamido-2-deoxy-D-mannose +

phosphoenolpyruvate + H_2O

Ref.

Equilibrium constant

The reaction is essentially irreversible [R].　　　　　　(1)

Specificity

The enzyme isolated from Neisseria meningitidis is highly specific.
Thus, N-acetyl-D-mannosamine could not be replaced by N-acetyl-D-glucosamine, N-acetyl-D-galactosamine, N-acetyl-D-mannosamine 6-phosphate or
their deacylated forms, D-mannosamine, D-mannose, D-glucose, D-galactose,
D-glucose 6-phosphate, D-ribose, D-ribose 5-phosphate, D-erythrose, D-
rhamnose, D-arabinose, UDP-N-acetylglucosamine, UDPglucose or GDP-
mannose.　Phosphoenolpyruvate could not be replaced by pyruvate, lactate, 2-phospholactate, oxaloacetate or 3-phosphoglycerate.　　(1)

Michaelis constants

source	substrate	$K_m(M)$	conditions	
N. meningitidis	N-acetyl-D-mannosamine	6.25×10^{-3}	pH 8.3, Tris, $37°$	(1)
	phosphoenolpyruvate	4.2×10^{-5}		

References

1.　Blacklow, R. S. & Warren, L.　(1962)　JBC, 237, 3520.

4-METHYL-4-HYDROXY-2-OXOGLUTARATE LYASE

(4-Methyl-4-hydroxy-2-oxoglutarate pyruvate-lyase)

4-Methyl-4-hydroxy-2-oxoglutarate = 2 pyruvate

Ref.

Equilibrium constant

The reaction is essentially irreversible [F].   (1)

Michaelis constants

source	substrate	$K_m(M)$	conditions
Peanut cotyledons	4-methyl-4-hydroxy-2-oxoglutarate	8.6×10^{-5}	pH 8.0, Tris, 30° (1)

Inhibitors

source	inhibitor	type	$K_i(M)$	conditions
Peanut cotyledons	2-oxoglutarate	C (4-methyl-4-hydroxy-2-oxoglutarate)	1.5×10^{-3}	pH 8.0, Tris, 30° (1)
	pyruvate	NC (4-methyl-4-hydroxy-2-oxoglutarate)	-	

References

1. Shannon, L. M. & Marcus, A. (1962) JBC, 237, 3342.

CARBONIC ANHYDRASE

(Carbonate hydro-lyase)

$$H_2CO_3 \text{ (or } H^+ + HCO_3^-) = CO_2 + H_2O$$

Ref.

Equilibrium constant

$$\frac{[CO_2]}{[H^+][HCO_3^-]} = 10^{6.4} M^{-1} \tag{6}$$

Molecular weight

source	value	conditions	
Bovine erythrocyte[a]	31,000	pH 8.2	(2)
Human erythrocyte[a]	28,000	pH 7.0	(8)

[a] Carbonic anhydrase preparations from bovine or human erythrocytes contain at least three distinct molecular forms of the enzyme of similar or identical molecular weights.

Specificity and kinetic constants

Carbonic anhydrase is a powerful catalyst for the reversible hydration of carbon dioxide and, also, acetaldehyde and related carbonyl compounds. It possesses esterase activity. (1,3,4,7)

source		substrate	k_0(sec^{-1})	K_m(M)	conditions	
Human erythrocyte	B	HCO_3	23,000	3.2×10^{-2}	pH 7.05 P_i, 25°	(6)
	C	HCO_3	365,000	6.8×10^{-2}		
	B	CO_2	15,000	2.8×10^{-3}		
	C	CO_2	620,000	1.4×10^{-2}		

Specificity and kinetic constants contd.   Ref.

source		substrate	$k_0(\text{sec}^{-1})$	$K_m(M)$	conditions
Human erythrocyte	B	p-nitrophenyl acetate	0.8	5.2×10^{-3}	pH 7.0, P_i, $25°$
	C	p-nitrophenyl acetate	35.9	2.2×10^{-2}	(7)
Bovine erythrocyte		HCO_3 CO_2	25,500 67,000	9.6×10^{-3} 8.4×10^{-3}	pH 7.0, P_i, $0.5°$ (5)

Inhibitors

source	inhibitor	type	$K_i(M)$	conditions
Bovine erythrocyte	acetazolamide	NC(acet-aldehyde)	6.1×10^{-7}	pH 7.22, P_i, $0°$ (4)

Carbonic anhydrase is inhibited by several anions and alcohols.   (7)

References

1. Davis, R. P. (1961) The Enzymes, 5, 545.

2. Lindskog, S. (1960) BBA, 39, 218.

3. Pocker, Y. & Stone, J. T. (1967) B, 6, 668.

4. Pocker, Y. & Meany, J. E. (1965) B, 4, 2535.

5. DeVoe, H. & Kistiakowsky, G. B. (1961) JACS, 83, 274.

6. Gibbons, B. H. & Edsall, J. T. (1964) JBC, 239, 2539.

7. Verpoorte, J. A., Mehta, S. & Edsall, J. T. (1967) JBC, 242, 4221.

8. Armstrong, J. McD., Myers, D. V. Verpoorte, J. A. & Edsall, J. T. (1966) JBC, 241, 5137.

FUMARATE HYDRATASE

(L-Malate hydro-lyase)

L-Malate = fumarate + H_2O

Ref.

Equilibrium constant

$$\frac{[\text{fumarate}]}{[\text{L-malate}]} \quad = \quad 0.23 \qquad (\text{pH} > 6.5,\ 25^\circ) \tag{2}$$

Molecular weight

source	value	conditions	
Pig heart	194,000[4]	pH 7.3	(3)

Specificity and kinetic constants

Fumarase is absolutely specific for fumarate and L-malate. The following compounds were inactive as substrates: D-malate, DL-thio-malate, maleate, cis- and trans-aconitate, citrate, mesaconate, citraconate, D-,L-, and meso-tartrate, and the mono- and diesters of fumarate. (1,5)

source	substrate	$k_0(\text{sec}^{-1})$[a]	$K_m(M)$[a]	conditions	
Pig heart	L-malate	1130	3.79×10^{-6}	1×10^{-2}M Tris-acetate, 21°	(4)
	fumarate	2520	1.74×10^{-6}		

[a] The values given are the pH independent maximum velocities and Michaelis constants.

A detailed analysis of the kinetics of fumarase will be found in reference (4). The kinetic constants depend on the temperature, pH and ionic strength of the reaction medium.

Inhibitors				Ref.

source	inhibitor[a]	$K_i(M)$	conditions	
Pig	adipate	1.0×10^{-1}		
heart	succinate	5.2×10^{-2}		
	glutarate	4.6×10^{-2}		
	malonate	4.0×10^{-2}		
	D-tartrate	2.5×10^{-2}		
	mesaconate	2.5×10^{-2}	pH 6.35,	(5)
	L-2-hydroxy-3-sulphopropionate	1.65×10^{-2}	23°	
	D-malate	6.3×10^{-3}		
	maleate	1.1×10^{-2}		
	citrate	3.5×10^{-3}		
	trans-aconitate	6.3×10^{-4}		

[a]C(fumarate)

Light absorption data

Fumarate	ε, (250 mμ)	1400 M^{-1}cm^{-1} (pH 4.5)	(2)
	ε, (290 mμ)	109 M^{-1}cm^{-1} (pH 7.3)	(2)
	ε, (250 mμ)	1450 M^{-1}cm^{-1} (pH 7.3)	(2)

References

1. Alberty, R. A. (1961) The Enzymes, 5, 531.

2. Bock, R. M. & Alberty, R. A. (1953) JACS, 75, 1921.

3. Kanarech, L., Marler, E., Bradshaw, R. A., Fellows, R. E. & Hill, R. L. (1964) JBC, 239, 4207.

4. Brant, D. A., Barnett, L. B. & Alberty, R. A. (1963) JACS, 85, 2204.

5. Massey, V. (1953) BJ, 55, 172.

ACONITATE HYDRATASE
(Citrate (isocitrate) hydro-lyase)
Citrate = cis-aconitate + H$_2$O

Equilibrium constant

At equilibrium,

$$\begin{aligned}
\text{citrate} &= 90.9\% \\
\text{cis-aconitate} &= 2.9\% \\
\text{isocitrate} &= 6.2\%
\end{aligned}$$

(pH 7.4, 25°)

Mg^{2+} shifts the equilibrium towards citrate.   (2)

Molecular weight

source	value	conditions	
Sinapas alba (mustard)	S$_{20}$,w = 4.7	-	(3)

Specific activity

S. alba (221 x) 2.4 isocitrate (pH 8.0, Tris.)   (3)

Specificity

Aconitase **from** pig heart **exhibits complete specificity for its three** substrates (1) but that isolated from S. alba also attacks 2-**methyl** cis-aconitate.   (3)

Michaelis constants

source	substrate	V(relative)	K$_m$(M)	conditions	
S. alba	citrate	1.00	4.0×10^{-3}		
	cis-aconitate	-	1.0×10^{-4}	pH 8.0,	(3)
	isocitrate	0.71	1.5×10^{-4}(a)	Tris.	
			1.5×10^{-2}(b)		
Pig heart	citrate	1.00	3.6×10^{-3}		
	cis-aconitate	-	1.2×10^{-4}	pH 7.7,	(4)
	isocitrate	3.00	4.8×10^{-4}	P$_i$, 22°	

(a) S $< 3 \times 10^{-3}$M
(b) S $1 - 7.5 \times 10^{-2}$M

The mechanism of action of aconitase is discussed in reference (6).

Inhibitors

source	inhibitor	type	K$_i$(M)	conditions	
Pigeon breast muscle	fluorocitrate(a)	C(isocitrate)	$\sim 2 \times 10^{-4}$	pH 7.2, P$_i$	(5)

(a) Biosynthetic

References

1. Dickman, S. R. (1961) The Enzymes, 5, 495.
2. Krebs, H. A. (1953) BJ, 54, 78.
3. Palmer, M. J. (1964) BJ, 92, 404.
4. Morrison, J. F. (1954) Australian J. Exptl. Biol and Med. Sci., 32, 867.
5. Peters, R. A. & Wilson, T. H. (1952) BBA, 9, 310.
6. Rose, I. A. & O'Connell, E. L. (1967) JBC, 242, 1870.

ALTRONATE DEHYDRATASE

(D-Altronate hydro-lyase)

D-Altronate = 2-keto-3-deoxy-D-gluconate + H_2O

Ref.

Equilibrium constant

The reaction is essentially irreversible[F]. (1,2)

Specificity

The Escherichia coli enzyme is highly specific for D-altronate: D-altronolactone, D-mannonate, D-allonate, D-talonate, D-idonate, D-gluconate, D-arabonate, L-galactonate, L-gulonate and D-arabo-ascorbate are all inactive as substrates. (1,2)

Michaelis constants

source	substrate	$K_m(M)$	conditions	
E. coli	D-altronate	2.5×10^{-3}	pH 7.6, glycyl-glycine, 37°	(1,2)

References

1. Ashwell, G. (1962) Methods in Enzymology, 5, 199.
2. Smiley, J. D. & Ashwell, G. (1960) JBC, 235, 1571.

MANNONATE DEHYDRATASE

(D-Mannonate hydro-lyase)

D-Mannonate = 2-keto-3-deoxy-D-gluconate + H_2O

Ref.

Equilibrium constant

The reaction is essentially irreversible[F].   (1,2)

Specificity

The **Escherichia coli** enzyme is highly specific for D-mannonate: D-mannonolactone, D-altronate, D-gluconate, D-talonate, D-idonate, D-allonate, D-arabonate, D-galactonate, L-gulonate and 6-phospho-D-gluconate are all inactive.   (1,2)

Michaelis constants

source	substrate	$K_m(M)$	conditions	
E. coli	D-mannonate	3×10^{-3}	pH 5.4, P_i, 37°	(1,2)

References

1. Ashwell, G. (1962) Methods in Enzymology, 5, 203.
2. Smiley, J. D. & Ashwell, G. (1960) JBC, 235, 1571.

DIHYDROXYACID DEHYDRATASE
(2,3-Dihydroxyacid hydro-lyase)

2,3-Dihydroxyisovalerate = 2-oxoisovalerate + H_2O

Ref.

Molecular weight

source	value	conditions	
Neurospora crassa[a]	$S_{20,w} = 5.0$	-	(2)

[a] This enzyme has a high lipid content ($\sim 50\%$).

Specific activity

N. crassa (123 x) 2.15 DHV (pH 8.1, Tris, 37°) (2)

Specificity and Michaelis constants

Dihydroxyacid dehydratase is active with DHV (a valine precursor) and DHI (an isoleucine precursor). (4)

source	substrate	relative velocity	K_m(M)	conditions	
Escherichia coli	DHV	1.00	1.7×10^{-4}	pH 7.8, Tris, 37°	(4)
	DHI	0.42	8×10^{-5}		
N. crassa	DHV	1.00	1.2×10^{-3}	pH 7.7, Tris, 37°	(2)
	DHI	1.00	5.8×10^{-4}	pH 8.3, Tris, 37°	(2)
Spinacea oleracea[a]	DHV	1.00	6.3×10^{-3}	pH 8.0, Tris, 37°	(3)
	DHI	0.47	2.0×10^{-3}		
	2,3-threo-dihydroxybutyrate	0.47	-		
	2,3-erythro-dihydroxybutyrate	0.34	-		

[a] The following compounds were inactive: 2,3-threo-dihydroxynonanate and 2,3-erythro-dihydroxynonanate.

Abbreviations

DHV   2,3-dihydroxyisovalerate
DHI   2,3-dihydroxy 3-methylvalerate

References

1. Malmström, B. G. (1961) The Enzymes, 5, 465.
2. Kiritani, K., Narise, S. & Wagner, R. P. (1966), JBC, 241, 2042.
3. Kanamore, M. & Wixom, R. L. (1963) JBC, 238, 998.
4. Myers, J. W. (1961) JBC, 236, 1414.

5-DEHYDROQUINATE DEHYDRATASE

(5-Dehydroquinate hydro-lyase)

5-Dehydroquinate = 5-dehydroshikimate + H_2O

Ref.

Equilibrium constant

$$\frac{[\text{5-dehydroshikimate}]}{[\text{5-dehydroquinate}]} = 15 \quad (\text{pH } 7.4, \text{ P}_i, 29°) \tag{1}$$

Specificity

5-Dehydroquinate dehydratase is highly specific for 5-dehydroquinate. Thus the **enzy**me from Escherichia coli was inactive with quinate, malate, isocitrate and citrate (1) and that from cauliflower was inactive with 3-deoxy-2-oxoheptanoate 7-phosphate, fumarate, aconitate, malate and citrate (2).

Michaelis constants

source	substrate	$K_m(M)$	conditions	
E. coli	5-dehydroquinate	4.4×10^{-4}[a]	pH 7.4, P$_i$, 29°	(1)
Cauliflower	5-dehydroquinate	6.1×10^{-5}	pH 7.4, P$_i$.	(2)

[a] A value of 4.4×10^{-5}M is reported in reference (3).

Light absorption data

5-dehydroshikimate ε, (234 mμ) = 11,900 M^{-1} cm^{-1} (pH 7.4)   (3)

References

1. Mitsuhashi, S. & Davis, B. D. (1954) BBA, 15, 54.
2. Balinsky, D. & Davies, D. D. (1961) BJ, 80, 300.
3. Davis, B. D., Gilvarg, C. & Mitsuhashi, S. (1955) Methods in Enzymology, 2, 305.

PHOSPHOPYRUVATE HYDRATASE

(2-Phospho-D-glycerate hydro-**lyase**)

2-Phospho-D-glycerate = phospho-enolpyruvate + H_2O

Ref.

Equilibrium constant

$$\frac{[\text{phospho-enolpyruvate}]}{[\text{2-phospho-D-glycerate}]} = 6.3 \qquad 25° \qquad (2)$$

(this is a pH and metal independent constant)

Molecular weight

source	value	conditions	
Rabbit muscle	82,000 [2]	pH 7.1	(3,7)
Yeast	67,300	various	(1)

Specific activity

Yeast	84.7	2-phospho-D-glycerate	(pH 7.4, Tris)	(1)
Rabbit muscle	28.2	2-phospho-D-glycerate	(pH 7.8, imidazole)	(1)

Specificity

The enzyme isolated from yeast is highly specific **and** the
following were not attacked: D-erythro-2,3-dihydroxybutyrate 2-
phosphate, D-erythro-2,3-dihydroxybutyrate 3-phosphate, D-lactate,
D-glyceraldehyde 3-phosphate, dihydroxyacetone phosphate, β-glycerol
phosphate, β-phosphohydroxypropionate, D-phospholactate or D-3-
phosphoglycerate. (4)

The enzyme isolated from rabbit muscle attacks erythronate
3-phosphate, but the corresponding 2- and 4-phosphates are inactive. (6)

Michaelis constants

source	substrate	$\underline{V}$ (**relative**)	$K_m(M)$	conditions	
Rabbit muscle	2-phospho-D-glycerate	1.0	7×10^{-5}	pH 6.8, imi-dazole	(6)
	erythronate 3-phosphate	1.0	3×10^{-4}		
Yeast	2-phospho-D-glycerate	-	1.01×10^{-4}	pH 7.8, imi-dazole	(4)

Inhibitors

source	inhibitor	type	$K_i(M)$	conditions	
Yeast	D-phospholactate	c^*	3.5×10^{-4}	pH 7.8, imi- dazole	(4,5)
	3-phospho-D-glycerate	c^*	4.5×10^{-4}		
	P_i	NC^*	6.4×10^{-3}		
	3-hydroxypropionate phosphate	c^*	4.5×10^{-4}		
Yeast	D-erythro-2,3-dihydroxy-butyrate 2-phosphate	c^*	6.0×10^{-4}	pH 6.8, imi- dazole	(6)
	D-erythro-2,3-dihydroxy-butyrate 3-phosphate		6.3×10^{-3}		

*With respect to 2-**phospho-D-glycerate**

References

1. Malmström, B. G. (1961) The Enzymes, 5, 471.
2. Wold, F. & Ballou, C. E. (1957) JBC, 227, 301.
3. Winstead, J. A. & Wold, F. (1965) B, 4, 2145.
4. Wold, F. & Ballou, C. E. (1957) JBC, 227, 313.
5. Wold, F. & Ballou, C. E. (1959) JACS, 81, 2368.
6. Wold, F. & Barker, R. (1964) BBA, 85, 475.
7. Winstead, J. A. & Wold, F. (1964) B, 3, 791.
8. Bücher, T. (1955) Methods in Enzymology, 1. 427.

PHOSPHOGLUCONATE DEHYDRATASE

(6-Phospho-D-gluconate hydro-lyase)

6-Phospho-D-gluconate = 2-keto-3-deoxy-6-phospho-D-gluconate + H_2O

Ref.

Equilibrium constant

The reaction is essentially irreversible [F].   (3)

Michaelis constants

source	substrate	$K_m(M)$	conditions	
Pseudomonas fluorescens	6-phosphogluconate	6×10^{-4}	pH 8, imidazole	(2)

References

1. Malmström, B. G. (1961) The Enzymes, 5, 463.

2. Kovachevich, R. & Wood, W. A. (1955) JBC, 213, 745, 757.

3. Meloche, H. P. & Wood, W. A. (1966) Methods in Enzymology, 9, 653.

L-SERINE DEHYDRATASE

(L-Serine hydro-lyase (deaminating))

L-Serine + H_2O = pyruvate + NH_3 + H_2O

Ref.

Molecular weight

source	value	conditions	
Rat liver	21,000	pH 7.5	(2)
	63,500	-	(3)

Specificity

Rat liver (1250 x)	155 L-serine	(pH 8.0, P_i, 37°)	(3)
(74 x)	33 L-serine	(pH 8.3, borate, 37°)	(2)

Specificity and Michaelis constants

source	substrate	relative velocity	K_m(M)	conditions	
Rat liver	L-serine	1.00	7×10^{-2}	pH 8.3, P_i, 37°	(3)
	L-threonine	0.67	-		
	pyridoxal-phosphate	-	3×10^{-7}		
	L-serine	1.00	5.2×10^{-2}	pH 8.3, borate, 37°	(2)
	L-threonine	1.16	5.9×10^{-2}		
	DL-homocysteine[a]	0.60	2.5×10^{-2}		
	3-chloro-L-alanine	1.43	2.86×10^{-1}		

[a] In the cystathionine synthesis reaction. L-Serine dehydratase and cystathionine synthetase (4.2.1.21) activities have now been separated (3,4).

References

1. Greenberg, D. M. (1961) The Enzymes, 5, 563.

2. Nagabhushanam, A. & Greenberg, D. M. (1965) JBC, 240, 3002.

3. Nakagawa, H., Kimura, H. & Miura, S. (1967) BBRC, 28, 359.

4. Brown, F. C., Mallady, J. & Roszell, J. A. (1966) JBC, 241, 5220.

D-SERINE DEHYDRATASE

(D-Serine hydro-lyase (deaminating))

D-Serine + H_2O = pyruvate + NH_3 + H_2O

Ref.

Molecular weight

source	value	conditions	
Escherichia coli	40,000	sucrose gradient	(1)
	37,000	pH 7.4	(2)

Specific activity

E. coli	(350 x)	300 D-serine	(pH 7.8, P_i, 37°)	(1)
	(780 x)	280 D-serine	(pH 7.4, P_i, 37°)	(2)

Specificity

D-Serine dehydratase is specific for D-serine and D-threonine.
Thus, the enzyme from E. coli was inactive with the following compounds:
L-serine, L-threonine, D-cysteine, DL-homoserine, DL-tryptophan, D-alanine, D-aspartate, O-methyl-DL-serine and DL-homocysteine. Slight
activity was shown towards DL-allothreonine. (1,2)

Michaelis constants

source	substrate	$\frac{V}{(relative)}$	$K_m(M)$	conditions	
E. coli	D-serine	1.00	1.3×10^{-3}	pH 7.8, P_i, 37°	(1)
	D-threonine	0.16	3.2×10^{-3}		
	pyridoxal-phosphate	-	1.5×10^{-6}		
Earthworm	D-serine	-	4.9×10^{-4}	pH 8.3, Tris, 37°	(3)

Inhibitors

source	inhibitor	type	$K_i(M)$	conditions	
E. coli[a]	D-threonine	C(D-serine)	3.4×10^{-3}	pH 7.8, P_i, 37°	(1)
	O-methyl-DL-serine	C(D-serine)	1.3×10^{-3}		

[a] At high concentrations (0.1 M) the following compounds were inhibitory:
glycine, DL-allothreonine, β-alanine, α-D-alanine, α-methyl-DL-serine
and DL-homoserine.

References

1. Dupourque, D., Newton, A. W. & Snell, E. E. (1966) JBC, 241, 1233.
2. Labouw, R. & Robinson, W. G. (1966) JBC, 241, 1239.
3. Fujimoto, D. & Adams, E. (1965) BBA, 105, 596.

HOMOSERINE DEHYDRATASE

(L-Homoserine hydro-lyase (deaminating))

L-Homoserine + H_2O = 2-oxobutyrate + NH_3 + H_2O

Ref.

Equilibrium constant

It has been demonstrated that the enzyme can catalyze the synthesis of L-cystathionine from L-cysteine and L-homoserine as well as the decomposition of L-cystathionine to 2-oxobutyrate, NH_3 and L-cysteine. (1)

Molecular weight

source	value	conditions	
Rat liver	190,000[a]	pH 7.5	(2)

[a] 1 mole of the enzyme contains 4 moles of pyridoxal-phosphate.

Specific activity

Rat liver (580 x) 33.7[a] L-homoserine (pH 7.5, P_i, 37°)   (2)
                    12.3[a] L-cystathionine

[a] These are maximum figures.

Specificity and Michaelis constants

source	substrate	relative velocity	K_m(M)	conditions	
Rat liver[a]	L-homoserine	1.00	2×10^{-2}		
	L-cystathionine	0.80	3×10^{-3}		
	L-djenkolate	0.30	−		
	L-(and meso)-lanthionine	0.17	−	pH 7.5, P_i, 37°	(2,3)
	L-cysteine	0.05	−		
	L-serine	0.02	−		
	O-acetyl-DL-homoserine	0.02	−		
	pyridoxal-phosphate	−	4.3×10^{-7}		

Specificity and Michaelis constants contd.

source	substrate	$\dfrac{V}{\text{(relative)}}$	$K_m(M)$	conditions	
Neurospora crassa[b]	cystathionine (Li)	1.00	5.2×10^{-4}		
	cystathionine (C)	1.28	6.9×10^{-4}		
	lanthionine	1.05	3.9×10^{-4}	pH 7.3, P_i, $30°$	(4)
	meso-cystine	0.51	1.2×10^{-4}		
	L-cystine	0.24	3.2×10^{-5}		
	L-homoserine	0.11	–		

[a] The following compounds exhibited no or very low activities: L-threonine, L-allothreonine, DL-2-amino-5-hydroxyvalerate, DL-2-amino-6-hydroxycaproate, β-hydroxy-DL-aspartate, β-hydroxy-DL-glutamate, glucosamine, DL-homodjenkolate, S-methyl-L-cysteine, S-ethyl-L-cysteine, S-carbamidomethyl-L-cysteine, S-carboxypropyl-L-cysteine, L-penicillamine, DL-homocysteine, L-methionine, DL-ethionine, S-carbamidomethyl-DL-homocysteine, S-carboxyethyl-L-homocysteine and S-carboxypropyl-L-homocysteine.

[b] The following compounds exhibited no or very low activities: L-methionine, S-methyl-L-cysteine, N-succinyl-DL-homoserine, S-carboxymethylcysteine, L-cysteine, L-homocysteine, D-cystine, D-homocystine, DL-serine, D-homoserine, O-phospho-L-homoserine, DL-homoserine lactone, DL-threonine, S-carbamidomethylcysteine and L-cystine diamide.

Inhibitors

source	inhibitor	type	$K_i(M)$	conditions	
N. crassa	L-homoserine	C(cystathionine(Li))	8×10^{-3}		
	L-homoserine	C(L-cystine)	6×10^{-3}	pH 7.3, P_i, $30°$	(4)
	L-serine	C(cystathionine(Li))	1.3×10^{-2}		
	L-serine	C(L-cystine)	1.3×10^{-2}		

References

1. Greenberg, D. M. (1961) The Enzymes, 5, 563.
2. Matsuo, Y. & Greenberg, D. M. (1958) JBC, 230, 545, 561.
3. Matsuo, Y. & Greenberg, D. M. (1959) JBC, 234, 507, 516.
4. Flavin, M. & Segal, A. (1964) JBC, 239, 2220.

THREONINE DEHYDRATASE

(L-Threonine hydro-lyase (deaminating))

L-Threonine + H_2O = 2-oxobutyrate + NH_3 + H_2O

Ref.

Molecular weight

source	value	conditions	
Escherichia coli	155,000	+AMP ⎰ sucrose	(9)
(AMP activated enzyme)	78,000	no AMP ⎱ gradient	
Clostridium tetanomorphum	160,000[4]	various	(7)

Specific activity

C. tetanomorphum (700 x) 333 L-threonine (pH 9.5, Tris, 37°) (3)

Specificity and Michaelis constants

source	substrate	$\frac{V}{\text{(relative)}}$	$K_m(M)$	conditions	
E. coli	L-threonine	1.00	4.2×10^{-3}	pH 7.4, P_i, 37°	(2)
(AMP activated	L-serine	0.21	4.0×10^{-3}	+ 1×10^{-3}M AMP	
enzyme)	L-threonine	0.08	2.0×10^{-2}	pH 7.4, P_i, 37°	(2)
	L-serine	0.02	1.8×10^{-2}	no AMP	
	5'-AMP	1.00	$5 \quad \times 10^{-4}$		
	5'-GMP	0.66	$4 \quad \times 10^{-3}$	pH 7.4, P_i, 37°	
	5'-CMP	0.80	$5 \quad \times 10^{-3}$	+ 1×10^{-2}M L-	(2)
	5'-IMP	0.80	$1 \quad \times 10^{-2}$	threonine	
	5'-UMP	0.66	$1 \quad \times 10^{-2}$		
C. tetanomorphum	L-threonine	1.00	3.7×10^{-2}	pH 8.4, Tris, 37° no ADP	(4)
		1.19	3.5×10^{-3}	pH 8.4, Tris, 37° ADP = 1×10^{-3}M	(4)
	ADP	-	2.3×10^{-5}	pH 8.4, Tris, 37° L-threonine = 1×10^{-3}M	(4)
Salmonella typhimurium	L-threonine	-	9.2×10^{-3}	pH 8.1, P_i, 30°	(5)
Sheep liver	L-threonine	1.00	2.9×10^{-2}	pH 7.2, 37°	(6)
	L-serine	0.03	-	pH 7.2, 37°	(6)

Two distinct L-threonine deaminases are present in E. coli (1). One of these is specifically activated by several ribonucleoside 5'-monophosphates but deoxyribonucleotides, nucleoside polyphosphates and nucleoside monophosphates linked at positions other than 5' are ineffective (2). The other enzyme (biosynthetic L-threonine deaminase) is subject to end-product inhibition by isoleucine (8) and exhibits complex kinetics (10).

The kinetics exhibited by the enzyme isolated from C. tetanomorphum are complex. In the presence of ADP, normal Michaelis-Menton kinetics are observed but in its absence plots of reaction rates against L-threonine concentrations give sigmoid curves. ATP abolishes the effect

Specificity and Michaelis constants contd.	Ref.
of ADP.	(3,4)

The enzyme isolated from S. typhimurium is also subject to end-product inhibition by L-isoleucine. (5)

The enzyme (sheep liver) does not attack D-serine, D-threonine, DL-allo-threonine, DL-homocysteine, DL-cysteine or β-phenylserine. (6)

Inhibitors

source	inhibitor	type	$K_i(M)$	conditions	
E. coli	D-threonine	C(L-threonine)	5.6×10^{-2}	pH 7.4, P_i, $37°$ no AMP(a)	(2)
		C(L-serine)	6.3×10^{-2}		
	D-serine	C(L-threonine)	4.5×10^{-2}		
		C(L-serine)	4.5×10^{-2}		
S. typhimurium	allothreonine	C(L-threonine)	7×10^{-5}	pH 8.5, P_i, $\sim 25°$	(5)
	2-oxoglutarate	C(L-threonine)	1.48×10^{-1}		
	ammonia	C(L-threonine)	9.5×10^{-2}		
C. tetanomorphum	D-threonine	C(L-threonine)	7.5×10^{-2}	pH 8.4, Tris, $37°$ ADP = 1×10^{-3}M	(4)
		C(L-threonine)	1.3×10^{-2}	pH 8.4, Tris, $37°$ no ADP	(4)
	ATP	-	7×10^{-5}	pH 8.4, Tris, $37°$ L-threonine = 1×10^{-3}M	(4)

(a)The K_i values were not appreciably effected by the presence of AMP.

References

1. Greenberg, D. M. (1961) The Enzymes, 5, 563.
2. Hirata, M., Tokushige, M., Inagaki, A. & Hayaishi, O. (1965) JBC, 240, 1711.
3. Whiteley, H. R. & Tahara, M. (1966) JBC, 241, 4881.
4. Nakazawa, A. & Hayaishi, O. (1967) JBC, 242, 1146.
5. Maeba, P. & Sanwal, B. D. (1966) B, 5, 525.
6. Sayre, F. W. & Greenberg, D. M. (1956) JBC, 220, 787.
7. Whiteley, H. R. (1966) JBC, 241, 4890.
8. Umbarger, H. E. & Brown, B. (1957) J. Bacteriol., 73, 105.
9. Phillips, A. T. & Wood, W. A. (1964) BBRC, 15, 530.
10. Changeux, J. P. (1961) Cold Spring Harbor Symp. Quant. Biol., 26, 313.

ENOYL-CoA HYDRATASE

(L-3-Hydroxyacyl-CoA hydro-lyase)

An L-3-hydroxyacyl-CoA = a 2,3-(or 3,4-)trans-enoyl-CoA + H_2O

Ref.

Equilibrium constant

$$\frac{[\text{crotonoyl-CoA}]\,[\text{H}_2\text{O}]}{[\text{L}(+)\text{-3-hydroxybutyryl-CoA}]} = 16.2 \quad \text{(independent of pH)} \qquad (1,3)$$

Molecular weight

source	value	conditions	
Ox liver	210,000	light scattering	(2)

Specific activity

Ox liver	(810 x)	3480 crotonoyl-CoA (pH 7.5, Tris, 25°)		(2)
		6700 crotonoyl-CoA (pH 9.4, 25°)		(2)

Specificity and Michaelis constants

Enoyl-CoA hydratase has several catalytic activities. Thus, it is at once a hydratase, a positional isomerase, a thioltranscrotonylase, a racemase and an irreversible cis-trans isomerase. (1)

As a hydratase the enzyme exhibits low specificity and acts on the CoA and pantetheine esters of ethylenic and 3-hydroxy fatty acids. It hydrates both the cis and trans isomers of 2-ethylenic acyl-CoA compounds of chain lengths from C_4 to at least C_9. Substitution at the ethylenic bond decreases the reactivity of the substrate. The enzyme is without activity on the 4-ethylenic bond of CoA esters. (3)

source	substrate	relative velocity	K_m(M)	conditions	
Ox	trans-crotonoyl-CoA	1.00	2.0×10^{-5}		
liver	trans-2-pentenoyl-CoA	0.77	-		
	cis-isocrotonoyl-CoA	0.30	-		
	cis-2-hexenoyl-CoA	0.20	-	pH 7.5,	(3)
	trans-2-hexenoyl-CoA	0.15	2.5×10^{-5}	Tris, 25°	
	3-methylcrotonoyl-CoA	0.14	-		
	vinylacetyl-CoA	0.01	-		
	trans-3-hexenoyl-CoA	0.01	-		

Light absorption data

Crotonoyl-CoA and higher 2-ethylenic acyl-CoA compounds have an absorption band at 263 mμ ($\varepsilon = 6700$ $M^{-1}cm^{-1}$). (2)

References

1. Stern, J. R. (1961) The Enzymes, 5, 511.
2. Stern, J. R., Del Campillo, A. & Raw, I. (1956) JBC, 218, 971.
3. Stern, J. R. & Del Campillo, A. (1956) JBC, 218, 985.

METHYLGLUTACONYL-CoA HYDRATASE

(3-Hydroxy-3-methylglutaryl-CoA hydro-lyase)

3-Hydroxy-3-methylglutaryl-CoA =

trans-3-methylglutaconyl-CoA + H_2O

Ref.

Equilibrium constant

The reaction is reversible.   (1)

Specificity

The enzyme from sheep liver is highly specific. The following compounds were inactive in the place of 3-hydroxy-3-methylglutaryl-CoA: 3-hydroxy-3-methylglutaryl-pantetheine, crotonoyl-CoA and 3-methylcrotonoyl-CoA.   (1)

Michaelis constants

source	substrate	$K_m(M)$	conditions	
Ox liver	3-hydroxy-3-methyl-glutaryl-CoA	1×10^{-4}	pH 7.16, P_i, 18°	(1)

Light absorption data

trans-3-methylglutaconyl-CoA $\varepsilon,(268\ m\mu) = 11,300\ M^{-1}\ cm^{-1}$ (pH 7.16) (1)

References

1. Hilz, H., Knappe, J., Ringelmann, E. & Lynen, F. (1958) BZ, 329, 476.

IMIDAZOLEGLYCEROLPHOSPHATE DEHYDRATASE

(D-erythro-Imidazoleglycerolphosphate hydro-lyase)

D-erythro-Imidazoleglycerol phosphate =

imidazoleacetol phosphate + H_2O

Ref.

Equilibrium constant

The reaction is essentially irreversible [F].   (1)

Molecular weight

source	value	conditions	
Salmonella typhimurium	145,000	sucrose gradient	(2)

Michaelis constants

source	substrate	$K_m(M)$	conditions	
Neurospora crassa	D-erythro-imidazole-glycerol phosphate	2.4×10^{-4}	pH 7.5, triethanol-amine, 30°	(1)

The enzyme requires Mn^{2+} (Mg^{2+} is inactive) and a reducing agent (mercaptoethanol) for activity.   (1)

Light absorption data

imidazoleacetol phosphate ε, (280 mμ) = 7860 M^{-1} cm^{-1} (pH 14)   (1)

References

1. Ames, B. N. (1957) JBC, 228, 131.

2. Whitfield, H. J. Jr., Smith, D. W. E. & Martin, R. G. (1964) JBC, 239, 3288.

TRYPTOPHAN SYNTHASE

(L-Serine hydro-lyase (adding indole))

L-Serine + indole = L-tryptophan + H_2O

Ref.

Equilibrium constant

The reactions catalyzed by this enzyme (a, b and c) are given in the specificity section. Reactions b and c are essentially irreversible[F] but reaction a is freely reversible.

(3,8)

Molecular weight

source		value	conditions	
Escherichia coli	α subunit[a]	29,000	various	(1,2)
	$β_2$ subunit[b]	117,000[2]	various	(1,2)
Neurospora crassa[c]		135,000[4]	-	(4)

[a] also called A protein
[b] also called B protein
[c] enzymically active components analogous to the α and $β_2$ subunits of E. coli have not been obtained.

Specific activity

source	specific activity	sub-strate	reaction	conditions	
E. coli ($α_2$ $β_2$ complex)	0.64	In GP	a	pH 7.8, Tris, 37°	
(100 x)	20.0	indole	b	pH 7.8, Tris, 37°	(8)
	5.8	In GP	c	pH 7.0, Tris, 23°	
N. crassa (125 x)	4.2	indole	b	pH 6.7, P_i, 37°	(5)

Specificity

The enzyme isolated from E. coli is composed of a complex of sub-units, $α_2$ $β_2$. Subunit α catalyzes reaction a and subunit $β_2$ reaction b (see below). Subunit $β_2$ also catalyzes the deamination of L-serine, L-threonine and L-cysteine but the complex does not. On combination, the complex $α_2$ $β_2$ catalyzes reactions a and b 30 - 100 times as effectively as the individual subunits and, in addition, reaction c which is thought to be the physiologically significant one.

a In GP   = indole + 3-phosphoglyceraldehyde
b Indole + serine = tryptophan + H_2O
c In GP + serine = tryptophan + 3-phosphoglyceraldehyde

Reactions b and c require pyridoxal-phosphate but reaction a does not.

(1,2,9)

The enzyme (N. crassa) also catalyzes reactions a, b and c. It is highly specific for L-serine in reaction b which cannot be replaced by D-serine, glycine, DL-alanine, L-cysteine, L-cystine, DL-threonine, DL-methionine, L-aspartate, L-glutamate, acetate, pyruvate

Specificity contd.   Ref.

or maleate. In the same reaction, indole can be replaced by 6-
methylindole or 7-hydroxyindole.   (3,4,6)

Michaelis constants

source	substrate	$K_m(M)$	reaction[a]	conditions	
E. coli $(\alpha_2\,\beta_2)$	indole	1.65×10^{-4}	b		
	L-serine	2.46×10^{-2}	b		
	pyridoxal-phosphate	1.1×10^{-6}	b		
β_2	indole	2.3×10^{-4}	b	pH 7.8, Tris, 37°	(8)
	L-serine	1.7×10^{-2}	b		
	pyridoxal-phosphate	2.25×10^{-5}	b		
	L-serine	1.45×10^{-2}	-[b]	pH 7.8, Tris, 37°	(9)
α	In GP	4.7×10^{-4}	a	pH 6.5, P_i, 37°	(7)
N. crassa	In GP	1.4×10^{-4}	a	pH 6.1, P_i, 37°	(3)
	indole	5.6×10^{-5}	b		
	L-serine	3.4×10^{-3}	b	pH 7.8, P_i, 37°	(6)
	pyridoxamine-phosphate	$\sim 1 \times 10^{-6}$	b		

[a] The reactions catalyzed (a, b or c) are given in the specificity
section.

[b] L-serine = pyruvate + NH_3. This reaction is completely inhibited
in the presence of the α subunit.

Abbreviations

In GP   indoleglycerol phosphate

References

1. Reed, L. J. & Cox, D. J. (1966) Ann. Rev. Biochem., 35 (1), 75.
2. Creighton, T. E. & Yanofsky, C. (1966) JBC, 241, 980.
3. Carsiotis, M. & Suskind, S. R. (1964) JBC, 239, 4227.
4. Carsiotis, M., Appella, E., Provost, P., Germershausen, J. &
    Suskind, S. R. (1965) BBRC, 18, 877.
5. Ensign, S., Kaplan, S. & Bonner, D. M. (1964) BBA, 81, 357.
6. Yanofsky, C. (1955) Methods in Enzymology, 2, 233.
7. Hardman, J. K. & Yanofsky, C. (1965) JBC, 240, 725.
8. Hatanaka, M., White, E. A., Horibata, K. & Crawford, I. P.
    (1962) ABB, 97, 596.
9. Crawford, I. P. & Ito, J. (1964) PNAS, 51, 390.

CYSTEINE SYNTHASE

(L-Serine hydro-lyase (adding hydrogen sulphide))

$$L\text{-Serine} + H_2S = L\text{-cysteine} + H_2O$$

Ref.

Specificity

Neurospora crassa is thought to possess separate enzymes responsible for the synthesis of cysteine (from serine and H_2S) and of homocysteine (from homoserine and H_2S). Neither enzyme could utilize phosphohomoserine, phosphoserine or threonine as the amino acid substrate. (1)

Michaelis constants

source	substrate	$K_m(M)$	conditions	
N. crassa	L-serine[a]	7.8×10^{-4}	pH 8.2, PP_i, 37°	(1)
	L-homoserine[b]	5.5×10^{-4}		
Hen liver	DL-serine	3.5×10^{-3}	pH 9.0, Tris, 38°	(2)
Baker's yeast	pyridoxal-phosphate	3.1×10^{-5}	pH 8.0, Tris, 37°	(3)

[a] Cysteine synthase activity.
[b] Homocysteine synthase activity.

Inhibitors

source	inhibitor	type	$K_i(M)$	conditions	
N. crassa	L-methionine[a]	NC(L-serine or L-homoserine)	1.8×10^{-2}[b] 2.2×10^{-2}[c]	pH 8.2, PP_i, 37°	(1)
Hen liver	L-cysteine	C(DL-serine)	8×10^{-3}	pH 9.1, Tris, 38°	(2)

[a] End product feedback inhibitor
[b] Cysteine synthase activity
[c] Homocysteine synthase activity

Both cysteine and homocysteine inhibit their own reactions and each others synthesis. (1)

References

1. Wiebers, J. L. & Garner, H. R. (1967) JBC, 242, 12.
2. Sentenac, A. & Fromageot, P. (1964) BBA, 81, 289.
3. Schlossmann, K., Brüggemann, J. & Lynen, F. (1962) BZ, 336, 258.

PORPHOBILINOGEN SYNTHASE

(5-Aminolaevulinate hydro-lyase (adding 5-aminolaevulinate and cyclizing))

2 5-Aminolaevulinate = porphobilinogen + 2 H_2O

Ref.

Specificity

The enzyme from ox liver could not utilize aminoacetone, 2,5-diaminolaevulinate or 6-amino-5-oxohexanoate in the place of 5-aminolaevulinate.

(4)

Michaelis constants

source	substrate	$K_m(M)$	conditions	
Saccharomyces cerevisiae	5-amino-laevulinate	1.5×10^{-3}	pH 9.6, glycine, 55°	(1)
Rhodopseudomonas spheroides	5-amino-laevulinate	3.0×10^{-4}	pH 8, carbonate, 34°	(2)
Ox liver	5-amino-laevulinate	1.6×10^{-4}	pH 6.7, P_i, 38°	(4)

Inhibitors

The enzyme from R. spheroides is inhibited by haemin. (3)

The enzyme from ox liver is inhibited by Tris. The inhibition is abolished by P_i or arsenate. (4)

References

1. De Barreiro, O. L. C. (1967) BBA, 139, 479.

2. Shemin, D. (1962) Methods in Enzymology, 5, 883.

3. Burnham, B. F. & Lascelles, J. (1963) BJ, 87, 462.

4. Gibson, K. D., Neuberger, A. & Scott, J. J. (1955) BJ, 61, 618.

AMINODEOXYGLUCONATE DEHYDRATASE

(2-Amino-2-deoxy-D-gluconate hydro-lyase (deaminating))

2-Amino-2-deoxy-D-gluconate + H_2O =

2-keto-3-deoxy-D-gluconate + NH_3 + H_2O

<u>Ref.</u>

Equilibrium constant

The reaction is essentially irreversible [F].   (1,2)

Specificity

The enzyme (unidentified organism) was unable to utilize the D-
or L-isomers of serine or threonine in the place of 2-amino-2-deoxy-D-
gluconate. It requires pyridoxal-phosphate for activity.   (1,2)

Michaelis constant

source	substrate	$K_m(M)$	conditions	
"unidentified organism"	2-amino-2-deoxy-D-gluconate	8.8×10^{-3}	pH 8.0, P_i, 37°	(1,2)

References

1. Merrick, J. M. & Roseman, S. (1960) JBC, 235, 1274.
2. Merrick, J. M. & Roseman, S. (1966) Methods in Enzymology, 9, 657.

MALONATE SEMIALDEHYDE DEHYDRATASE

(Malonate-semialdehyde hydro-lyase)

Malonate semialdehyde =

acetylene monocarboxylate + H_2O

Specificity

The enzyme from Pseudomonas sp. is highly specific for acetylene monocarboxylate which could not be replaced by acetylenedicarboxylate, propynol or ethynylbenzene. (1)

Michaelis constants

source	substrate	$K_m(M)$	conditions	
Pseudomonas sp.	acetylene mono-carboxylate	8×10^{-5}	pH 8.0, P_i, 23°	(1)

References

1. Yamada, E. W. & Jakoby, W. B. (1959) JBC, 234, 941.

PROPANEDIOL DEHYDRATASE

(Propanediol hydro-lyase)

Propanediol = propionaldehyde + H_2O

Ref.

Equilibrium constant

The reaction is essentially irreversible [F].　　　　　　(1)

Specific activity

Aerobacter aerogenes (200 x) 47 propanediol (pH 8.0, P_i, 37°)　　(1)

Specificity

Propanediol dehydratase catalyzes the following reactions:

propanediol   = propionaldehyde + H_2O

ethylene glycol   = acetaldehyde + H_2O

The following compounds were inactive: glycerol; ribitol; 1,2,4-butanetriol; 2,3-butanediol; 1,2-dihydroxy-2-methylpropane; 1,2-butylene glycol; cyclohexanediol; mercaptoethanol; isopropanolamine; ethanolamine; chloroethanol; fluoroethanol; lactaldehyde and 1,2-dithiopropane.　　　　　　(1)

The enzyme requires coenzyme B_{12} for activity.　　　　　(1)

Inhibitors

The enzyme is inhibited by cyano- and hydroxocobalamin.　　(1)

References

1. Lee H. A. Jr. & Abeles, R. H. (1963) JBC, 238, 2367.

GALACTARATE DEHYDRATASE

(Galactarate hydro-lyase)

Galactarate = 5-keto-4-deoxy-D-glucarate + H_2O

Specificity

The enzyme (Escherichia coli) is specific for galactarate. Thus, it cannot utilize D-glucarate, mannarate, and neither D- nor L-idarate. Specificity studies are difficult, however, because of the lability of the enzyme in the absence of its substrate. (1)

Michaelis constants

source	substrate	K_m(M)	conditions
E. coli	galactarate	4×10^{-4}	pH 8, Tris, 30°	(1)

References

1. Blumenthal, H. J. & Jepson, T. (1966) Methods in Enzymology, 9, 665.

D-GLUCARATE DEHYDRATASE

(D-Glucarate hydro-lyase)

D-Glucarate = 5-keto-4-deoxy-D-glucarate (85%) + 2-keto-
3-deoxy-D-glucarate (15%) + H_2O

Ref.

Equilibrium constant

The reaction is essentially irreversible [F].   (1)

Specificity

The enzyme (Escherichia coli) is highly specific: only D-
glucarate (saccharate) and L-idarate are cleaved. The following
are inactive: galactarate, D-mannarate, D-idarate, xylarate, D-,
L- and meso-tartrate, D-glucosaminate, DL-threonine, L-serine,
D-gulonate, D-gluconate, D-galactonate, L-galactonate, α-D-
glucoheptonate and 6-phospho-D-gluconate.   (1)

Michaelis constants

source	substrate	$K_m(M)$	conditions	
E. coli	D-glucarate	8×10^{-4}	pH 8, Tris, 30°	(1)

References

1. Blumenthal, H. J. (1966) Methods in Enzymology, 9, 660.

L-(+)-TARTRATE DEHYDRATASE

(L-(+)-Tartrate hydro-lyase)

L-(+)-Tartrate = oxaloacetate + H_2O

Ref.

Molecular weight

source	value	conditions	
Pseudomonas putida	145,000 [4]	pH 7.0	(1,2)

Specificity

The enzyme (P. putida) is specific for L-(+)-tartrate; neither D-(-)-tartrate nor mesotartrate are active. (1)

Michaelis constants

source	substrate	$K_m(M)$	conditions	
P. putida	L-(+)-tartrate	8×10^{-4} [a]		
		and 2×10^{-3} [a]	pH 8.5, Tris, 25°	(1)
		2×10^{-3} [b]		

[a] In the absence of air
[b] In the presence of air

Inhibitors

source	inhibitor	type	$K_i(M)$	conditions	
P. putida	mesotartrate	C (L-(+)-tartrate)	2×10^{-3} [a]		
			and 8×10^{-3} [a]	pH 8.5, Tris, 25°	(1)
			2×10^{-3} [b]		

[a] In the absence of air
[b] In the presence of air

References
1. Hurlbert, R. E. & Jakoby, W. B. (1966) Methods in Enzymology, 9, 680.
2. Hurlbert, R. E. & Jakoby, W. B. (1964) JBC, 240, 2772.

MESACONASE

((+)-Citramalate hydro-lyase)

(+)-Citramalate = mesaconate + H_2O

Ref.

Equilibrium constant

The reaction is reversible. The reverse reaction is favoured. (1)

Molecular weight

source		value	conditions	
Clostridium	component I*	20 - 40,000	Sephadex G100,	
tetanomorphum	component II*	> 100,000	pH 7.0	(1)

---

*Column chromatography on DEAE-cellulose separates the enzyme
into two protein components (I and II) both of which are required
for activity.

Light absorption data

Mesaconate $\varepsilon,(250 \text{ m}\mu) = 2260 \text{ M}^{-1}\text{cm}^{-1}$ (pH 8.0) (1)

References

1. Blair, A. H. & Barker, H. A. (1966) JBC, 241, 400.

TRYPTOPHANASE

L-Tryptophan + H_2O = pyruvate + NH_3 + indole

Ref.

Equilibrium constant

The reaction is essentially irreversible [F].   (1)

Molecular weight

source	value	conditions	
Escherichia coli	281,000	pH 7.0	(1)
	490,000	pH 6.8	(3)
	220,000 [4]	pH 8.0	(4)

Specific activity

E. coli   (9 x)   26 L-tryptophan[*] (pH 8.0, P_i, 37°)   (1)

Bacillus alvei (3400 x)   14 L-tryptophan[*] (pH 8.0, P_i, 37°)   (2)

_____

[*]In the α,β-elimination reaction (I).

Specificity

The enzyme (E. coli) catalyzes several α,β-elimination and β-replacement reactions described by equations (I) and (II), respectively:

$$RCH_2CHNH_2COOH + H_2O = RH + NH_3 + CH_3COCOOH \qquad (I)$$

$$RCH_2CHNH_2COOH + R'H = R'CH_2CHNH_2COOH + RH \qquad (II)$$

Several amino acids can serve as substrates of these reactions: tryptophan, 4-,5-, or 6-methyltryptophan, cysteine, S-methylcysteine or serine (R'H = indole).   (1)

The enzyme isolated from B. alvei is not inhibited by cysteine, serine or threonine and it is thought, therefore, that this enzyme does not catalyze α,β-elimination reactions with these amino acids as substrates.   (2)

Both enzymes require pyridoxal-phosphate for activity.   (1,2)

Michaelis constants

source	substrate	reaction	$V^{(a)}$	$K_m(M)$	conditions
E. coli	L-tryptophan	(I)	26	3.3×10^{-4}	
	L-serine	(I)	14	1.6×10^{-1}	
	L-cysteine	(I)	10	1.1×10^{-2}	pH 8.0, P_i, (1)
	L-serine$^{(b)}$	(II)	10	1.6×10^{-1}	$37°$
	L-cysteine$^{(b)}$	(II)	7-8	$9\text{-}10 \times 10^{-3}$	
	indole$^{(c)}$	(II)	12	1.1×10^{-4}	
	indole$^{(d)}$	(II)	8	1.3×10^{-4}	
B. alvei	L-tryptophan	(I)	-	2.72×10^{-4}	pH 8.0, P_i, (2) $37°$

$^{(a)}$ μmoles min^{-1}mg^{-1}
$^{(b)}$ with indole as cosubstrate
$^{(c)}$ with L-serine as cosubstrate
$^{(d)}$ with L-cysteine as cosubstrate

Inhibitors

source	inhibitor	type	reaction	$K_i(M)$	conditions
E. coli	indole	C (tryptophan)	(I)	5×10^{-5}	pH 8.0,
	S-methyl-L-cysteine	C (tryptophan)	(I)	8.8×10^{-3}	P_i, (1) $37°$
B. alvei	L-phenylalanine	C (tryptophan)	(I)	3.23×10^{-3}	pH 8.0,
	anthranilate	C (tryptophan)	(I)	1.07×10^{-4}	P_i, (2)
	kynurenine	C (tryptophan)	(I)	7.1×10^{-4}	$37°$

References

1. Newton, W. A., Morino, Y. & Snell, E. E. (1965) JBC, 240, 1211.
2. Hoch, J. A., Simpson, F. J. & DeMoss, R. D. (1966) B, 5, 2229.
3. Burns, R. O. & DeMoss, R. D. (1962) BBA, 65, 233.
4. Morino, Y. & Snell, E. E. (1967) JBC, 242, 5591.

PECTATE LYASE

(Poly-α-1,4-D-galacturonide lyase)

Eliminates Δ-4,5-D-galacturonate residues from pectate,

thus bringing about depolymerization

Ref.

Specificity

Pectate lyase from Aspergillus fonsecaeus attacks pectin by a trans elimination process. The enzyme is specific for polymeric methyl galacturonate residues and is not active with unesterified galacturonans or polymers containing glucuronate or mannuronate. Pectate lyase catalyzed the lysis of polymethyl polygalacturonate methyl glycoside (1.00); pectin, 68% methylated (0.75); hexamethyl hexagalacturonate (0.026); pentamethyl pentagalacturonate (0.0065) and tetramethyl tetragalacturonate (0.00049). Trimethyl trigalacturonate and dimethyl digalacturonate were not hydrolyzed. Exhaustive treatment of polymethyl polygalacturonate with the enzyme yielded mainly the methyl esters of unsaturated tri-, tetra - and penta galacturonate, small amounts of unsaturated diester and trace amounts of longer chain esters.(1,2)

References

1. Edstrom, R. D. & Phaff, H. J. (1964) JBC, 239, 2409.
2. Albersheim, P. (1966) Methods in Enzymology, 8, 628.

ASPARTATE AMMONIA-LYASE

(L-Aspartate ammonia-lyase)

L-Aspartate = fumarate + NH_3

Ref.

Equilibrium constant

$$\frac{[\text{fumarate}][NH_4^+]}{[\text{L-aspartate}]} = 2.3 \times 10^{-2} \quad (pH\ 6.8,\ P_i,\ 37^o) \qquad (2)$$

Molecular weight

source	value	conditions	
Enterobacter aerogenes	180,000 [4]	sucrose gradient	(3)

Specificity and kinetic properties

The enzyme is highly specific for L-aspartate and fumarate. Thus, that from Lactobacillus helveticus (or Pseudomonas fluorescens) was inactive towards D-aspartate, L-cysteate, 2,3-diaminosuccinate and the protein amino acids. (5)

The kinetics of the enzyme from E. aerogenes are complex. At pH 6.0 typical Michaelis-Menton kinetics were observed with L-aspartate as the substrate. At higher pH values homotropic effects of the substrate gave rise to sigmoid curves (from substrate versus velocity plots). Several mononucleotides exhibited heterotropic effects. (3)

source	substrate	relative velocity	K_m(M)	conditions	
E. aerogenes	L-aspartate	–	1.5×10^{-3}	pH 7.0, Tris, 30°	(3)
Bacillus cadavaris	L-aspartate hydroxylamine[a]	1.00 0.80	3×10^{-2} 3×10^{-2}	} pH 6.8, P_i, 28°	(4)

[a] In the reaction fumarate + hydroxylamine = N-hydroxyaspartate.

Inhibitors

source	inhibitor	type	K_i(M)	conditions	
B. cadavaris	L-aspartate hydroxylamine	C(fumarate) C(aspartate)	8×10^{-3} 3×10^{-2}	} pH 6.8, P_i, 28°	(4)

Light absorption data

Fumarate ε, (240 mμ) = 2530 M^{-1} cm^{-1} (pH 6.8) (4)

References

1. Ellfolk, N. (1956) Ann. Acad. Sci. Finnicae, Ser. A, II, 79, 1.
2. Williams, V. R. & McIntyre, R. T. (1955) JBC, 217, 467.
3. Williams, V. R. & Lartigue, D. J. (1967) JBC, 242, 2973.
4. Emery, T. F. (1963) B, 2, 1041.
5. Virtanen, A. I. & Ellfolk, N. C. (1955) Methods in Enzymology, 2, 386.

METHYLASPARTATE AMMONIA-LYASE

(L-threo-3-Methylaspartate ammonia-lyase)

L-threo-3-Methylaspartate = mesaconate + NH_3

Ref.

Equilibrium constant

$$\frac{[\text{mesaconate}]\,[NH_3]}{[\text{L-threo-3-methylaspartate}]} = 0.3 \text{ M (pH 9.7, ethanolamine, } 25^\circ) \quad (1)$$

Molecular weight

source	value	conditions	
Clostridium tetanomorphum	100,000[2]	pH 5.9-9.7	(2)

Specific activity

C. tetanomorphum (80 x) 390[a] methylaspartate (pH 9.7, ethanolamine, 25° + Mg^{2+} + K^+) (2)

[a] A maximum value of 600 is reported in reference (1).

Specificity

The enzyme (C. tetanomorphum) attacks L-threo-3-methylaspartate, L-erythro-3-methylaspartate and L-aspartate in the forward reaction but it is without effect on the α-D-enantiomorphs of methyl-aspartate. Mesaconate can be replaced by fumarate but ammonia cannot be replaced by methylamine or ethylamine in the reverse reaction. (1)

The mechanism of the reaction is discussed in reference (3).

Michaelis constants

source	substrate	V (relative)	K_m(M)	conditions	
C. tetano-morphum	L-threo-3-methylaspartate	1.000	6.5×10^{-4}		
	L-erythro-3-methylaspartate	0.009	6.5×10^{-4}		
	L-aspartate	0.007	2.3×10^{-3}	pH 9.76, ethanol-amine, 25°	(1)
	mesaconate	-	2.5×10^{-3}		
	fumarate	-	1.1×10^{-2}		
	NH_4Cl	-	7.5×10^{-2}		
	Mg^{2+}	-	1.2×10^{-4}		
	K^+	-	3×10^{-3}		

References

1. Barker, H. A., Smyth, R. D., Bright, H. J. & Ingraham, L. L. (1962) Methods in Enzymology, 5, 827.
2. Hsiang, M. W. & Bright, H. J. (1967) JBC, 242, 3079.
3. Bright, H. J. (1964) JBC, 239, 2307.

HISTIDINE AMMONIA-LYASE

(L-Histidine ammonia-lyase)

L-Histidine = urocanate + NH$_3$

Ref.

Equilibrium constant

$$\frac{[\text{urocanate}]\,[\text{NH}_4^+]}{[\text{L-histidine}]} \quad = \quad 3 \quad (\text{pH 8.0, Tris-acetate}) \tag{1}$$

Molecular weight

source	value	conditions	
Pseudomonas fluorescens	198,000	sucrose gradient	(1)

Specific activity

P. fluorescens (125 x) 35 L-histidine (pH 8.0, Tris-acetate) (1)

Specificity

The enzyme (P. fluorescens) appears to be specific for L-histidine. (2)

In addition to the deamination reaction, the enzyme catalyzes two partial reactions, a hydrogen and a urocanate exchange into histidine. Other amino acids than histidine do not undergo hydrogen exchange and unsaturated acids other than urocanate do not accept the amino group of histidine. (4)

Michaelis constants

source	substrate	$K_m(M)$	conditions	
P. fluorescens	L-histidine	$0.9-2.4 \times 10^{-2}$	pH 8.5-9.0, P$_i$, Tris, or carbonate, 25°	(4)
P. fluorescens	L-histidine	8.9×10^{-3}	pH 9.2, PP$_i$, 25°	(3)

Inhibitors

source	inhibitor[a]	$K_i(M)$	conditions
P. fluorescens	L-cysteine	8.0×10^{-4}	
	D-cysteine	6.0×10^{-4}	
	L-cysteinylglycine	2.0×10^{-3}	
	L-cysteine methyl ester	8.0×10^{-4}	
	DL-homocysteine	1.2×10^{-3}	pH 9.2,
	glycine	1.0×10^{-2}	PP_i, 25° (3)
	mercaptoethylamine	4.6×10^{-3}	
	thienylalanine	2.4×10^{-2}	
	biguanine	2.6×10^{-3}	
	EDTA	1.0×10^{-5}	

[a]
   C(L-histidine)

   The following compounds did not inhibit: cysteate, methionine, serine and alanine. (3)

Light absorption data

   Urocanate, $\varepsilon(277\ m\mu) = 18,800\ M^{-1}\ cm^{-1}$ (pH 8.0)   (1)

References

1. Williams, V. R. & Hiroms, J. M. (1967) BBA, 139, 214.

2. Tabor, H. & Mehler, A. H. (1955) Methods in Enzymology, 2, 228.

3. Peterkofsky, A. & Mehler, L. N. (1963) BBA, 73, 159.

4. Peterkofsky, A. (1962) JBC, 237, 787.

FORMIMINOTETRAHYDROFOLATE CYCLODEAMINASE

(5-Formiminotetrahydrofolate ammonia-lyase (cyclizing))

5-Formiminotetrahydrofolate =

5,10-methenyltetrahydrofolate + NH_3

Ref.

Equilibrium constant

The reaction may be reversible. The forward reaction is strongly favoured. (2)

Molecular weight

source	value	conditions	
Clostridium cylindrosporum	38,000	pH 7.5	(2)

Specific activity

C. cylindrosporum (40 x) 720 5-formiminoTHF (pH 7.0, maleate, 25°)(2)

Specificity and Michaelis constants

source	substrate	$\frac{V}{(relative)}$	$K_m(M)$	conditions	
C. cylindrosporum	5-formiminoTHF	1.00	3.1×10^{-5}		
	5-formiminotetra-hydropteroyl-L-aspartate	0.21	4.0×10^{-5}	pH 7.0, maleate, 25°	(2)
	5-formiminotetra-hydropteroyltri-L-glutamate (γ-linkage)	3.3	2.9×10^{-5}		
Hog liver	5-formiminoTHF	— —	$2.6 \times 10^{-5(a)}$ $1.75 \times 10^{-4(b)}$	pH 6.5, maleate	(4,5)
	K^+	—	1.3×10^{-4}		

[a] In the presence of K^+
[b] In the absence of K^+

Specificity and Michaelis constants contd.

The enzyme also attacked the following compounds: tetrahydropteroyl-D-glutamate, tetrahydropteroate and tetrahydropteroyltri-L-glutamate. 2-Hydroxy-2-deaminotetrahydrofolate was inactive. (2)

Inhibitors

source	inhibitor[a]	K_i (M)	conditions
C. cylindrosporum	4-amino-4-deoxyfolate	9.4×10^{-6}	
	4-amino-4-deoxy-10-methylfolate	8.2×10^{-6}	
	4-amino-4-deoxytetra-hydrofolate	1.4×10^{-7}	
	4-amino-4-deoxy-10-methyltetrahydrofolate	1.1×10^{-4}	pH 7.0, maleate, 25o (2)
	tetrahydrofolate	4.0×10^{-6}	
	10-methyltetrahydro-folate	2.4×10^{-5}	
	2-hydroxy-2-deamino-tetrahydrofolate	1.02×10^{-4}	

[a] C(5-formiminoTHF)

Light absorption data

5,10-methenyltetrahydrofolate ε, (350 mμ) =

$24,900 \ M^{-1} \ cm^{-1}$ (in acid solution) (4)

Abbreviations

5-formiminoTHF   5-formiminotetrahydrofolate

References

1. Rabinowitz, J. C. (1960) The Enzymes, 2, 222.
2. Uyeda, K. & Rabinowitz, J. C. (1967) JBC, 242, 24.
3. Uyeda, K. & Rabinowitz, J. C. (1965) JBC, 240, 1701.
4. Tabor, H. (1962) Methods in Enzymology, 5, 789.
5. Tabor, H. & Wyngarden, L. (1959) JBC, 234, 1830.

PHENYLALANINE AMMONIA-LYASE
(L-Phenylalanine ammonia-lyase)

L-Phenylalanine = trans-cinnamate + NH_3

Ref.

Equilibrium constant

The reaction is essentially irreversible [F]. (1)

Specificity

The enzyme from Hordeum vulgare (barley) is highly specific for L-phenylalanine and the following compounds were inactive: D-phenyl-alanine, DL-aspartate, L-histidine, L-alanine, 3,4-dihydroxyphenyl-DL-alanine, DL-leucine, β-phenyl-DL-serine, glycine, L-cysteine, L-tryptophan, L-tyrosine and DL-m-tyrosine. (1)

Michaelis constants

source	substrate	$K_m(M)$	conditions	
H. vulgare	L-phenylalanine	1.7×10^{-3}	pH 8.8, borate, $40°$	(1)
Sweet potato	L-phenylalanine	1×10^{-4}	pH 8.8, borate, $40°$	(2)

Inhibitors

The enzyme is inhibited by several aromatic acids including L-tyrosine and m- and p-coumarates. The inhibition is competitive (L-phenylalanine). (1,3)

References

1. Koukol, J. & Conn, E. E. (1961) JBC, 236, 2692.

2. Minamikawa, T. & Uritani, I. (1965) J. Biochem. (Tokyo), 57, 678.

3. Minamikawa, T. & Uritani, I. (1965) J. Biochem. (Tokyo), 58, 53.

β-ALANYL-CoA AMMONIA-LYASE

(β-Alanyl-CoA ammonia-lyase)

β-Alanyl-CoA = acrylyl-CoA + NH₃

Equilibrium constant

$$\frac{[\text{acrylyl-pantetheine}]\,[\text{NH}_3]}{[\beta\text{-alanyl-pantetheine}]} = 1.22 \times 10^{-6}\ M$$
(pH 7.5, triethanolamine, 25°)

The reaction with acryl-CoA and NH₃ as the substrates is also reversible. (1)

Specificity

The enzyme from Clostridium propionicum was active with acrylyl-CoA (1.00), crotonoyl-CoA (0.052), acrylyl-pantetheine (0.016), crotonoyl-pantetheine (0.0025) and acrylyl-N-acetyl thioethanolamine (0.00003) but not with acrylyl-S-thiopropionate or crotonoyl-N-acetyl-thioethanolamine. The enzyme is highly specific for NH₃ which could not be replaced by a number of amino acids or by urea. (1)

References

1. Vagelos, P. R., Earl, J. M. & Stadtman, E. R. (1959) JBC, 234, 490.

erythro-3-HYDROXYASPARTATE DEHYDRATASE

(erythro-3-Hydroxyaspartate ammonia-lyase)

erythro-3-Hydroxyaspartate = oxaloacetate + NH_3

Ref.

Equilibrium constant

The reaction is essentially irreversible [F].   (1)

Specificity

The enzyme (Micrococcus denitrificans) is highly specific
and the following compounds were not cleaved: threo-DL-3-hydroxy-
aspartate, erythro- and threo-DL-3-hydroxy-3-methylaspartate, allo-
DL-DL-3-hydroxyglutamate and the L- and D-isomers of serine, threonine
and allothreonine. The enzyme requires pyridoxal-phosphate for activity.   (1)

Michaelis constants

source	substrate	$K_m(M)$	conditions	
M. denitrificans	erythro-L-3-hydroxyaspartate	2.1×10^{-3}	pH 7.6, Tris-carbonate, 30^0	(1)

Inhibitors

source	inhibitor	type	K_i	conditions	
M. denitrificans	maleate	C (erythro-L-3-hydroxyaspartate	3.2×10^{-2}	pH 7.6, Tris-carbonate, 30^0	(1)

References

1. Gibbs, R. G. & Morris, J. G. (1965) BJ, 97, 547.

ARGININOSUCCINATE LYASE

(L-Argininosuccinate arginine-lyase)

L-Argininosuccinate = fumarate + L-arginine

Equilibrium constant

$$\frac{[\text{fumarate}]\,[\text{L-arginine}]}{[\text{L-argininosuccinate}]} = 1.14 \times 10^{-2}M \quad (\text{pH } 7.5,\ P_i,\ 38^\circ) \tag{2}$$

Molecular weight

source	value	conditions	
Steer liver	202,000[a]	pH 7.5	(3)

[a] In Tris buffer at 0° inactivation concomitant with dissociation into subunits occurred. The inactivation was reversible and it was prevented by L-arginine, L-argininosuccinate or P_i.

Specific activity

Steer liver (240 x) 15.3 L-argininosuccinate (pH 7.5, P_i, 38°) (3)

Specificity

The enzyme (beef liver) also catalyzes the following reaction:
L-canavaninosuccinate = L-canavanine + fumarate (4)

L-Aspartate, guanidinosuccinate, the cyclic anhydride of argininosuccinate and adenylosuccinate were inactive in the forward reaction. (1,4)

In the reverse reaction the only substrates known are L-arginine and L-canavanine and the following compounds were inactive: creatine, creatinine, glycocyamine, guanidine and methyl guanidine. Fumarate could not be replaced by malate, trans-aconitate, trans-crotonate or itaconate. (1,2,4)

Michaelis constants

source	substrate	V (relative)	$K_m(M)$	conditions	
Beef	L-argininosuccinate	1.0	1.5×10^{-3}	pH 7.5,	
liver	L-arginine	1.4	1.5×10^{-2}	P_i, 38°	(2)
	fumarate	1.4	1.5×10^{-2}		

Inhibitors

With the enzyme from beef liver, L-argininosuccinate inhibited the cleavage of L-canavaninosuccinate and L-canavaninosuccinate the cleavage of L-argininosuccinate. (1,4)

References

1. Ratner, S. (1962) The Enzymes, 6, 502.
2. Ratner, S., Anslow, W. P. & Petrack, B. (1953) JBC, 204, 115.
3. Havir, E. A., Tamir, H., Ratner, S. & Warner, R. C. (1965) JBC, 240, 3079.
4. Walker, J. B. (1953) JBC, 204, 139.

ADENYLOSUCCINATE LYASE

(Adenylosuccinate AMP-lyase)

Adenylosuccinate = fumarate + AMP

Ref.

Equilibrium constant

$$\frac{[\text{fumarate}]\,[\text{AMP}]}{[\text{adenylosuccinate}]} = 6.8 \times 10^{-3}\text{M} \quad (\text{pH } 6.0\text{-}7.0,\ P_i,\ 35°) \quad (2)$$

$$\frac{[\text{fumarate}]\,[\text{AICAR}]}{[\text{succino-AICAR}]} = 2.3 \times 10^{-3}\text{M} \quad (\text{pH } 7.2,\ P_i,\ 37°) \quad (3)$$

Molecular weight

source	value	conditions	
Neurospora sp.	200,000 [6-8]	pH 7.1	(4)

Specific activity

Neurospora sp. (1970 x) 18,700 adenylosuccinate (pH 8.0, Tris, 37°) (4)

Specificity

Adenylosuccinate lyase is a bifunctional enzyme that catalyzes two non-sequential reactions in purine biosynthesis:

adenylosuccinate   =   fumarate + AMP
succino-AICAR   =   fumarate + AICAR

It is thought that a single active site is involved in the catalysis of both reactions. (1,3,4)

The enzyme is highly specific for its substrates. Thus that from baker's yeast could not utilize adenosine 2'-phosphate or adenosine 3'-phosphate in the place of AMP. dAMP was as active as AMP. Fumarate could not be replaced by maleate, oxaloacetate, 2-oxoglutarate, malate or malonate and adenylosuccinate could not be replaced by argininosuccinate. (1,2)

Michaelis constants

source	substrate	relative velocity	$K_m(M)$	conditions	
Baker's yeast	adenylosuccinate	-	1.2×10^{-5}	pH 7.0, P_i, $35°$	(2)
	fumarate	-	5.2×10^{-4}		
	AMP	-	4.8×10^{-5}		
Neurospora sp.	adenylosuccinate	-	1.2×10^{-6}	pH 8.0, Tris, $37°$	(4)
Chicken liver	succino-AICAR	1.00	1.1×10^{-4}	pH 7.2, P_i, $38°$	(3)
	adenylosuccinate	3.85	-		

Inhibitors

With the enzyme from chicken liver, adenylosuccinate inhibited the cleavage of succino-AICAR and succino-AICAR the cleavage of adenylosuccinate. (1,3)

Light absorption data

$\Delta\epsilon$(adenylosuccinate -- AMP) at 280 mµ = 10,700 M^{-1} cm^{-1}
290 mµ = 4,200 M^{-1} cm^{-1} (pH 7.0) (2)

$\Delta\epsilon$(succino-AICAR -- AICAR) at 267 mµ = 700 M^{-1} cm^{-1} (pH 7.2) (4)

Abbreviations

AICAR	5'-phosphoribosyl-4-carboxamide-5-aminoimidazole
succino-AICAR	5'-phosphoribosyl-4-(N-succinocarboxamide)-5-aminoimidazole

References

1. Ratner, S. (1962) The Enzymes, 6, 506, 509.
2. Carter, C. E. & Cohen, L. H. (1956) JBC, 222, 17.
3. Miller, R. W., Lukens, L. N. & Buchanan, J. M. (1959) JBC, 234, 1806.
4. Woodward, D. O. & Braymer, H. D. (1966) JBC, 241, 580.

CYSTEINE DESULPHHYDRASE

(L-Cysteine hydrogensulphide-lyase (deaminating))

L-Cysteine + H_2O = pyruvate + NH_3 + H_2S

Ref.

Equilibrium constant

The reaction may be reversible. (1)

Specificity

The desulphhydrase from rat liver is highly specific for L-cysteine (or L-cystine) which could not be replaced by D-cysteine, D-cystine, methionine, glutathione, thioglycollate or 2-amino-3-thiolbutylate. (2)

The enzyme from Escherichia coli could utilize either L-cysteine or D-cysteine. Pyridoxal-phosphate - required as a cofactor - could not be replaced by adenosine 5-phosphate or biotin. (3,4)

Michaelis constants

source	substrate	$K_m(M)$	conditions	
E. coli	L-cysteine	1.76×10^{-2}	pH 7.8, $40°$	(3)

Inhibitors

The enzyme from E. coli was inhibited by 2-oxoglutarate, tryptophan, glutamate, alanine and Tris. (3)

References

1. Smythe, C. V. & Halliday, D. (1942) JBC, 144, 237.
2. Smythe, C. V. (1955) Methods in Enzymology, 2, 315.
3. Metaxas, M. A. & Delwiche, E. A. (1955) J. Bacteriol., 70, 735.
4. Saz, A. K. & Brownell, L. W. (1954) ABB, 52, 291.

ALLIIN LYASE

(Alliin alkylsulphenate-lyase)

An S-alkyl-L-cysteinesulphoxide =

2-aminoacrylate + an alkyl sulphenate

Specificity and Michaelis constants

Alliin lyase from <u>Allium</u> <u>cepa</u> (onion) is highly specific for S-substituted L-cysteine sulphoxides and the following compounds were not attacked: methionine, its sulphoxide, cycloalliin and S-substituted derivatives of L-cysteine. The enzyme requires pyridoxal-phosphate for activity. $\qquad$ (3)

source	substrate	$\frac{V}{(relative)}$	$K_m(M)$	conditions	
A. cepa	$(\pm)$S-methyl-[a]	1.0	1.66×10^{-2}		
	$(\pm)$S-ethyl-[a]	1.0	5.7×10^{-3}		
	$(\pm)$S-propyl-[a]	1.0	3.8×10^{-3}	pH 8.5,	(2)
	$(\pm)$S-butyl-[a]	1.0	4.7×10^{-3}	PP_i, $37°$	
	$(+)$S-propyl-[a]	1.0	2.3×10^{-3}		
	$(-)$S-propyl-[a]	1.0	1.17×10^{-2}		
	$(\pm)$S-propyl-[a]	-	4×10^{-3}	pH 8.4, Tris, $37°$	(3)

[a]-L-Cysteinesulphoxide

Inhibitors[a]

inhibitor	$\frac{K_i}{(x\ 10^3M)}$[c]	$\frac{K_i}{(x\ 10^3M)}$[d]	$\frac{K_i}{(x\ 10^3M)}$[e]	$\frac{K_i}{(x\ 10^3M)}$[f]	conditions
S-methyl-[b]	5.82	2.63	1.09	0.77	
S-ethyl-[b]	4.21	1.92	0.81	0.35	pH 8.5,
S-propyl-[b]	4.90	1.49	0.48	0.26	PP_i, $37°$ (2)
S-butyl-[b]	4.78	1.32	0.41	0.22	

[a]The data given are those for the enzyme from A. cepa. The inhibitors are partially competitive with respect to the substrate given.
[b]-L-Cysteine
[c]Substrate = $(\pm)$S-methyl-L-cysteinesulphoxide
[d]Substrate = $(\pm)$S-ethyl-L-cysteinesulphoxide
[e]Substrate = $(\pm)$S-butyl-L-cysteinesulphoxide
[f]Substrate = $(\pm)$S-propyl-L-cysteinesulphoxide

References

1. Stoll, A. & Seebeck, E. (1951) <u>Advances</u> <u>in</u> <u>Enzymology</u>, <u>11</u>, 377.

2. Schwimmer, S., Ryan, C. A. & Wong, F. F. (1964) <u>JBC</u>, <u>239</u>, 777.

3. Schwimmer, S. & Mazelis, M. (1963) <u>ABB</u>, <u>100</u>, 66.

LACTOYL-GLUTATHIONE LYASE

(S-Lactoyl-glutathione methylglyoxal-lyase (isomerizing))

S-Lactoyl-glutathione = glutathione + methylglyoxal

Ref.

Equilibrium constant

The reaction is essentially irreversible [R].   (1,2)

Specificity and Michaelis constants

The enzymes lactoyl-glutathione lyase (glyoxylase I) and hydroxy-acylglutathione hydrolase (glyoxylase II: 3.1.2.6) are responsible for the "glyoxylase reaction" which transforms methylglyoxal to DL-lactate with glutathione as cofactor.   (1)

Glyoxylase I from baker's yeast could utilize the following compounds in the place of methylglyoxal: glyoxal, phosphohydroxypyruvate aldehyde and phenylglyoxal. Glutathione could be replaced by isoglutathione, asparthione, γ-D-Glu-L-Cys-Gly and S-acetylglutathione but not by thioglycollate, oxidized glutathione, thioneine, ascorbate, cysteine, cysteinylglycine γ-glutamylcysteine or S-methylglutathione. (1,3)

source	substrate	V (relative)	$K_m(M)$	conditions	
Baker's yeast	methylglyoxal	1.0	1×10^{-3}	pH 6.6, P_i, 21°	(2)
	phosphohydroxy-pyruvate aldehyde	1.0	4×10^{-3}		
	glutathione	1.0	7.4×10^{-4}	0.2M NaHCO$_3$, 25°	(3)
	asparthione	1.0	3.7×10^{-3}		
	isoglutathione	1.0	1.23×10^{-2}		

Inhibitors

source	inhibitor	type	$K_i(M)$	conditions	
Baker's yeast	ophthalmate	C(glutathione)	9.5×10^{-4}	pH 6.6, P_i, 20°	(4)

The following compounds also inhibited the enzyme from baker's yeast: S-methylglutathione, γ-DL-glutamyl-DL-alanylglycine and S(N-ethylsuccinyl)-glutathione.   (1,5)

Light absorption data

S-lactoyl-glutathione ε, (240 mμ) = 3300 M^{-1} cm^{-1} (pH 6.6)   (4)

References

1. Knox, W. E. (1960) The Enzymes, 2, 271.
2. Weaver, R. H. & Lardy, L. A. (1961) JBC, 236, 313.
3. Behrens, O. K. (1941) JBC, 141, 503.
4. Cliffe, E. E. & Waley, S. G. (1961) BJ, 79, 475.
5. Kermack, W. O. & Matheson, N. A. (1957) BJ, 65, 48.

S-ALKYLCYSTEINE LYASE

(S-Alkyl-L-cysteine methylmercaptan-lyase (deaminating))

S-Methyl-L-cysteine = pyruvate + NH_3 + methyl mercaptan

Ref.

Specificity and Michaelis constants[a]

source	substrate	relative velocity	$K_m(M)$
Pseudomonas cruciviae	S-methyl-L-cysteine	1.00	2.3×10^{-3}
	S-methyl-L-cysteine sulphoxide[b]	0.34	2.4×10^{-3}
	S-ethyl-L-cysteine	1.05	-
	S-ethyl-L-cysteine sulphoxide	1.17	-
	S-allyl-L-cysteine	0.26	-
	S-allyl-L-cysteine sulphoxide	0.34	-
	S-n-propyl-L-cysteine	0.56	-
	S-n-butyl-L-cysteine	0.60	-
	S-isobutyl-L-cysteine	0.42	-
	S-n-amyl-L-cysteine	0.50	-
	S-isoamyl-L-cysteine	0.40	-
	S-(2-carboxyisobutyl)-L-cysteine	0.56	-
	S-(1-carboxy-n-butyl)-L-cysteine	0.46	-
	S-(2-carboxy-1, 1-dimethylethyl)-L-cysteine	0.60	-
	S-(2-carboxy-n-propionyl)-L-cysteine	0.52	-
	S-(2-carboxy-2-methyl-n-propionyl)-L-cysteine	0.50	-
	pyridoxal-phosphate	-	8×10^{-6}

[a]Conditions: pH 8.8, Tris, 23°. The data are from reference (1).

[b]In the reaction

S-methyl-L-cysteine sulphoxide = methyl methanethiosulphinate + pyruvate + NH_3

The enzyme was inactive with the following compounds: L-methionine, L-cysteine, L-serine and L-alanine. Pyridoxal-phosphate could not be replaced by pyridoxamine-phosphate, pyridoxal, pyridoxamine or pyridoxine.(1)

References

1. Nomura, J., Nishizuka, Y. & Hayaishi, O. (1963) JBC, 238, 1441.

DDT-DEHYDROCHLORINASE

(1,1,1-Trichloro-2,2-bis-(p-chlorophenyl)-ethane
hydrogenchloride-lyase)

1,1,1-Trichloro-2,2-bis-(p-chlorophenyl)-ethane =
1,1-dichloro-2,2-bis-(p-chlorophenyl)-ethylene + HCl

Ref.

Equilibrium constant

The reaction is essentially irreversible [F].   (1)

Specificity

The enzyme from DDT resistant Musca domestica (house fly) utilized the following compounds as substrates: 1,1,1-trichloro-2,2-bis-
(p-chlorophenyl)-ethane (1.00); 1,1,1-trichloro-2,2-bis-(p-bromo-
phenyl)-ethane (1.00); 1,1,1-trichloro-2,2-bis-(p-fluorophenyl)-ethane
(0.54); 1,1,1-trichloro-2,2-bis-(p-tolyl)-ethane (0.36); 1,1,1-tri-
chloro-2,2-bis-(p-methoxyphenyl)-ethane (0.23); 1,1,1-trichloro-2,2-
bis-(p-iodophenyl)-ethane (0.08); 1,1-dichloro-2,2-bis-(p-chlorophenyl)-ethane (3.77); 1-chloro-2,2-bis-(p-chlorophenyl)-ethane (1.19)
and 2,2-bis-(p-chlorophenyl)-ethane (0.03). 1,1,1-Trichloro-2,2-bis-
(phenyl)-ethane was inactive.   (1)

The enzyme has been purified 50,000 x from M. domestica.   (2)

Michaelis constants

source	substrate	$K_m(M)$	conditions	
M. domestica	DDT glutathione[a]	5×10^{-7} 2.5×10^{-4}	pH 7.4, Pi, 25^6	(1)

[a]Activator

Light absorption data

1,1-dichloro-2,2-bis-(p-chlorophenyl)-ethylene ε, (260 mμ) =
14,500 M^{-1} cm^{-1} (pH 7.4)   (1)

Abbreviations

DDT   1,1,1-trichloro-2,2-bis-(p-chlorophenyl)-ethane

References

1. Lipke, H. & Kearns, C. W. (1959) JBC, 234, 2123, 2129.
2. Lipke, H. & Kearns, C. W. (1957) FP, 16, 212.

ALANINE RACEMASE

(Alanine racemase)

L-Alanine = D-alanine

Molecular weight

source	value	conditions	
Bacillus subtilis	~50,000	pH 8.1	(1)

Specific activity

B. subtilis (140 x)   23   D or L-alanine   (-)   (3)

Specificity

The enzyme is highly specific for D- or L-alanine. The enzyme from Streptococcus faecalis utilized D- or L-alanine at equal rates. The other protein amino acids and 2-aminobutyrate were inactive. Of several vitamin B6 analogs tested, only pyridoxal-phosphate was effective as cofactor (2). The enzyme from B. subtilis, however, was inactive with pyridoxal-phosphate and required FAD instead which could not be replaced by FMN, NAD, reduced NAD or NADP.   (3)

Michaelis constants

source	substrate	$K_m(M)$	conditions	
S. faecalis	L-alanine	8.5×10^{-3} ⎫	pH 8.1,	
	pyridoxal-phosphate	2×10^{-6} ⎬	P_i, 37°	(2)
	pyridoxal-phosphate	4.4×10^{-7}	pH 8.3, P_i, 37°	(4)
Pseudomonas sp.	L-alanine	3×10^{-2}	pH 8.9, Tris, 37°	(5)

Inhibitors

source	inhibitor	type	$K_i(M)$	conditions	
Pseudomonas sp.	aminoxyacetate	C(L-alanine)	4×10^{-7} ⎫	pH 8.9,	
	hydroxylamine	C(L-alanine)	1×10^{-5} ⎬	Tris, 37°	(5)
Staphylococcus aureus	D-cycloserine[a]	C(L-alanine)	5×10^{-5}	-	(6)
	hydroxylamine	C(L-alanine)	1.2×10^{-5}	-	(6)
S. faecalis	N-nitrosalicylaldehyde	C[b]	4.0×10^{-5} ⎫		
	5-deoxypyridoxal	C[b]	8.9×10^{-5}		
	pyridoxal	C[b]	3.2×10^{-4}		
	ω-methylpyridoxal	C[b]	5.3×10^{-4} ⎬	pH 8.3,	(4)
	pyridoxamine	C[b]	5.9×10^{-4}	P_i, 37°	
	ω-methylpyridox-amine	C[b]	2.7×10^{-3}		
	pyridoxine	C[b]	2.3×10^{-2} ⎭		

[a] L-Cycloserine did not inhibit
[b] With respect to pyridoxal-phosphate

References

1. Diven, W. F., Scholz, J. J. & Johnston, R. B. (1964) BBA, 85, 322.
2. Wood, W. A. & Gunsalus, I. C. (1951) JBC, 190, 403.
3. Diven, W. F., Scholz, J. J. & Johnston, R. B. (1963) FP, 22, 535.
4. Olivard, J. & Snell, E. E. (1955) JBC, 213, 203.
5. Free, C. A., Julius, M., Arnow, P. & Barry, G. T. (1967) BBA, 146, 608.
6. Roze, U. & Strominger, J. L. (1966) Mol. Pharmacol., 2, 92.

METHIONINE RACEMASE

(Methionine racemase)

L-Methionine $=$ D-methionine

<u>Ref.</u>

<u>Michaelis constants</u>

<u>source</u>	<u>substrate</u>	$K_m(M)$	<u>conditions</u>	
<u>Pseudomonas</u> sp.	L-methionine	8.0×10^{-3}	pH 8.2,	(1)
	pyridoxal-phosphate	2×10^{-6}	P_i, 30°	

<u>References</u>

1. Kallio, R. E. & Larson, A. D. (1955) in <u>Amino Acid Metabolism</u> (eds. McElroy, W. D. & Glass, H. B.) John's Hopkins Press: Baltimore, p624.

GLUTAMATE RACEMASE

(Glutamate racemase)

L-Glutamate = D-glutamate

Ref.

Equilibrium constant

$$\frac{[\text{D-glutamate}]}{[\text{L-glutamate}]} = \quad \sim 1 \tag{1}$$

Michaelis constants

source	substrate	relative velocity	$K_m(M)$	conditions	
Lactobacillus arabinosus	D-glutamate	1.0	3.6×10^{-3}	pH 7.5, P_i, 37°	(1)
	L-glutamate	1.0	-		
L. fermentii	D-glutamate	-	4.7×10^{-2}	-	(2)

Inhibitors

The enzyme (L. arabinosus) was inhibited by hydroxylamine (C(D-glutamate)). (1)

References

1. Glaser, L. (1960) JBC, 235, 2095.
2. Tanaka, M., Kato, Y. & Kinoshita, S. (1961) BBRC, 4, 114.

HYDROXYPROLINE EPIMERASE

(Hydroxyproline 2-epimerase)

L-Hydroxyproline = D-allohydroxyproline

Equilibrium constant

$$\frac{[\text{D-allohydroxyproline}]}{[\text{L-hydroxyproline}]} = 0.99 \quad (\text{pH 8.1, Tris, } 25^\circ)$$ (1)

Molecular weight

source	value	conditions	
Pseudomonas striata	18,000	various	(1)

Specific activity

P. striata (200 x)   60 L-hydroxyproline   (pH 8.1,
                     152 D-allohydroxyproline   Tris, 25°)   (1)

Specificity

The enzyme (P. striata) also catalyzes the conversion of D-hydroxy-proline to L-allohydroxyproline. 3-Hydroxyproline is also a substrate but the following proline analogs were inactive: N-acetylhydroxy-L-proline, β-alanylhydroxy-L-proline, glycylhydroxy-L-proline, carbobenzoxy-glycylhydroxy-L-proline, hydroxy-L-prolylglycine and hydroxy-L-proline amide. None of the protein amino acids was active except L-proline.   (1)

The enzyme does not require pyridoxal-phosphate as a cofactor.   (1)

Michaelis constants

source	substrate	$K_m(M)$	conditions	
P. striata	L-hydroxyproline	2.2×10^{-2}	pH 8.1,	
	D-allohydroxyproline	5.3×10^{-2}	Tris, 25°	(1)

Inhibitors

High substrate concentrations (L-hydroxyproline or D-allohydroxy-proline) are inhibitory.   (1)

References

1. Adams, E. & Norton, I. L. (1964) JBC, 239, 1525.

LACTATE RACEMASE

(Lactate Racemase)

L-Lactate = D-lactate

Specificity

The enzyme from rabbit liver was active with lactate, malate and isocitrate but not with alanine or 3-hydroxyglutarate. (1)

Michaelis constants

source	substrate	$\frac{V}{(\text{relative})}$	$K_m(M)$	conditions	
Clostridium butylicum	L-lactate D-lactate	1 1	8×10^{-3} 8×10^{-3}	pH 5.0, acetate, 37°	(2)

References

1. Huennekens, F. M., Mahler, H. R. & Nordmann, J. (1951) AB, 30, 77.

2. Dennis, D. (1962) Methods in Enzymology, 5, 426.

RIBULOSEPHOSPHATE 3-EPIMERASE

(D-Ribulose-5-phosphate 3-epimerase)

D-Ribulose 5-phosphate = D-xylulose 5-phosphate

Equilibrium constant

$$\frac{[\text{D-xylulose 5-phosphate}]}{[\text{D-ribulose 5-phosphate}]} = 1.5 - 3.0 \qquad (25^\circ) \qquad (4)$$

Molecular weight

source	value	conditions	
Yeast	46,000		(5)

Specific activity

Yeast (675 x)   262   D-ribulose 5-phosphate   (pH 7, imidazole) (5)

Specificity

The enzyme isolated from a variety of sources is highly specific. Thus, that purified from Lactobacillus pentosus did not attack tagatose 6-phosphate or ribulose diphosphate (3) and the enzyme from calf spleen was inactive with xylose 5-phosphate, ribulose diphosphate, ribulose, xylulose, sedoheptulose 7-phosphate, hexose diphosphate or fructose 6-phosphate (2).

Michaelis constants

source	substrate	$K_m(M)$	conditions	
L. pentosus	D-xylulose 5-phosphate	5×10^{-4}	pH 7.5, Tris,	(3)
	D-ribulose 5-phosphate	1×10^{-3}	25°	

References

1. Maxwell, E. S. (1961) The Enzymes, 5, 450.

2. Ashwell, G. & Hickman, J. (1957) JBC, 226, 65.

3. Hurwitz, J. & Horecker, B. L. (1956) JBC, 223, 993.

4. Hurwitz, J. (1962) Methods in Enzymology, 5, 247.

5. Williamson, W. T. & Wood, W. A. (1966) Methods in Enzymology, 9, 605.

UDPGLUCOSE EPIMERASE

(UDPglucose 4-epimerase)

UDPglucose = UDPgalactose

Ref.

Equilibrium constant

$$\frac{[\text{UDPgalactose}]}{[\text{UDPglucose}]} = 0.284 \quad (\text{pH } 7.1\text{-}8.7, \text{ P}_i\text{-glycine, } 27^\circ) \tag{2}$$

Molecular weight

source	value	conditions	
Escherichia coli	79,000 [2]	pH 7.0	(2)

Specific activity

E. coli (260 x) $380^{(a)}$ UDPgalactose (pH 8.5, glycine, 27°)   (2)

(a) This is a maximum value

Specificity

The enzyme (calf liver or E. coli) requires NAD specifically for full activity: the cofactor could not be replaced by reduced NAD, NADP or any NAD analog tested (2,3). The enzyme from yeast contains tightly bound NAD. This enzyme was not stimulated by additional NAD.   (4,5)

Michaelis constants

source	substrate	$K_m(M)$	conditions	
E. coli	UDPgalactose	1.6×10^{-4}	pH 8.5, glycine, 27°	(2)
Calf liver	UDPglucose	9×10^{-5}	pH 8.7, glycine, room temperature	(3)
	UDPgalactose	5×10^{-5}		
	NAD	2×10^{-7}		

Inhibitors

The enzyme (calf liver) is inhibited by reduced NAD; the inhibition is partially overcome by NAD.   (3)

References

1. Maxwell, E. S. (1961) The Enzymes, 5, 444.
2. Wilson, D. B. & Hogness, D. S. (1964) JBC, 239, 2469.
3. Maxwell, E. S. (1957) JBC, 229, 139.
4. Maxwell, E. S., de Robichon-Szulmajster, H. & Kalckar, H. M. (1958) ABB, 78, 407.
5. Maxwell, E. S. & de Robichon-Szulmajster, H. (1960) JBC, 235, 308.

ALDOSE MUTAROTASE

(Aldose 1-epimerase)

$$\alpha\text{-D-Glucose} = \beta\text{-D-glucose}$$

Ref.

Equilibrium constant

The reaction is reversible. (1,2)

Molecular weight

source	value	conditions	
Penicillium notatum	70,000	pH 7.0	(2)
Hog kidney	54,300	pH 7.1	(5)

Specific activity

Hog kidney	(100 x)	25.5	α-D-glucose	(pH 7.1, Tris, 26°)	(5)
P. notatum	(15 x)	14.0	β-D-glucose	(pH 5.7, P_i, 20°)	(2)

Specificity and Michaelis constants

source	substrate	relative velocity	K_m(M)	conditions	
P. notatum	α-D-glucose	1.00	–		
	α-D-galactose	1.05	–		
	β-cellobiose	0.19	–		
	β-L-arabinose	1.19	–	pH 5.7, P_i, 20°	(2)
	β-D-glycero-D-galacto-heptopyranose	0.19	–		
	α-D-xylose	0.36	–		
Hamster intestine	D-glucose	–	2.5×10^{-2}	pH 7, P_i, 24°	(1)
	D-galactose	–	8.4×10^{-3}		

Inhibitors

source	inhibitor	type	K_i(M)	conditions	
Hamster intestine	6-deoxyglucose		5.7×10^{-3}		
	1-deoxyglucose	C (glucose)	2.6×10^{-2}	pH 7, P_i, 24°	(1)
	phlorizin		9×10^{-5}		

A number of sugar and sugar alcohols are competitive inhibitors of the enzyme. (3,4)

References

1. Keston, A. S. (1964) JBC, 239, 3241.
2. Bentley, R. & Bhate, D. S. (1960) JBC, 235, 1219, 1225.
3. Keston, A. S. (1963) ABB, 102, 306.
4. Bentley, R. (1962) Methods in Enzymology, 5, 219.
5. Li, Lu-Ku. (1965) ABB, 110, 156.

RIBULOSEPHOSPHATE 4-EPIMERASE

(L-Ribulose-5-phosphate 4-epimerase)

L-Ribulose 5-phosphate = D-xylulose 5-phosphate

Ref.

Equilibrium constant

$$\frac{[\text{D-xylulose 5-phosphate}]}{[\text{L-ribulose 5-phosphate}]} = \begin{array}{l} 1.86(\text{pH } 8.4, \text{ glycylglycine } 24^\circ) \\ 1.2 \ (\text{pH } 6.0, \text{ succinate, } 37^\circ \ ) \end{array}$$

(2)
(3)

Specificity

The epimerase is highly specific for its substrates. Thus the enzyme from <u>Aerobacter aerogenes</u> was inactive with the following compounds: D-tagatose 6-phosphate, α-D-xylose 1-phosphate, D-xylose 5-phosphate and D-ribulose 5-phosphate.

(2)

Michaelis constants

source	substrate	$K_m(M)$	conditions	
<u>A. aerogenes</u>	L-ribulose 5-phosphate	1×10^{-4}	pH 8.6, glycyl-glycine	(2)
<u>Lactobacillus plantarum</u>	L-ribulose 5-phosphate	1.1×10^{-3}	pH 7.5, Tris, 37°	(3)

References

1. Maxwell, E. S. (1961) The Enzymes, 5, 452.
2. Wolin, M. J., Simpson, F. J. & Wood, W. A. (1958) JBC, 232, 559.
3. Burma, D. P. & Horecker, B. L. (1958) JBC, 231, 1053.

N-ACYLGLUCOSAMINE 2-EPIMERASE

(N-Acyl-2-acetamido-2-deoxy-D-glucose 2-epimerase)

N-Acyl-2-acetamido-2-deoxy-D-glucose =

N-acyl-2-acetamido-2-deoxy-D-mannose

Ref.

Equilibrium constant

$$\frac{[\text{N-acetyl-D-mannosamine}]}{[\text{N-acetyl-D-glucosamine}]} = 0.26 \qquad (\text{pH } 7.6, \text{ Tris, } 37^\circ) \qquad (1,2)$$

Specificity

The enzyme (hog kidney) was active with N-acetyl-D-mannosamine, N-acetyl-D-glucosamine and the corresponding N-glycolyl derivatives. No activity was detected towards N-acetylglucosamine 1-phosphate, N-acetylglucosamine 6-phosphate, N-acetylmannosamine 6-phosphate, glucosamine, mannosamine, glucosamine 6-phosphate, mannosamine 6-phosphate, UDP-N-acetylglucosamine, N-acetylgalactosamine, glucose or mannose. (1,2)

The enzyme showed an absolute requirement for ATP. dATP exhibited 35% the activity of ATP, but the following were inactive: UTP, GTP, CTP, ADP, AMP, ITP, CMP, UMP, dCTP, dGTP, TTP, cyclic 3',5'-AMP, NAD, NADP or PP_i, (1,2)

Michaelis constants

source	substrate	$K_m(M)$	conditions
Hog kidney	N-acetylglucosamine	3.4×10^{-4}	pH 7.6, Tris, 37°
	N-acetylmannosamine	3.0×10^{-3}	1×10^{-4} M ATP (1,2)
	ATP	1.1×10^{-3}	pH 7.6, Tris, 37°, with either substrate

References

1. Ghosh, S. & Roseman, S. (1965) JBC, 240, 1531.
2. Ghosh, S. & Roseman, S. (1966) Methods in Enzymology, 8, 191.

N-ACYLGLUCOSAMINE 6-PHOSPHATE 2-EPIMERASE

(N-Acyl-2-acetamido-2-deoxy-D-glucose 6-phosphate 2-epimerase)
N-Acyl-2-acetamido-2-deoxy-D-glucose 6-phosphate =
N-acyl-2-acetamido-2-deoxy-D-mannose 6-phosphate

Ref.

Equilibrium constant

$$\frac{[\text{N-acetyl-D-mannosamine 6-phosphate}]}{[\text{N-acetyl-D-glucosamine 6-phosphate}]} = 0.43 \qquad \text{(pH 7.6, Tris-}\atop\text{maleate, 37}^{\circ}) \qquad (1,2)$$

Specific activity

Aerobacter cloacae (266 x) 478 N-acetyl-D-mannosamine (pH 7.6,   (1,2)
Tris-maleate,
37°)

Specificity

N-Glycolylhexosamine 6-phosphate ester can replace the corresponding acetyl derivatives but the following compounds are inactive: N-
acetylglucosamine and N-acetylmannosamine, glucosamine 6-phosphate and
mannosamine 6-phosphate, N-acetylgalactosamine 6-phosphate and mannose
6-phosphate.   (1,2)

Michaelis constants

source	substrate	$K_m(M)$	conditions	
A. cloacae	N-acetyl-D-mannosamine 6-phosphate	2.4×10^{-3}	pH 7.6, Tris-maleate, 37°	(1,2)
	N-acetyl-D-glucosamine 6-phosphate	1.6×10^{-3}		

References

1. Ghosh, S. & Roseman, S. (1965) JBC, 240, 1525.

2. Ghosh, S. & Roseman, S. (1966) Methods in Enzymology, 8, 185.

UDP-N-ACETYL-D-GLUCOSAMINE 2-EPIMERASE

(UDP-2-acetamido-2-deoxy-D-glucose 2-epimerase (UDP liberating))

UDP-2-acetamido-2-deoxy-D-glucose + H_2O =

UDP + 2-acetamido-2-deoxy-D-mannose

Ref.

Equilibrium constant

The reaction is essentially irreversible [F].   (1)

Specificity and kinetic properties

The enzyme (rat liver) is specific for UDP-N-acetylglucosamine: UDP-glucose, N-acetyl-D-glucosamine, N-acetyl-D-glucosamine 1-phosphate and UDP-N-acetylgalactosamine are inactive. It is thought that the enzyme acts in two discrete steps - epimerization followed by hydrolysis.   (1)

The enzyme is subject to feedback inhibition by CMP-N-acetyl-neuraminate which cannot be replaced by N-acetylneuraminate, 5'-CMP, CDP, CTP, CDP-D-glucose, CDP-paratose, CDP-L-fucose, UDP-D-glucose or N-acetylneuraminosyl lactose. The affinity of the enzyme for CMP-N-acetylneuraminate increases as it becomes more saturated with the inhibitor and this results in sigmoidal shapes when curves of concentration of inhibitor versus percent inhibition are plotted. The inhibitor decreases both the K_m and V of the reaction.   (2)

source	substrate	$K_m(M)$	conditions	
Rat liver	UDP-N-acetyl-glucosamine	2×10^{-3}	pH 7.5, Tris, 37°	(1)

References

1. Spivak, C. T. & Roseman, S. (1966) Methods in Enzymology, 9, 612.

2. Kornfeld, S., Kornfeld, R., Neufeld, E. F. & O'Brien, P. J. (1964) PNAS, 52, 371.

METHYLMALONYL-CoA RACEMASE

(Methylmalonyl-CoA racemase)

D-Methylmalonyl-CoA = L-methylmalonyl-CoA

Equilibrium constant

$$\frac{[\text{L-methylmalonyl-CoA}]}{[\text{D-methylmalonyl-CoA}]} = 1.0 \quad (\text{pH 7.3, Tris, } 30^\circ) \qquad (1)$$

Molecular weight

source	value	conditions	
Propionibacterium shermanii	$S_{20,w} = 2.92$	pH 7.4	(1)

Specific activity

P. shermanii (23 x)   33.4   L-methylmalonyl-CoA   (1)
                                    (pH 7.3, Tris, 30°)

Methylmalonyl-CoA racemase has also been purified from sheep liver.   (2)

References

1. Allen, S. H. G., Kellermeyer, R., Stjernholm, R., Jacobson, B. & Wood, H. G. (1963) JBC, 238, 1637.
2. Mazumder, R., Sasakawa, T., Kaziro, Y. & Ochoa, S. (1962) JBC, 237, 3065.

MALEYLACETOACETATE ISOMERASE

(4-Maleylacetoacetate cis-trans-isomerase)

4-Maleylacetoacetate = 4-fumarylacetoacetate

Ref.

Specificity

Maleylacetoacetate isomerase can utilize both maleylacetoacetate and maleylpyruvate as substrates. The ratio of the activity obtained with maleylacetoacetate to that obtained with maleylpyruvate varied widely with the source of enzyme. Thus with the enzyme from rat liver the ratio was 0.75 and with that from Pseudomonas sp. 0.04. The following compounds were inactive as substrates with the liver enzyme: maleate; angelate; tiglate; cis, cis-muconate; cis, trans-muconate, isocrotonate and crotonate. (2,3)

The isomerase requires glutathione specifically as a cofactor and the following compounds were inactive: CoA, dithiopropanol (BAL), thiomalate, glycyl-L-cysteine, oxidized glutathione, L-cysteinyl-glycine, L-cysteine, ascorbate, thioglycollate or hydrogen sulphide. The K_m for glutathione was 1×10^{-5} (pH 7.5, P_i, 26°). (1,3)

References

1. Knox, E. W. (1960) The Enzymes, 2, 282.
2. Lack, L. (1961) JBC, 236, 2835.
3. Edwards, S. W. & Knox, W. E. (1956) JBC, 220, 79.

RETINENE ISOMERASE

(all-trans-Retinene 11-cis-trans-isomerase)

all-trans-Retinene = 11-cis-retinene

Equilibrium constant

$$\frac{[11\text{-}cis\text{-}retinene]}{[all\text{-}trans\text{-}retinene]} = 0.052^{(a)} \quad (pH\ 7,\ P_i,\ 37^\circ) \tag{3}$$

[a] Obtained in the dark. Light shifts the equilibrium towards 11-cis-retinene (also called neo-b retinene).

Specificity

The enzyme (bovine retina) is highly specific for its substrates and the following compounds were inactive: all-trans-vitamin A and neo-b vitamin A. (1,3)

Michaelis constants

source	substrate	$K_m(M)$	conditions	
Bovine retina	11-cis-retinene	2×10^{-5}	pH 7, P_i, 37°	(3)

References

1. Topper, Y. J. (1961) The Enzymes, 5, 417.
2. Wald, G. & Hubbard, R. (1960) The Enzymes, 3, 369.
3. Hubbard, R. (1956) J. Gen. Physiol., 39, 935.

TRIOSEPHOSPHATE ISOMERASE

(D-Glyceraldehyde-3-phosphate ketol-isomerase)

D-Glyceraldehyde 3-phosphate = dihydroxyacetone phosphate

Ref.

Equilibrium constant

$$\frac{[\text{dihydroxyacetone phosphate}]}{[\text{D-glyceraldehyde 3-phosphate}]} = 22 \qquad \text{(pH 8.0, veronal-acetate, } 25°\text{)} \qquad (2)$$

Molecular weight

source	value	conditions	
Rabbit muscle	43,000	Sephadex G100, pH 7.8	(4)

Specific activity

Rabbit and calf muscle (100 x)	11,600	D-glyceraldehyde 3-phosphate	(pH 7.9, triethanol-amine, 25°)	(4)

Michaelis constants

source	substrate	$K_m(M)$	conditions	
Calf muscle	D-glyceraldehyde 3-phosphate	3.9×10^{-4}	pH 7.5, tri-ethanolamine, 26°	(3)

Inhibitors

P_i (2,5)

References

1. Topper, Y. J. (1961) The Enzymes, 5, 429.

2. Oesper, P. & Meyerhof, O. (1950) ABB, 27, 223.

3. Meyer-Arendt, E., Beisenherz, G. & Bücher, Th. (1953) Naturwissenschaften, 40, 59.

4. Burton, P. M. & Waley, S. G. (1966) BJ, 100, 702.

5. Beisenherz, G. (1955) Methods in Enzymology, 1, 387.

ARABINOSE ISOMERASE

(D-Arabinose ketol-isomerase)

D-Arabinose = D-ribulose

Ref.

Equilibrium constant

$$\frac{[\text{D-ribulose}]}{[\text{D-arabinose}]} = 0.179 \qquad (\text{pH } 6 - 8, \text{ glycyl-glycine}) \quad (2)$$

$$\frac{[\text{L-fuculose}]}{[\text{L-fucose}]} = 0.123 \qquad (\text{pH } 8.0, \text{ P}_i, 37^\circ) \quad (3)$$

Specificity

The enzyme (<u>Escherichia coli</u>) catalyzes the isomerization of D-arabinose, L-fucose, L-galactose and D-altrose. (3)

The enzyme isolated from <u>Aerobacter aerogenes</u> catalyzes the isomerization of L-xylose and L-fucose in addition to that of D-arabinose. (4)

Michaelis constants

source	substrate	K_m(M)	conditions	
E. coli	L-fucose	1.7×10^{-2}		
	D-arabinose	3.5×10^{-2}	pH 8, P$_i$,	(3)
	L-fuculose	1.4×10^{-3}	37°	
	D-ribulose	1.1×10^{-2}		
A. aerogenes	D-arabinose	2.2×10^{-1}	pH 7, Tris	(4)

References

1. Topper, Y. P. (1961) The Enzymes, <u>5</u>, 430.

2. Cohen, S. S. (1953) JBC, <u>201</u>, 71.

3. Green, M. & Cohen, S. S. (1956) JBC, <u>219</u>, 557.

4. Mortlock, R. P. (1966) Methods in Enzymology, <u>9</u>, 583.

L-ARABINOSE ISOMERASE

(L-Arabinose ketol-isomerase)

L-Arabinose = L-ribulose

Equilibrium constant

$$\frac{[\text{L-ribulose}]}{[\text{L-arabinose}]} = \sim 0.11 \qquad (38^\circ) \qquad (1)$$

Specificity

The enzyme (<u>Aerobacter</u> <u>aerogenes</u>) does not isomerize L-lyxose or L-ribose. It is specific for sugars with an L-<u>cis</u> hydroxyl configuration at C-3 and C-4 (4). The enzyme isolated from <u>Lactobacillus</u> <u>plantarum</u> is also highly specific and the following sugars are not attacked: D-arabinose, L-xylose, D-xylose, D-lyxose or D-ribose. Aldo- or keto-hexoses were similarly inactive. (2)

Michaelis constants

source	substrate	relative velocity	$K_m(M)$	conditions	
L. plantarum	L-arabinose	-	2.8×10^{-2}	pH 7.5, Tris, 23°	(2)
	L-ribulose	-	1.8×10^{-2}		
A. aerogenes	L-arabinose	1.00	3.3×10^{-2}	pH 6.9, maleate, 38°	(4)
	D-galactose	0.23	3.7×10^{-1}		
	D-fucose	0.22	2.7×10^{-1}		

Inhibitors

source	inhibitor	type	$K_i(M)$	conditions	
A. aerogenes	L-arabitol	c^* (L-arabinose)	2.3×10^{-3}	pH 6.9, maleate, 38°	(4)
	ribitol		3.5×10^{-4}		

*The inhibition is also competitive with D-galactose or D-fucose as the substrate.

References

1. Topper, Y. J. (1961) The Enzymes, 5, 431.
2. Heath, E. C., Horecker, B. L., Smyrniotis, P. Z. & Yakagi, Y. (1958) JBC, 231, 1031.
3. Smyrniotis, P. Z. (1962) Methods in Enzymology, 5, 344.
4. Yamanaka, K. & Wood, W. A. (1966) Methods in Enzymology, 9, 596.

XYLOSE ISOMERASE

(D-Xylose ketol-isomerase)

D-Xylose = D-xylulose

Equilibrium constant

$$\frac{[\text{D-xylulose}]}{[\text{D-xylose}]} = 0.16 \qquad (\text{pH } 7.5, P_i, 30^\circ) \qquad (2)$$

Specificity

The enzyme (<u>Lactobacillus brevis</u>) attacks D-glucose and D-ribose in addition to D-xylose but D-mannose, D-galactose, 2-deoxy glucose, L- and D-arabinose, L-xylose, gluconate, glucuronate, D-sorbitol, D-mannitol or xylitol are inactive (5). The enzyme isolated from <u>Pasteurella pestis</u> is inactive with D-arabinose, D-ribose, D-lyxose, D-ribulose, D-glucose or D-mannose (2). The enzyme from <u>Pseudomonas hydrophilia</u> also converts glucose to fructose (3).

Michaelis constants

source	substrate	K_m(M)	conditions	
P. pestis	D-xylose	3.0×10^{-3}		
	Mg^{2+}	2.8×10^{-4}	pH 7.5, P_i, 30°	(2)
	Mn^{2+}	1.1×10^{-5}		
P. hydrophilia	D-glucose	5×10^{-1}	pH 8, arsenate, 40°	(3)
L. brevis	D-xylose	5×10^{-3}	pH 7, maleate, 40°	(5)
	D-glucose	9.2×10^{-1}	pH 7, maleate, 50°	

Inhibitors

source	inhibitor	type	K_i(M)	conditions	
L. brevis	xylitol	C (D-xylose)	1.5×10^{-3}		
		C (D-glucose)	4.5×10^{-3}	pH 6.6, maleate, 35°	(5)
	D-sorbitol	C (D-xylose)	–		
		C (D-glucose)	–		

Tris inhibits (5).

References
1. Topper, Y. J. (1961) The Enzymes, 5, 432.
2. Slein, M. W. (1955) JACS, 73, 1663.
3. Marshall, R. O. & Kooi, E. R. (1957) Science, 125, 648.
4. Slein, M. W. (1962) Methods in Enzymology, 5, 347.
5. Yamanaka, K. (1966) Methods in Enzymology, 9, 588.

RIBOSEPHOSPHATE ISOMERASE

(D-Ribose-5-phosphate ketol-isomerase)

D-Ribose 5-phosphate = D-ribulose 5-phosphate

Equilibrium constant

$$\frac{[\text{D-ribulose 5-phosphate}]}{[\text{D-ribose 5-phosphate}]} = 0.30 \quad (\text{pH 7.6, Tris, } 37^\circ) \tag{2}$$

Specific activity

Alfalfa (380 x) 2400 D-ribose 5-phosphate (pH 7.0, Tris, 37°)   (3)

Specificity

The enzyme is highly specific for D-ribose 5-phosphate and D-ribulose 5-phosphate. Thus, that isolated from alfalfa was inactive with D-arabinose 5-phosphate, D-ribose 3-phosphate, D-glucose 6-phosphate, DL-glyceraldehyde phosphate, dihydroxyacetone phosphate and ribose.   (3)

Michaelis constants

source	substrate	$K_m(M)$	conditions	
Pedicoccus pentosareus	D-ribose 5-phosphate	2.8×10^{-3}	pH 7.6, Tris, 37°	(2)
Red blood cells	D-ribose 5-phosphate	2.2×10^{-3}	pH 7.5, Tris.	(4)

Inhibitors

The enzyme (alfalfa) is inhibited by 5-phosphoribonate.   (3)

References

1. Topper, Y. J. (1961) The Enzymes, 5, 432.
2. Dobrogosz, W. J. & De Moss, R. D. (1963) BBA, 77, 629.
3. Axelrod, B. & Jang, R. (1954) JBC, 209, 847.
4. Bruns, F. H., Noltmann, E. & Vahlhaus, E. (1958) BZ, 330, 483.

MANNOSE ISOMERASE

(D-Mannose ketol-isomerase)

D-Mannose = D-fructose

Equilibrium constant

$$\frac{[\text{D-fructose}]}{[\text{D-mannose}]} = 2.45 \quad (\text{pH } 7.4,\ 30^\circ) \tag{2}$$

$$\frac{[\text{D-xylulose}]}{[\text{D-lyxose}]} = 0.39 \quad (\text{pH } 7.4,\ 30^\circ) \tag{2}$$

$$\frac{[\text{D-rhamnulose}]}{[\text{D-rhamnose}]} = 0.58 \quad (\text{pH } 7.4,\ 30^\circ) \tag{2}$$

Molecular weight

source	value	conditions	
Aerobacter aerogenes	40,000	pH 7.0	(3)

Specific activity

A. aerogenes (140 x) 7.7 D-lyxose (pH 7.0, cacodylate, 25°) (3)

Specificity and Michaelis constants

source	substrate	product	relative velocity	K_m(M)	conditions	
Pseudomonas sacchoro-philia[a]	D-mannose	D-fructose	1.00	-		
	D-lyxose	D-xylulose	0.11	-	pH 7.4, Tris, 30°	(2)
	D-rhamnose	D-rhamnulose	0.07	-		
A. aerogenes[b]	D-lyxose	D-xylulose	1.00	3.6×10^{-3}	pH 7.0,	
	D-mannose	D-fructose	1.00	1.0×10^{-2}	cacody-	(3)
	Mn^{2+}	-	-	4×10^{-6}	late, 25°	

[a] The enzyme was inactive with the following compounds: D-xylose, D-arabinose, D-ribose, L-xylose, L-arabinose, D-glucose, D-talose, D-galactose, L-idose, L-gulose, L-glucose, L-mannose, L-rhamnose, D-mannuronate, D-mannose 6-phosphate, D-glycero-D-galaheptose, D-glycero-D-taloheptose, L-glycero-L-idoheptose and L-glycero-L-guloheptose.

[b] The enzyme was inactive with the following compounds: D- and L-xylose, D-mannose 6-phosphate, D-glucose 6-phosphate, D-glucose, D-ribose and D- and L-arabinose.

References

1. Topper, Y. J. (1961) The Enzymes, 5, 433.
2. Palleroni, N. J. & Doudoroff, M. (1956) JBC, 218, 535.
3. Anderson, R. L. & Allison, D. P. (1965) JBC, 240, 2367.

MANNOSEPHOSPHATE ISOMERASE

(D-Mannose-6-phosphate ketol-isomerase)

D-Mannose 6-phosphate = D-fructose 6-phosphate

Ref.

Equilibrium constant

$$\frac{[\text{D-fructose 6-phosphate}]}{[\text{D-mannose 6-phosphate}]} = 1.78 \ (\text{pH } 6.8, \ P_i, \ 37^\circ) \tag{2}$$

Michaelis constants

source	substrate	$K_m(M)$	conditions	
Yeast	mannose 6-phosphate	8×10^{-4}	pH 6.8, P_i, 37°	(2)

References

1. Topper, Y. J. (1961) The Enzymes, 5, 435.
2. Noltmann, E. & Bruns, F. H. (1958) BZ, 330, 514.

GLUCOSEPHOSPHATE ISOMERASE

(D-Glucose-6-phosphate ketol-isomerase)

D-Glucose 6-phosphate = D-fructose 6-phosphate

Ref.

Equilibrium constant

$$\frac{[\text{D-fructose 6-phosphate}]}{[\text{D-glucose 6-phosphate}]} = 0.298 \qquad \text{(pH 8, Tris, 30}^\circ) \qquad (2)$$

Molecular weight

source	value	conditions	
Brewer's yeast	145,000	pH 7.0	(3)
Bovine mammary gland	48,000	pH 7.5	(4)
	125,000	--	(5)

Specific activity

Rabbit muscle (100 x)	544	glucose 6-phosphate	(pH 8, Tris, 30°)	(6)
Brewer's yeast (118 x)	675	fructose 6-phosphate	(pH 8, Tris, 30°)	(9)
Bovine mammary gland (5000 x)	384	glucose 6-phosphate	(pH 8, Tris, 30°)	(5)

Specificity

No substrates other than glucose 6-phosphate and fructose 6-phosphate have been found. (1)

Michaelis constants

source	substrate	K_m(M)	conditions	
Bovine mammary gland	glucose 6-phosphate	1.2×10^{-4}	pH 8, Tris, 30°	(5)
	fructose 6-phosphate	7.0×10^{-5}		
Rabbit brain and skeletal muscle; human erythrocytes	glucose 6-phosphate	3×10^{-5}	pH 8, Tris, 30°	(2)
	fructose 6-phosphate	1×10^{-5}		
Mouse brain	glucose 6-phosphate	2.1×10^{-4}	pH 7.1, imidazole, 38°	(7)

Inhibitors

source	inhibitor	type	K_i(M)	conditions	
Various mammals	ATP	C (fructose 6-phosphate)	4×10^{-4}	pH 8, Tris, 30°	(2)
	phosphoenol pyruvate		1.1×10^{-3}		
	6-phosphogluconate		5×10^{-6}		

Inhibitors   (contd.)

source	inhibitor	type	$K_i(M)$	conditions
Various mammals	P_i	C (fructose 6-phosphate)	1.7×10^{-3}	pH 8, Tris, $30°$ (2)

Other inhibitors include PP_i, high concentrations of Mg^{2+} (1) and 2-deoxy-D-glucose 6-phosphate (8).

References

1. Topper, Y. T. (1961)   The Enzymes, 5, 434.

2. Kahana, S. E., Lowry, O. H., Schulz, D. W., Passonneau, J. V. & Crawford, E. J. (1960)   JBC, 235, 2178.

3. Noltmann, E. A. & Bruns, F. H. (1959)   BZ, 331, 436.

4. Baich, A., Wolfe, R. G. & Reithel, F. J. (1960)   JBC, 235, 3130.

5. Hines, M. C. & Wolfe, R. G. (1963)   B, 2, 770.

6. Noltmann, E. A. (1964)   JBC, 239, 1545.

7. Lowry, O. H. & Passonneau, J. V. (1964)   JBC, 239, 31.

8. Wick, A. N., Drury, D. R., Nakada, H. J. & Wolfe, J. B. (1957) JBC, 224, 963.

9. Nakagawa, Y. & Noltmann, E. A. (1965)   JBC, 240, 1877.

GLUCOSAMINEPHOSPHATE ISOMERASE
(2-Amino-2-deoxy-D-glucose-6-phosphate ketol-isomerase (deaminating))

2-Amino-2-deoxy-D-glucose 6-phosphate + H_2O =
D-fructose 6-phosphate + NH_3

Ref.

Equilibrium constant

The forward reaction is favoured. (2,3)

Specificity

The enzyme (Proteus vulgaris) was inactive with glucosamine, N-acetyl-glucosamine or N-acetylglucosamine 6-phosphate (3) and that from Escherichia coli was inactive with glucosamine, N-acetyl glucosamine 6-phosphate, galactosamine 6-phosphate or N-acetyl galactosamine 6-phosphate (2). The enzyme isolated from hog kidney exhibits similar specificity properties (2).

Michaelis constants

source	substrate	relative velocity	K_m(M)	conditions	
E. coli	glucosamine 6-phosphate	1.0	7.1×10^{-3}	pH 7.8, Tris,	(2)
		$1.0^{(a)}$	1.2×10^{-3}	37°	
Hog kidney	glucosamine 6-phosphate	1.0	1.4×10^{-2}	pH 7.8, Tris,	(2)
		$5.0^{(a)}$	6.6×10^{-4}	37°	

(a) In the presence of N-acetyl glucosamine 6-phosphate.

References

1. Topper, Y. J. (1961) The Enzymes, 5, 436.

2. Comb, D. G. & Roseman, S. (1958) JBC, 232, 807.

3. Nakada, H. I. (1966) Methods in Enzymology, 9, 575.

GLUCURONATE ISOMERASE

(D-Glucuronate ketol-isomerase)

D-Glucuronate = D-fructuronate

Equilibrium constant

$$\frac{[\text{D-fructuronate}]}{[\text{D-glucuronate}]} = \begin{array}{l} 0.82 \\ >49 \end{array} \begin{array}{l} (\text{pH 8, } P_i, 37^{\circ}) \\ (\text{pH 8, borate, } 37^{\circ}) \end{array}$$ (2,3)
(2,3)

$$\frac{[\text{D-tagaturonate}]}{[\text{D-galacturonate}]} = \begin{array}{l} 4.0 \\ 1.0 \end{array} \begin{array}{l} (\text{pH 8, } P_i, 37^{\circ}) \\ (\text{pH 8, borate, } 37^{\circ}) \end{array}$$ (2,3)
(2,3)

Specificity

The enzyme from Escherichia coli also catalyzes the isomerization of D-galacturonate to D-tagaturonate but the following compounds are inactive: D-mannuronate, L-iduronate, 5-keto-D-gluconate, 2-keto-D-gluconate, D-glucose, D-fructose, L-sorbose, D-arabinose, D-ribose and D-ribose 5-phosphate. (2,3)

Michaelis constants

source	substrate	$K_m(M)$	conditions	
E. coli	D-galacturonate	1.65×10^{-3}	pH 8.0, borate, 37°	(2,3)
	D-tagaturonate	7.5×10^{-4}		
	D-glucuronate	3.7×10^{-3}		

References

1. Topper, Y. J. (1961) The Enzymes, 5, 436.
2. Ashwell, G. (1962) Methods in Enzymology, 5, 190.
3. Ashwell, G., Wahba, A. J. & Hickman, J. (1960) JBC, 235, 1559.

ARABINOSEPHOSPHATE ISOMERASE

(D-Arabinose-5-phosphate ketol-isomerase)

D-Arabinose 5-phosphate = D-ribulose 5-phosphate

Equilibrium constant

$$\frac{[\text{D-ribulose 5-phosphate}]}{[\text{D-arabinose 5-phosphate}]} = 0.295 \quad (\text{pH 8, glycylglycine, } 37^\circ) \quad (1)$$

Specificity

The enzyme (Propionibacterium pentosaceum) is highly specific and the following could not replace D-arabinose 5-phosphate: L-arabinose, D-arabinose, D-xylose, D-ribose, D-ribose 5-phosphate or D-glucose 6-phosphate.

(1)

Michaelis constants

source	substrate	$K_m(M)$	conditions	
P. pentosaceum	D-arabinose 5-phosphate	1.98×10^{-3}	pH 8, gly-cylglycine, 37°	(1,2)

References

1. Volk, W. A. (1966) Methods in Enzymology, 9, 585.
2. Volk, W. A. (1960) JBC, 235, 1550.

L-RHAMNOSE ISOMERASE

(L-Rhamnose ketol-isomerase)

L-Rhamnose = L-rhamnulose

Ref.

Equilibrium constant

$$\frac{[\text{L-rhamnulose}]}{[\text{L-rhamnose}]} = \begin{array}{l} 1.5 \\ 0.75 \end{array} \qquad \begin{array}{l} (\text{pH } 7.6, \text{ Tris, } 37^\circ) \\ (\text{pH } 8.5, \text{ Tris, } 37^\circ) \end{array} \qquad \begin{array}{l} (2) \\ (3) \end{array}$$

Specificity

The enzyme is highly specific. Thus, the enzyme isolated from Escherichia coli will not attack D-glucose, D-galactose, D-mannose, L-arabinose, D-xylulose, D-rhamnose or D- or L-fucose (2), and that from Lactobacillus plantarum is inactive towards D-rhamnose, L-fucose, D-mannose, D- or L-arabinose and D- or L-xylose. L-Mannose was isomerized by this enzyme (3).

Michaelis constants

source	substrate	K_m(M)	conditions	
E. coli	L-rhamnose	2.0×10^{-3}	pH 7.6, Tris, 37°	(2)
	L-rhamnulose	1.7×10^{-3}		
L. plantarum	L-rhamnose	7×10^{-4}	pH 8.5, Tris, 37°	(3)
	L-mannose	5×10^{-3}		

References
1. Topper, Y. J. (1961) The Enzymes, 5, 433.
2. Takagi, Y. & Sawada, H. (1964) BBA, 92, 10.
3. Domagk, G. F. & Zech, R. (1966) Methods in Enzymology, 9, 579.

D-LYXOSE ISOMERASE

(D-Lyxose ketol-isomerase)

D-Lyxose = D-xylulose

Ref.

Equilibrium constant

$$\frac{[\text{D-xylulose}]}{[\text{D-lyxose}]} = 0.235 \qquad (\text{pH 7, cacodylate, } 25^\circ) \quad (1)$$

Molecular weight

source	value	conditions	
Aerobacter aerogenes	~ 40,000	pH 7.0	(1)

Specificity

The enzyme (A. aerogenes) isomerizes D-mannose (to D-fructose) at 40% the rate with D-lyxose but D-ribose, D- or L-xylose, D- or L-arabinose, D-glucose, D-glucose 6-phosphate or D-mannose 6-phosphate are not attacked. (2)

Michaelis constants

source	substrate	K_m(M)	conditions	
A. aerogenes	D-lyxose	3.6×10^{-3}	pH 7.0,	
	D-mannose	1.0×10^{-2}	cacodylate,	(1)
	Mn^{2+}	4.0×10^{-6}	35°	

References
1. Anderson, R. L. & Allison, D. P. (1965) JBC, 240, 2367.
2. Anderson, R. L. (1966) Methods in Enzymology, 9, 593.

STEROID Δ-ISOMERASE

(3-Ketosteroid $\Delta 4-\Delta^5$-isomerase)

A Δ^5-3-ketosteroid = a Δ^4-3-ketosteroid

Ref.

Equilibrium constant

    The reversibility of the reaction has been demonstrated. (5)

Molecular weight

source	value	conditions	
Pseudomonas testosteroni	40,800 [3]	pH 6.8	(4)

Specific activity

    Pseudomonas testosteroni   88,500 Δ^5-androstene-3,17-dione.   (2)
                                         (pH 7, P_i, 25°)

Specificity and Michaelis constants

source	substrate	relative velocity	K_m(M)	conditions
P. testos-teroni	Δ^5-androstene-3,17-dione	1.00	3.2×10^{-4}	
	17β-hydroxy-$\Delta^{5(10)}$-estren-3-one	0.0025	2.3×10^{-5}	
	5-pregnene-3,20-dione	1.50	–	
	Δ^5-cholesten-3-one	0.000013	–	
	5(10)-estrene-3,17-dione	0.0027	–	pH 7.0, P_i, 25° (3,4)
	17α-methyl-17-hydroxy-5(10) estren-3-one	0.0055	–	
	17α-ethyl-17-hydroxy-5(10) estren-3-one	0.0073	–	
	17α-ethynyl-17-hydroxy-5(10) estren-3-one	0.0065	–	

Inhibitors

source	inhibitor	type	K_i(M)	conditions
P. testos-teroni	17-β-estradiol	C (Δ^5-androstene-3,17-dione)	1.0×10^{-5}	pH 7, P_i, 25° (3)
	19-nortestosterone		5.2×10^{-6}	
	17β-dihydro-equilenin		6.3×10^{-6}	

Light absorption data

    Δ_ε (Δ^4-androstene-3,17-dione--Δ^5-androstene-3,17-dione)
        at 248 mμ = 16,300 M^{-1} cm^{-1} (4)

References

1. Talalay, P. (1965) Ann. Rev. Biochem., 34, 348.
2. Talalay, P. & Boyer, J. (1965) BBA, 105, 389.
3. Wang, S-F., Kawahara, F. S. & Talalay, P. (1963) JBC, 238, 576.
4. Kawahara, F. S., Wang, S-F., & Talalay, P. (1962) JBC, 237, 1500.
5. Ward, M. G. & Engel, L. L. (1966) JBC, 241, 3154.

ISOPENTENYLPYROPHOSPHATE ISOMERASE

(Isopentenylpyrophosphate Δ^3-Δ^2-isomerase)

Dimethylallyl pyrophosphate = isopentenyl pyrophosphate

Ref.

Equilibrium constant

$$\frac{[\text{isopentenyl pyrophosphate}]}{[\text{dimethylallyl pyrophosphate}]} = 0.15 \qquad (\text{pH } 8,\ 37^\circ) \qquad (1)$$

Molecular weight

source	value	conditions	
Hog liver	60,000	pH 8.0	(1)

Michaelis constants

source	substrates	$K_m(M)$	conditions	
Hog liver	isopentenyl pyrophosphate	8.2×10^{-6}	pH 8.0,	(1)
	Mg^{2+}	1.0×10^{-3}	Tris, 37°	
Yeast	isopentenyl pyrophosphate	3.6×10^{-5}	pH 8.6, Tris, 37°	(2)

References

1. Shah, D. H., Cleland, W. W. & Porter, J. W. (1965) JBC, 240, 1946.

2. Agranoff, B. W., Eggerer, H., Henning, V. & Lynen, F. (1960) JBC, 235, 326.

VINYLACETYL-CoA ISOMERASE

(Vinylacetyl-CoA Δ^3- Δ^2-isomerase)

Vinylacetyl-CoA = crotonoyl-CoA

Equilibrium constant

The reverse reaction (with either crotonoyl-CoA or 3-methyl crotonoyl-CoA as the substrate) could not be demonstrated. (1)

Specificity

The enzyme isolated from ox liver attacked vinylacetyl-CoA (1.00), 3-methylvinylacetyl-CoA (0.50), 3-hexenoyl-CoA (~0.10) and vinylacetyl pantetheine (~0.001). The following compounds were inactive: 4-pentenoyl-CoA, 3-methylvinylacetate and its ethyl ester, 5-androstene-3,17-dione, 5-cholestenone and 5-pregnene-3, 20-dione. (1)

Michaelis constants

source	substrate	$K_m(M)$	conditions	
Ox liver	vinylacetyl-CoA	6×10^{-5}	pH 7.4, Tris, 25°	(1)
	3-methylvinylacetyl-CoA	6×10^{-5}		

Light absorption data

crotonoyl-CoA $\quad \varepsilon$, (266 mμ) = 6,500 M^{-1} cm^{-1} (pH 7.4) (1)

References

1. Rilling, H. C. & Coon, M. J. (1960) JBC, 235, 3087.

PHOSPHOGLYCERATE PHOSPHOMUTASE

(D-Phosphoglycerate 2,3-phosphomutase)

2-Phospho-D-glycerate = 3-phospho-D-glycerate

Ref.

Equilibrium constant

$$\frac{[\text{3-phospho-D-glycerate}]}{[\text{2-phospho-D-glycerate}]} = 5.0 \qquad (\text{pH } 6.8, \text{ imidazole}, 37°) \qquad (3)$$

Molecular weight

source	value	conditions	
Wheat germ	~ 35,000	-	(2)

Michaelis constants

source	substrate	K_m(M)	conditions	
Wheat germ	3-phospho-D-glycerate	6×10^{-4}	pH 7, Tris, 30°	(1)
	2-phospho-D-glycerate	$5-1 \times 10^{-4}$		

Inhibitors

High concentrations of 2,3-diphospho-D-glycerate (but not of 2-phospho-D-glycerate) inhibit. (2)

References

1. Ito, N. & Grisolia, S. (1959) JBC, 234, 242.
2. Grisolia, S. (1962) Methods in Enzymology, 5, 236.
3. Cowgill, R. W. & Pizer, L. I. (1956) JBC, 223, 885.

METHYLASPARTATE MUTASE

(L-threo-3-Methylaspartate carboxy-aminomethylmutase)

L-threo-3-Methylaspartate = L-glutamate

Equilibrium constant

$$\frac{[\text{L-glutamate}]}{[\text{L-threo-3-methylaspartate}]} = 10.6 \qquad (\text{pH } 8.2, \text{ Tris}, 30^\circ) \qquad (1)$$

Molecular weight

source	value	conditions	
Clostridium tetanomorphum			
E component*	128,000	-	(1)
S component	17,000	various	(2)

*The enzyme consists of two separable protein moieties: components E and S. Both components are required for activity.

Specificity

The enzyme (C. tetanomorphum) appears to be absolutely specific for L-glutamate which cannot be replaced by the following compounds: D-glutamate, 2-, 3-, or 4-methyl-DL-glutamate, L-glutamine, the 4-methyl ester of L-glutamate or DL-2-amino-adipate. L-threo-3-Methylaspartate cannot be replaced by L-threo-3-ethylaspartate. (1)

Michaelis constants

source	substrate	relative velocity	$K_m(M)$	conditions	
Cl. tetanomor- phum	L-threo-3- methylaspar- tate	1.4	$\sim 5 \times 10^{-4}$	pH 8.2,	
	L-glutamate	1.0	$1\text{-}2 \times 10^{-3}$	Tris,	(1)
	benzimidazolylco- bamide coenzyme	-	$\sim 1 \times 10^{-7}$	$\sim 30^\circ$	

References

1. Barker, H. A., Rooze, V., Suzuki, F. & Iodice, A. A. (1964) JBC, 239, 3260.
2. Switzer, R. L. & Barker, H. A. (1967) JBC, 242, 2658.

L-METHYLMALONYL-CoA MUTASE

(L-Methylmalonyl-CoA CoA-carbonylmutase)

L-Methylmalonyl-CoA = succinyl-CoA

Ref.

Equilibrium constant

$$\frac{[\text{succinyl-CoA}]}{[\text{methylmalonyl-CoA}]} = \sim 20 \qquad (\text{pH } 7.3 - 7.5, \text{ Tris, } 30^\circ) \quad (1,2)$$

Molecular weight

source	value	conditions	
Sheep liver	165,000	pH 7.5	(2)
	75,000	minimum: cobamide content	(2)
Propionibacterium shermanii	56,000	pH 7.5	(1)

Specific activity

P. shermanii	(480 x)	127 methyl-malonyl-CoA	(pH 7.3, Tris, 30°)	(1,2)
		14.4 succinyl-CoA	(pH 7.3, Tris, 25°)	(1)
Sheep liver	(7000 x)	85.3 methyl-malonyl-CoA	(pH 7.5, Tris, 30°)	(2)
		5 succinyl-CoA	(pH 7.5, Tris, 25°)	(2)

Michaelis constants

source	substrate	K_m(M)	conditions	
Sheep liver	L-methylmalonyl-CoA	2.4×10^{-4}	pH 7.5, Tris, 25°	(2)
	succinyl-CoA	6.2×10^{-5}		
	dimethylbenzimidazolyl-cobamide	2.1×10^{-8}		
P. shermanii	methylmalonyl-CoA	8.5×10^{-5}	pH 7.3, Tris, 25°	(1)
	succinyl-CoA	3.45×10^{-5}		
	benzimidazolylcobamide	3.45×10^{-7}		

Inhibitors

The enzyme (sheep liver) is inhibited by D-methylmalonyl-CoA. (2)

References

1. Kellermeyer, R. W., Allen, S. H. G., Stjernholm, R. & Wood, H. G. (1964) JBC, 239, 2562.

2. Cannata, J. J. B., Focesi, A., Mazumder, R., Warner, R. C. & Ochoa, S. (1965) JBC, 240, 3249.

2-HYDROXYISOPROPYLMALATE ISOMERASE

(Hydroxyisopropylmalate 2,3-hydroxymutase)

2-Hydroxyisopropylmalate = 3-hydroxyisopropylmalate

Ref.

Equilibrium constant

At equilibrium 2-hydroxyisopropylmalate, 3-hydroxyisopropyl-
malate and dimethylcitraconate are present in the following propor-
tions: 3.4:8.7:1 (pH 7.0, Tris-succinate, $32°$).   (1)

Molecular weight

source	value	conditions	
Neurospora crassa	70,000-80,000	sucrose gradient	(1)

Michaelis constants

source	substrate	K_m(M)	conditions	
N. crassa	3-hydroxyisopropylmalate	6.7×10^{-4}	pH 7.0,	
	2-hydroxyisopropylmalate	6.4×10^{-5}	Tris-succinate,	(1)
	dimethylcitraconate	1.8×10^{-5}	$32°$	

Light absorption data

Dimethylcitraconate		
$\varepsilon, (225 \ m\mu) = 6,590 \ M^{-1}cm^{-1}$		
$\varepsilon, (235 \ m\mu) = 4,530 \ M^{-1}cm^{-1}$	pH 7.0	(1)
$\varepsilon, (245 \ m\mu) = 2,270 \ M^{-1}cm^{-1}$		

References

1. Gross, S. R., Burns, R. O. & Umbarger, H. E. (1963) B, 2, 1046.

MUCONATE CYCLOISOMERASE

(4-Carboxymethyl-4-hydroxyisocrotonolactone lyase (decyclizing))

(+)-4-Carboxymethyl-4-hydroxyisocrotonolactone =

cis-cis-muconate

Ref.

Equilibrium constant

$$\frac{[\text{cis-cis-muconate}]}{[(+)\text{-4-carboxymethyl-4-hydroxyisocrotonolactone}]} = 4.06 \times 10^{-2}$$ (pH 7.5, Tris.)   (1)

Specificity

Muconate cycloisomerase from Pseudomonas fluorescens was inactive with trans-trans-muconate. The cis-trans isomer was attacked at about 0.02% the rate at which the cis-cis isomer was utilized.   (1)

Michaelis constants

source	substrate	$K_m(M)$	conditions	
P. fluorescens	cis-cis-muconate	9.8×10^{-5}	pH 8.0, P_i	(1)

Light absorption data

cis-cis-muconate ε, (260 mµ) = 16,900 M^{-1} cm^{-1} (pH 7.0)   (1)

References

1. Sistrom, W. R. & Stanier, R. Y. (1954) JBC, 210, 821.

TETRAOXYPTERIDINE ISOMERASE

(Tetraoxypteridine isomerase (xanthine-8-carboxylate))

Tetraoxypteridine = xanthine 8-carboxylate

Equilibrium constant

$$\frac{[\text{xanthine 8-carboxylate}]}{[\text{tetraoxypteridine}]} = 1.6 \times 10^{-3} \quad (\text{pH 7.5, Tris, } 23^{\circ}) \tag{1}$$

Specificity

The enzyme (<u>Alcaligenes faecalis</u>) is highly specific and does not isomerize 6,7-dioxypteridine, 2-amino-6,7-dioxypteridine, 4,6,7-trioxypteridine, leucopterin, 1-,3-, or 8-monomethyltetraoxypteridine or 4-amino-5-oxalylamino-2,6-dioxypyrimidine. 1,3,8-Trimethyltetraoxypteridine was attacked at about 1-2% the rate at which tetraoxypteridine was isomerized.

(1)

References

1. McNutt, W. S. & Damle, S. P. (1964) JBC, 239, 4272.

TYROSYL-sRNA SYNTHETASE

(L-Tyrosine: sRNA ligase (AMP))

ATP + L-tyrosine + sRNA =

AMP + pyrophosphate + L-tyrosyl-sRNA

Ref.

Molecular weight

source	value	conditions	
Escherichia coli	95,000	pH 6.5	(2)
Bacillus subtilis	88,000	pH 6.5	(2)
Hog pancreas	$S_{20,w} = 4.2$	pH 7.5	(3)

Specific activity

E. coli	60	(600 x)	$PP_i^{(a)}$	pH 7.0, cacodylate, 37°	(2)
B. subtilis	48	(1200 x)	$PP_i^{(a)}$	pH 7.0, cacodylate, 37°	(2)
Hog pancreas	5.2	(400 x)	$PP_i^{(a)}$	pH 8.3, glycine, 37°	(3)
Hog pancreas[b]	14.7	(5000 x)	$PP_i^{(a)}$	pH 7.5, Tris, 37°	(4)

[a] In the ATP-PP_i exchange reaction

[b] Prepared from an acetone powder

Specificity

Tyrosyl-sRNA synthetase is highly specific for its substrates. Thus, that from hog pancreas could only utilize L-tyrosine and 3-fluoro-L-tyrosine of a number of substituted L-tyrosines tested. Of the protein amino acids only L-tyrosine was active.　　　　　　(3)

The enzymes from E. coli and B. subtilis were similarly highly specific in that they did not catalyze an ATP-PP_i exchange with any of the protein amino acids other than L-tyrosine. Of a variety of tyrosine analogs tested, only D-tyrosine, 3-fluorotyrosine, 3-hydroxy-tyrosine and 5-hydroxy-2-(3-DL-alanyl)-pyridine were active. The following nucleotides were inactive in the place of ATP with either enzyme: ADP, GTP, CTP, UTP, dATP, dGTP, dCTP, TTP and adenyl-5-methylenedi-phosphonate. Both enzymes cross-reacted completely with their hetero-logous s-RNA's but neither enzyme transferred tyrosine to yeast sRNA. (2)

Michaelis constants

source	substrate	$\frac{V}{(\text{relative})}$	$K_m(M)$	conditions	
Hog pancreas	L-tyrosine[a]	–	6×10^{-5}	pH 8.5, glycine, 37°	(3)
	ATP[a]	–	5×10^{-3}		
	PP_i[a]	–	3×10^{-4}		
	sRNA	–	3.2×10^{-8}	pH 7.5, Tris, 37°	(4)
E. coli	L-tyrosine[b]	1.00	2.7×10^{-5}	pH 7.0, cacodylate, 37°	(2)
	3-fluoro-DL-tyrosine[b]	0.85	4.8×10^{-4}		
	ATP[b]	–	4.0×10^{-4}		
B. subtilis	L-tyrosine[b]	–	4.8×10^{-5}		
	3-fluoro-DL-tyrosine[b]	–	2.4×10^{-4}		
	ATP[b]	–	2.9×10^{-4}		

[a] In the ATP-PP_i exchange reaction.
[b] In the formation of L-tyrosyl-sRNA reaction. The kinetic constants obtained in the ATP-PP_i exchange reaction catalyzed by the enzymes from E. coli and B. subtilis will be found in reference (2).

Inhibitors

source	inhibitor[a]	$K_i(M)$	conditions	
E. coli	L-tyrosinol	4.1×10^{-6}	pH 7.0, cacodylate, 30°	(2)
	tyramine	6.0×10^{-6}		
	L-tyrosine amide	8.1×10^{-6}		
	L-tyrosine methyl ester	1.7×10^{-5}		
B. subtilis	L-tyrosinol	1×10^{-5}		
	tyramide	4.2×10^{-5}		
	L-tyrosine amide	1.1×10^{-4}		
	L-tyrosine methyl ester	1.9×10^{-4}		

[a] C(L-tyrosine) in the ATP-PP_i exchange reaction.

References

1. Stulberg, M. P. & Novelli, G. D. (1962) The Enzymes, 6, 401.
2. Calendar, R. & Berg, P. (1966) B, 5, 1681, 1690.
3. Schweet, R. S. & Allen, E. H. (1958) JBC, 233, 1104.
4. Clark, J. M. Jr. & Eyzaguirre, J. P. (1962) JBC, 237, 3698.

TRYPTOPHANYL-sRNA SYNTHETASE

(L-Tryptophan: sRNA ligase (AMP))

ATP + L-tryptophan + sRNA =

AMP + pyrophosphate + L-tryptophanyl-sRNA

Ref.

Equilibrium constant

The reaction is reversible. (3)

Specific activity

Beef pancreas (215 x)   1.43 hydroxylamine[a] (pH 7.8, Tris, 37°) (1)
                        7.45 PP_i[b]   (pH 7.8, Tris, 37°) (1)

---
[a] In the reaction ATP + L-tryptophan + hydroxylamine = L-tryptophan
hydroxamate + AMP + PP_i
[b] In the ATP-PP_i exchange reaction

Specificity

Tryptophanyl-sRNA synthetase from beef pancreas is highly specific
for L-tryptophan and certain analogs of tryptophan (7-azatryptophan,
tryptazan, 6-fluorotryptophan and 5-fluorotryptophan).   5- and 6-Methyl-
tryptophan and a number of the protein amino acids were inactive (1,2).
The enzyme is specific for ATP which could not be replaced by any other
nucleotide tested. (3)

In the reverse reaction, the enzyme shows little specificity for
the formation of ATP from adenyl amino acid and PP_i.   Thus adenylate
prepared from D- or L-alanine, D- or L-valine, D- or L-phenylalanine
or D- or L-tryptophan produced ATP in the reverse reaction. (3)

Inhibitors

In the ATP-PP_i exchange assay various tryptophan analogs
(β-methyltryptophan, tryptophan hydroxamate, tryptamine, 5-hydroxy-
tryptophan, 5-methyltryptophan and 6-methyltryptophan) were inhibitory
(C(tryptophan)). (2)

References

1. Davie, E. W., Koningsberger, V. V. & Lipmann, F. (1956) ABB, 65, 21.
2. Sharon, N. & Lipmann, F. (1957) ABB, 69, 219.
3. Davie, E. W. (1962) Methods in Enzymology, 5, 718.

THREONYL-sRNA SYNTHETASE

(L-Threonine: sRNA ligase (AMP))

ATP + L-threonine + sRNA =
AMP + pyrophosphate + L-threonyl-sRNA

Ref.

Michaelis constants

source		substrate	$K_m(M)$	conditions
Rat liver[a]	Enzyme A	L-threonine	4.5×10^{-6}	pH 8.0, Tris, 37° (with rat liver sRNA) (1)
		ATP	5.6×10^{-5}	
	Enzyme B	L-threonine	4.2×10^{-6}	
		ATP	1.2×10^{-4}	

[a] Rat liver possesses two chromatographically distinct threonyl-sRNA synthetases (Enzymes A and B).

References

1. Allende, C. C., Allende, J. E., Gatica, M., Celis, J., Mora, G. & Matamala, M. (1966) JBC, 241, 2245.

LEUCYL-sRNA SYNTHETASE

(L-Leucine: sRNA ligase (AMP))

ATP + L-leucine + sRNA =

AMP + pyrophosphate + L-leucyl-sRNA

Ref.

Equilibrium constant

The reaction is reversible. (1)

Specificity and Michaelis constants

The effect of NaCl on the specificity of leucyl-sRNA synthetase is noteworthy. Thus, the esterification of L-leucine to Escherichia coli or yeast sRNA by their respective homologous enzymes is unaffected by NaCl. However, in the presence of NaCl, leucyl-sRNA synthetase undergoes a reversible modification to a form that can no longer attach leucine to heterologous sRNA. The ATP-PP$_i$ exchange reaction of the yeast enzyme is unaffected by NaCl. (2)

source	substrate	$K_m(M)$	conditions	
E. coli	E. coli sRNA	2.5×10^{-8}	pH 7.0,	
Yeast	E. coli sRNA	1.6×10^{-7}	cacodylate,	(2)
	yeast sRNA	4×10^{-7}	37°	

References

1. Berg, P., Bergmann, F. H., Ofengand, E. J. & Dieckmann, M. (1961) JBC, 236, 1726.
2. Peterkofsky, A., Gee, S. J. & Jesensky, C. (1966) B, 5, 2789.

ISOLEUCYL-sRNA SYNTHETASE

(L-Isoleucine: sRNA ligase(AMP))

ATP + L-isoleucine + sRNA =

AMP + pyrophosphate + L-isoleucyl-sRNA

Ref.

Molecular weight

source	value	conditions	
Escherichia coli	112,000	pH 7.0	(1)

Specific activity

E. coli   11 PP_i[a]   (pH 7.0, cacodylate, 30°)   (1)

---
[a] In the ATP-PP$_i$ exchange reaction.

Specificity

The enzyme (E. coli) is highly specific for L-isoleucine. Thus, of all the other protein amino acids only L-valine is active in the ATP-PP$_i$ exchange assay.   However, in the presence of sRNA the valyl adenylate enzyme complex breaks down and valyl adenylate is set free. Thus, the synthesis of valyl-sRNA is not catalyzed by isoleucyl-sRNA synthetase.   (2,3)

Michaelis constants

source	substrate	relative velocity	K_m(M)	conditions	
E. coli	sRNA	-	1.7×10^{-7}	pH 7.0, cacodylate, 30°	(1)
	L-isoleucine[a]	1.0	5×10^{-6}	pH 7.0, cacodylate, 30°	(2)
	L-valine[a]	0.5	-		

---
[a] In the ATP-PP$_i$ exchange assay.

The properties of the enzyme from Bacillus stearothermophilus are discussed in reference (4).

Inhibitors

source	inhibitor	type	K_i(M)	conditions	
E. coli	L-valine	C(L-isoleucine)	3.8×10^{-4}	pH 7.0, cacodylate, 30°	(2)

References
1. Baldwin, A. N. & Berg, P. (1966) JBC, 241, 831, 839.
2. Bergmann, F. H., Berg, P. & Dieckmann, M. (1961) JBC, 236, 1735.
3. Norris, A. T. & Berg, P. (1964) PNAS, 52, 330.
4. Arca, M., Calvori, C., Frontali, L. & Tecce, G. (1964) BBA, 87, 440.

LYSYL-sRNA SYNTHETASE

(L-Lysine: sRNA ligase (AMP))

ATP + L-lysine + sRNA = AMP + pyrophosphate + L-lysyl-sRNA

Ref.

Molecular weight

source	value	conditions	
Escherichia coli	100,000	pH 7.5	(4)
Yeast	113,000	-	(2)

Specific activity

E. coli	(850 x)	20.8 PP$_i$[a]	(pH 8.0, Tris, 37°)	(1)
		0.05 L-lysine	(pH 8.0, Tris, 37°)	(1)
	(790 x)	1.47 L-lysine	(pH 7.0, cacodylate, 37°)	(4)
Yeast	(450 x)	2.1 L-lysine	(37°)	(2)

[a] In the ATP-PP$_i$ exchange assay.

Specificity

The enzyme from E. coli utilized L-tryptophan at 0.5% the rate with L-lysine but the following L-amino acids were inactive: phenylalanine, valine, isoleucine, serine, threonine, alanine and aspartate (4). At high concentrations the following compounds were utilized: 4-oxalysine, 2,6-diamino-4-hexynoate and trans-4-dehydrolysine (3). The enzyme also catalyzes a lysine dependent ATP-PP$_i$ exchange reaction. (1,3)

<u>Michaelis constants</u>

source	substrate	$K_m(M)$	conditions	
E. coli	lysine	2×10^{-5}		
	ATP	4×10^{-3}		
	Mg^{2+}	7.6×10^{-3}	pH 8.0,	
	lysine[a]	5.9×10^{-5}	Tris, 37°	(3)
	oxalysine[a]	6.6×10^{-4}		
	trans-dehydrolysine[a]	9.9×10^{-4}		
	2,6-diamino-4-hexynoate[a]	5.5×10^{-4}		
	lysine	1.8×10^{-5}		
	ATP	1.5×10^{-5}	pH 7.0, caco-	(4)
	Mg^{2+}	3.0×10^{-3}	dylate, 37°	
	sRNA	1×10^{-6}		

[a]In the ATP-PP$_i$ exchange reaction.

<u>Inhibitors</u>

Several structural analogs of lysine (DL-4-oxalysine, <u>cis</u>-4-dehydrolysine, <u>trans</u>-4-dehydrolysine and DL-2,6-diamino-4-hexynoate) are inhibitors (C(L-lysine)) of the enzyme from <u>E</u>. <u>coli</u>.   (3)

<u>References</u>

1. Stern, R. & Mehler, A. H. (1965) <u>BZ</u>, <u>342</u>, 400.

2. Lagerkvist, U. & Waldenstrom, J. (1965) <u>JBC</u>, <u>240</u>, PC 2264.

3. Lansford, E. M. Jr., Lee, N. M. & Shive, W. (1967) <u>ABB</u>, <u>119</u>, 272.

4. Waldenstrom, J. (1968) <u>European J. Biochem.</u>, <u>3</u>, 483.

ALANYL-sRNA SYNTHETASE

(L-Alanine: sRNA ligase (AMP))

ATP + L-alanine + sRNA =

AMP + pyrophosphate + L-alanyl-sRNA

Ref.

Specific activity

Pig liver (3800 x)   0.027 L-alanine[a]   pH 7.5, Tris, 38°   (1)

                  114 PP_i[b]   pH 8.5, Tris, 38°   (1)

---

[a]In the formation of alanyl-sRNA reaction.

[b]In the ATP-PP_i exchange reaction.

Specificity

Alanyl-sRNA synthetase is highly specific for its substrates. Thus the enzyme from pig liver was unable to utilize the following L-amino acids in the place of L-alanine in the formation of alanyl-sRNA or in the ATP-PPi exchange assay: aspartate, cysteine, glutamate, glutamine, glycine, histidine, leucine, lysine, methionine, phenylalanine, serine, tryptophan, tyrosine and valine. The following compounds were also inactive: D-alanine, β-alanine, DL-2-aminobutyrate, pyruvate and lactate. Both the synthesis and exchange reactions exhibit a marked specificity for ATP; ADP, GTP, ITP, CTP and UTP were inactive. Both reactions proceeded only in the presence of Co^{2+} or Mg^{2+} which could not be replaced by Mn^{2+}, Ca^{2+}, Ba^{2+}, Sr^{2+}, Cd^{2+} or Zn^{2+}.   (1)

The enzyme is also highly specific for pig liver sRNA which could not be replaced by sRNA from the following sources: calf liver, yeast or the pea.   (1)

References

1. Webster, G. C. (1961) BBA, 49, 141.

VALYL-sRNA SYNTHETASE

(L-Valine: sRNA ligase (AMP))

ATP + L-valine + sRNA = AMP + pyrophosphate + L-valyl-sRNA

Ref.

Equilibrium constant

$$\frac{[AMP]\,[PP_i]\,[L\text{-valyl-sRNA}]}{[ATP]\,[L\text{-valine}]\,[sRNA]} \;=\; 0.32$$

(pH 7.0, cacodylate, 30°)   (1)

Molecular weight

source	value	conditions	
Escherichia coli	$S_{20,w} = 4.2$	-	(2)
Saccharomyces cerevisiae	112,000	various	(3)

Specific activity

E. coli (650 x)	0.22 L-valine[a]	(pH 7.0, 37°)	(2)
S. cerevisiae (1300 x)	0.40 L-valine	(pH 7.0, cacodylate, 37°)	(3)

[a] The reaction catalyzed was: ATP + L-valine + hydroxylamine = AMP + PP_i + L-valylhydroxamate.

Specificity

The enzyme from E. coli could utilize the following amino acids as substrates: L-valine (1.00), L-threonine (0.28) and L-2-amino-butyrate (0.31) but not DL-allothreonine, L-isoleucine, DL-alloisoleu-cine, L-tert-leucine, L-leucine, DL-norvaline, DL-isovaline, threo-3-methyl-DL-aspartate, L-penicillamine, 2-aminoisobutyrate, DL-homo-serine, DL-homocysteine, L-alanine, DL-valinol, DL-2-amino-3-methyl phosphonate or DL-2-aminobutyl phosphonate.   (2)

With the enzyme from S. cerevisiae, the following amino acids were active: L-valine (1.000), L-lysine (0.024), L-leucine (0.003),

Specificity contd.

L-alanine (0.003) and L-serine (0.003). Little activity was exhibited towards L-isoleucine, L-phenylalanine, L-threonine, L-tyrosine or L-tryptophan.   (3)

Michaelis constants

source	substrate	$\dfrac{V}{(\text{relative})}$	$K_m(M)$	conditions	
E. coli	L-valine[a]	-	2×10^{-4}	pH 7.0,	(2)
	ATP[a]	-	2×10^{-3}	P_i, 37°	
	L-valine[b]	1.00	1.0×10^{-4}	pH 7.0, caco-	(4)
	L-threonine[b]	0.30	1.2×10^{-2}	dylate, 30°	
	L-2-amino-3-chlorobutyrate[b]	1.00	3.3×10^{-4}	pH 7.0, caco-	(4)
	L-allo-2-amino-3-chlorobutyrate[b]	0.15	1×10^{-3}	dylate, 30°	
	L-2-aminobutyrate[b]	0.30	3.7×10^{-3}		
S. cerevisiae	L-valine	-	3×10^{-5}	pH 7.0, caco-	(3)
	ATP	-	4×10^{-5}	dylate, 37°	
	Mg^{2+}	-	8×10^{-3}		
	sRNA	-	1×10^{-6}		

[a] In the hydroxylamine assay.

[b] In the ATP-PP$_i$ exchange assay.

References

1. Berg, P., Bergmann, F. H., Ofengand, E. J. & Dieckmann, M. (1961) JBC, 236, 1726.

2. George, H. & Meister, A. (1967) BBA, 132, 165.

3. Lagerkvist, V. & Waldenstrom, J. (1967) JBC, 242, 3021.

4. Bergmann, F. H., Berg, P. & Dieckmann, M. (1961) JBC, 236, 1735.

METHIONYL-sRNA SYNTHETASE

(L-Methionine: sRNA ligase (AMP))

ATP + L-methionine + sRNA =

AMP + pyrophosphate + L-methionyl-sRNA

Ref.

Molecular weight

source	value	conditions	
Escherichia coli	190,000	Sephadex G200, pH 8.0	(1)

Specific activity

E. coli (200 x)   30 PP_i[a]   (pH 8.5, Tris, 37°)   (1)
                   0.98 methionine[b]   (pH 8.5, Tris, 37°)   (1)

---

[a] In the ATP-PP_i-exchange assay
[b] In the acylation (of sRNA) assay

Specificity

The enzyme (E. coli) is highly specific for all of its substrates. In E. coli a single enzyme catalyzes the methionylation of both $sRNA_F$ and $sRNA_M$. (1)

Michaelis constants

source	substrate	$\dfrac{V}{\text{(relative)}}$	$K_m(M)$	conditions	
E. coli	L-methionine[a]	-	2×10^{-4}	pH 8.5, Tris, 37°	(1)
	L-methionine[b]	-	2×10^{-5}		
Sarcina lutea	L-methionine[a]	1.00	5.7×10^{-4}	pH 8.0, Tris, 37°	(2)
	L-selenomethionine[a]	1.00	5.7×10^{-4}		
	L-ethionine[a]	0.93	2.94×10^{-3}		
	L-cystathionine[a]	0.87	3.22×10^{-3}		

Michaelis constants contd.

(a) In the ATP-PP$_i$-exchange assay
(b) In the acylation (of sRNA) assay

Inhibitors

source	inhibitor	type[a]	K_m(M)	conditions
S. lutea	methionine amide	NC	9.66×10^{-2}	
	N-acetylmethionine	NC	1.31×10^{-2}	
	2-aminobutyrate	C	1.25×10^{-2}	
	3-aminobutyrate	C	1.17×10^{-2}	
	4-aminobutyrate	C	1.04×10^{-1}	
	2-methylmethionine	C	8.6×10^{-3}	pH 8.0, Tris, 37° (2)
	2-hydroxymethionine	C	8.8×10^{-3}	
	homocysteine	C	3.1×10^{-3}	
	homoserine	C	8.6×10^{-3}	
	norleucine	C	1.00×10^{-1}	
	methionine sulphone	C	1.51×10^{-2}	
	methionine sulphoximine	C	1.65×10^{-2}	

(a) With respect to L-methionine

References

1. Heinrikson, R. L. & Hartley, B. S. (1967) BJ, 105, 17.

2. Hahn, G. A. & Brown, J. W. (1967) BBA, 146, 264.

SERYL-sRNA SYNTHETASE

(L-Serine: sRNA ligase (AMP))

ATP + L-serine + sRNA =

AMP + pyrophosphate + L-seryl-sRNA

Molecular weight

source	value	conditions	
Yeast	89,000	sucrose gradient	(1)

Specific activity

Yeast (197 x) 0.56 L-serine[a] (pH 7.5, P_i, 37°)   (1)

[a]In the formation of seryl-sRNA reaction

Michaelis constants

source	substrate		$\dfrac{V}{(\text{relative})}$	$K_m(M)$	conditions	
Yeast	sRNA	(yeast)	1.00	2.4×10^{-7}		
	sRNA	(E. coli)	0.24	2.6×10^{-6}	pH 7.5, Tris.	(2)
	L-serine[a]		-	1.0×10^{-5}		

[a]In the formation of seryl-sRNA reaction

Inhibitors

The enzyme (yeast) is inhibited by P_i.   (2)

References

1. Makman, M. H. & Cantoni, G. L. (1965) B, 4, 1434.
2. Makman, M. H. & Cantoni, G. L. (1966) B, 5, 2246.

ASPARTYL-sRNA SYNTHETASE

(L-Aspartate: sRNA ligase (AMP))

ATP + L-aspartate + sRNA =
AMP + pyrophosphate + L-aspartyl-sRNA

Ref.

Specificity

The enzyme from <u>Lactobacillus arabinosus</u> is highly specific for L-aspartate which cannot be replaced by any of the common amino acids or by D-aspartate, L-cysteate, <u>erythro</u>-3-DL-hydroxyaspartate, <u>threo</u>-3-DL-hydroxyaspartate or a mixture of the two diastereoisomers of 3-DL-methylaspartate. The enzyme also catalyzes an ATP-PP_i exchange reaction but not the formation of aspartyl-hydroxamate in the presence of L-aspartate, hydroxylamine and ATP. (1)

A separate enzyme (present in extracts of <u>L. arabinosus</u>) is responsible for the activation of L-asparagine. (2)

Michaelis constants

source	substrate	$K_m(M)$	conditions	
<u>L. arabinosus</u>	L-aspartate ATP Mg^{2+}	9×10^{-3} 9×10^{-4} 9×10^{-3}	pH 7.5, P_i, $37°$ (ATP-PP_i exchange reaction)	(1)

References

1. Norton, S. J., Ravel, J. M. & Shive, W. (1963) JBC, 238, 269.
2. Hedgcoth, C., Ravel, J. M. & Shive, W. (1963) BBRC, 13, 495.

D-ALANYL-POLYPHOSPHORIBITOL SYNTHETASE

(D-Alanine: polyphosphoribitol ligase (AMP))

ATP + D-alanine + polyribitolphosphate =

AMP + pyrophosphate + O-D-alanyl-polyribitolphosphate

Ref.

Specificity

The enzyme from Lactobacillus arabinosus exhibits an absolute
specificity for amino acids of the D-configuration although modifica-
tions introduced into the β-carbon atom of D-alanine are possible.
The enzyme is also specific for ATP; CTP, UTP and GTP showed less
than 5% the activity observed with ATP. (1)

Michaelis constants

source	substrate	relative velocity	$K_m(M)$	conditions	
L. arabinosus	D-alanine	1.00	$7 \times 10^{-2(a)}$	PP$_i$-ATP	
	D-2-amino-n butyrate	0.15	-	exchange	
	D-serine	0.07	-	assay	(1)
	ATP	-	2.5×10^{-3}	pH 7.8,	
	PP$_i$	-	1.3×10^{-4}	Tris, 37°	

---

[a] A value of 0.4 M was found in the hydroxamate assay (pH 7.4,
Tris, 37°)

References

1. Baddiley, J. & Neuhaus, F. C. (1960) BJ, 75, 579.

L-ARGINYL-sRNA SYNTHETASE

(L-Arginine:sRNA ligase (AMP))

$$ATP + L\text{-arginine} + sRNA = AMP + PP_i + L\text{-arginyl-sRNA}$$

Ref.

Specificity

The enzyme (rat liver) is highly specific for L-arginine
and the following compounds were inactive as substrates: L-ornithine,
L-2-amino-4-guanidinobutyrate, L-citrulline, L-homocitrulline, L-
lysine and L-canavanine.

(1)

Michaelis constants

source	substrate	$K_m(M)$	conditions	
Rat liver	arginine	3×10^{-6}	pH 7.5, Tris, 37° (with sRNA from yeast)	(1)

Inhibitors

source	inhibitor	type	K_i	conditions	
Rat liver	L-canavanine	C (L-arginine)	4.5×10^{-5}	pH 7.5, Tris, 37°	(1)

References

1. Allende, C. C. & Allende, J. E. (1964) JBC, 239, 1102.

PHENYLALANYL-sRNA SYNTHETASE

(L-Phenylalanine:sRNA ligase (AMP))

ATP + L-phenylalanine + sRNA =

AMP + PP$_i$ + L-phenylalanyl-sRNA

Ref.

Molecular weight

source	value	conditions	
Bakers' yeast	180,000	various	(2)

Specific activity

Bakers' yeast (180 x)   0.55 L-phenylalanine   (pH 7.5, P$_i$, 37°)   (2)

Specificity

The enzyme isolated from Escherichia coli catalyzes the activation of L-phenylalanine (1.00), p-fluorophenylalanine (0.95), β-2-thienyl-L-alanine (0.58), 1-cyclohexenealanine (0.20), 2-pyridinealanine (0.16), 4-thiazolealanine (0.15), 1-cyclopentenealanine (0.14), β-phenylserine (0.12), trans-crotylglycine (0.10) and trans-2-amino-4-heptenoate (0.10). The following compounds were unable to replace phenylalanine: tyrosine, tryptophan, leucine and a number of substituted amino acids. **(1)**

Michaelis constants

source	substrate	K_m(M)	conditions	
E. coli	phenylalanine	2×10^{-3}	pH 7.6, hydroxyl-	
	ATP	5×10^{-3}	amine, 37°	(1)
Baker's yeast	ATP	$5 - 10 \times 10^{-3}$	pH 7.5, P$_i$, 37°	(2)

References

1. Conway, T. W., Lansford, E. M. & Shive, W. (1962) JBC, 237, 2850.
2. Makman, M. H. & Cantoni, G. L. (1965) B, 4, 1434.

PROLYL-sRNA SYNTHETASE

(L-Proline: sRNA ligase (AMP))

$$ATP + L\text{-proline} + sRNA = AMP + PP_i + L\text{-prolyl-sRNA}$$

Ref.

Michaelis constants

source	substrate	$K_m(M)$	conditions	
Escherichia coli	L-proline	1.2×10^{-4}	pH 6.8, P_i, 37°	(1)
	ATP	6×10^{-4}		

Inhibitors

source	inhibitor	type	$K_i(M)$	conditions	
E. coli	L-3,4-dehydroproline	C (L-proline)	1.2×10^{-3}	pH 6.8, P_i, 37°	(1)

The presence of hydroxyprolyl-sRNA synthetase in chick embryo is reported in reference (2).

References

1. Norton, S. J. (1964) ABB, 106, 147.

2. Jackson, D. S., Watkins, D. & Winkler, A. (1964) BBA, 87, 152.

L-GLUTAMYL-sRNA SYNTHETASE

(L-Glutamate: sRNA ligase (AMP))

$$ATP + L\text{-glutamate} + sRNA = AMP + PP_i + L\text{-glutamyl-sRNA}$$

Ref.

Molecular weight

source	value	conditions	
Escherichia coli	50,000	sucrose gradient	(2)

Specificity

The enzyme (rat liver) is highly specific for its substrates. Thus glutamate could not be replaced by a number of analogs, and the enzyme was unable to utilize sRNA from yeast, E. coli or Bacillus subtilis. dATP could partially replace ATP. (1)

The enzyme isolated from E. coli is also highly specific for its substrates. (3)

Michaelis constants

source	substrate	$K_m(M)$	conditions	
Rat liver	L-glutamate	1.3×10^{-4}	pH 7.0, Tris-acetate, 37°	(1)
	ATP	2.1×10^{-4}		
	Mg^{2+}	1.25×10^{-3}		
	sRNA (rabbit liver)	2.9×10^{-7}		
E. coli	L-glutamate	1.2×10^{-4}	pH 7.7, Tris, 37°	(3)
	ATP	4.2×10^{-4}		
	Mg^{2+}	1.2×10^{-2}		
	sRNA (E. coli)	0.6 mg ml^{-1}		

Inhibitors

The enzyme (E. coli) is strongly inhibited by AMP but not by IMP, UMP, GMP, ADP or IDP. The inhibition is complex and is not competitive with respect to ATP. (2)

The presence of glutaminyl-sRNA synthetase in rat liver (1) and E. coli (2,3) has been demonstrated.

References

1. Deutscher, M. P. (1967) JBC, 242, 1123, 1132.
2. Lazzarini, R. A. & Mehler, A. H. (1964) B, 3, 1445.
3. Ravel, J. M., Wang, S-F., Heinemeyer, C. & Shive, W. (1965) JBC, 240, 432.

GLYCYL-sRNA SYNTHETASE

(Glycine: sRNA ligase (AMP))

$$ATP + glycine + sRNA = AMP + PP_i + glycyl\text{-}sRNA$$

Specific activity

Staphylococcus aureus (218 x) $\begin{matrix} 11 \\ 23 \end{matrix}$ $\begin{matrix} (a) \\ (b) \end{matrix}$ $\begin{matrix} sRNA \\ PP_i \end{matrix}$ (pH 7.5, Tris, 25°)   (1)

(a) A maximum value.

(b) A maximum value obtained by the ATP-PP$_i$ exchange reaction

Specificity

The enzyme from S. aureus is highly specific for ATP: very low activities were observed when ATP was replaced by CTP, UTP, ITP, GTP or TTP.   (1)

Glycyl-sRNA synthetase also catalyzes an ATP-PP$_i$ exchange reaction and a reaction between ATP, glycine and hydroxamate.   (1,2,3,4)

The enzyme from Photobacterium fischeri could not utilize L-serine or acetate in the place of glycine.   (4)

Michaelis constants

source	substrate	$K_m(M)$	conditions	
S. aureus	glycine ATP	6.7×10^{-4} } 2.2×10^{-4}	glycyl-sRNA synthesis pH 7.5, Tris, 25°	(1)
	glycine ATP	1×10^{-3} } 1.9×10^{-4}	ATP-PP$_i$ exchange assay pH 7.5, Tris, 25°	(1)

Michaelis constants contd.

source	substrate	$K_m(M)$	conditions	
Rat liver	glycine	6.0×10^{-4}	ATP-PP_i exchange assay pH 7.5, Tris, 37°	(2)
	ATP	7.6×10^{-5}		
	PP_i	2.1×10^{-4}		
	glycine	4×10^{-6}	glycyl-sRNA synthesis pH 7.5, Tris, 37°	(2)
	ATP	7.9×10^{-4}		
P. fischeri	glycine	6.9×10^{-3}	glycine hydroxamate reaction pH 7.8, Tris, 37°	(4)
	ATP	5.2×10^{-3}		

Inhibitors

source	inhibitor[a]	type	$K_i(M)$	conditions	
Rat liver	methylamine	C(glycine)	6.3×10^{-3}	pH 7.5, Tris, 37°	(2)
	L-serine	NC(glycine)	5.2×10^{-2}		
	L-alanine	UC(glycine)	-		

[a] Other inhibitors are N-substituted glycines (e.g. sarcosine, betaine, hippurate) and C-substituted glycines (e.g. glycinamide, glycyl-L-valine).

The enzyme from the chick embryo was not inhibited by sarcosine, dimethylglycine, betaine or alanine. (3)

References

1. Niyomporn, B., Dahl, J. L. & Strominger, J. L. (1968) JBC, 243, 773.
2. Boyko, J. & Fraser, M. J. (1964) Can. J. Biochem., 42, 1677.
3. Bublitz, C. (1966) BBA, 113, 158.
4. Cormier, M. J. & Novelli, G. D. (1958) BBA, 30, 135.

ACETYL-CoA SYNTHETASE

(Acetate: CoA ligase (AMP))

ATP + acetate + CoA = AMP + pyrophosphate + acetyl-CoA

Ref.

Equilibrium constant

$$\frac{[AMP]\,[PP_i]\,[acetyl\text{-}CoA]}{[ATP]\,[acetate]\,[CoA]} = 0.86 \quad (\text{pH } 7.5, 8.0, \text{ or } 8.5, \text{ Tris, } 38°) \qquad (3)$$

Molecular weight

source	value	conditions	
Beef heart	70,000	2×10^{-2}M KHCO$_3$ + 5×10^{-4}M EDTA	(2)

Specific activity

Beef heart (100 x) 13.7 acetate (pH 8.0, Tris, 37°)   (2)

Specificity and Michaelis constants

source	substrate	$\dfrac{V}{\text{(relative)}}$	K_m(M)	conditions	
Beef	acetate	1.00	1.5×10^{-3}		
heart	propionate	1.07	5.0×10^{-3}	pH 8.0, Tris, 38°	(3)
	acrylate	0.86	2.9×10^{-3}		
Beef[a]	acetate	-	7.9×10^{-4}		
heart	propionate	-	1.1×10^{-2}		
	acrylate	-	1.1×10^{-2}		
	ATP	-	1.8×10^{-3}	pH 8.0, Tris, 37°	(2)
	Mg^{2+}	-	1.4×10^{-3}		
	CoA	-	1.4×10^{-3}		

[a] The following compounds could not replace acetate: formate, L- and DL-lactate, pyruvate, 3-hydroxypyruvate, succinate, malate, glycollate, glyoxylate, benzoate, salicylate, 4-aminobutyrate, glycine, alanine and β-alanine. ATP could not be replaced by ADP, AMP, GTP or CTP nor could CoA be replaced by glutathione.

The enzyme from yeast could also utilize propionate in the place of acetate but the following compounds were inactive: formate, butyrate, caproate and octanoate. ATP could not be replaced by UTP, CTP, ITP or GTP.   (4)

Inhibitors

The following compounds were found to inhibit the enzyme (beef heart) in the forward reaction: high concentrations of acetate, propionate and acrylate; and PP$_i$, ATP, Mg^{2+} and CoA.   (2)

References

1. Jencks, W. P. (1962) The Enzymes, 6, 378.
2. Campagnari, F. & Webster, L. T. (1963) JBC, 238, 1628.
3. Hele, P. (1954) JBC, 206, 671.
4. Berg, P. (1956) JBC, 222, 991.

ACYL-CoA SYNTHETASE

(Acid: CoA ligase (AMP))

ATP + an acid + CoA = AMP + pyrophosphate + an acyl-CoA

Ref.

Equilibrium constant

$$\frac{[AMP]\ [PP_i]\ [an\ acyl\text{-}CoA]}{[ATP]\ [an\ acid]\ [CoA]} \qquad \sim 1.5\ (pH\ 8.0,\ 38^\circ) \qquad (2,4)$$

Molecular weight

source	value	conditions	
Beef liver	30–60,000	–	(2)

Specificity

The enzyme has low specificity. It activates straight-chain fatty acids with four to eleven carbon atoms with maximal activities towards the seven and eight carbon acids. The following compounds also act as substrates: benzoate, substituted benzoates, phenylacetate, 2,4-dichlorophenoxyacetate, p-aminobenzoate, benemid, p-aminophenylacetate, phenylpropionate, cinnamate, α-picolinate, nicotinate, vinylacetate, crotonate and a number of branched-chain, hydroxy and unsaturated fatty acids.   (1)

Michaelis constants

source	substrate	$\frac{V}{(relative)}$	$K_m(M)$	conditions	
Beef liver	octanoate	1.00	1.53×10^{-4}		
	heptanoate	2.37	4.08×10^{-4}	pH 9.0,	
	butyrate	0.62	1.59×10^{-3}	diol buffer,	(2)
	3-hydroxyoctanoate	0.51	9.45×10^{-4}	38°	
	sorbate	1.45	4.0×10^{-4}		
	ATP[a]	–	5×10^{-4}		

[a] ATP could not be replaced by AMP or ADP.

The properties of the enzyme from hog liver are discussed in reference (3). This enzyme is active in the presence of high concentrations of acetate ($K_m = 2 \times 10^{-2}$M).

Inhibitors

The enzyme (beef liver) is inhibited by P_i, AMP and ADP.   (1,2)

References

1. Jencks, W. P. (1962) The Enzymes, 6, 380.
2. Mahler, H. R., Wakil, S. J. & Bock, R. M. (1953) JBC, 204, 453.
3. Jencks, W. P. & Lipmann, F. (1957) JBC, 225, 207.
4. Jencks, W. P. (1962) Methods in Enzymology, 5, 467.

ACYL-CoA SYNTHETASE

(Acid: CoA ligase (AMP))

ATP + an acid + CoA =

AMP + pyrophosphate + an acyl-CoA

Ref.

Specificity and Michaelis constants

Acyl-CoA synthetase has low specificity and attacks six to twenty carbon acids. The enzyme from **Bacillus megaterium**, for instance, exhibited maximum activity with dodecanoate and tridecanoate. Michaelis constants in the region $2-6 \times 10^{-4}$M were obtained with straight-chain fatty acids with twelve to sixteen carbon atoms. The branched-chain acid 12-methyltetradecanoate exhibited low activity. (4)

The enzyme from guinea-pig liver could utilize oleate (1.00), linoleate (0.32), linolenate (0.34), palmitate (1.62) and chaulmoograte (2.00) but the following compounds were inactive: suberate, azeleate and sebaceate. (1)

source	substrate	$\frac{V}{(\text{relative})}$	$K_m(M)$	conditions	
Guinea-pig liver	octanoate	1.00	3×10^{-4}	} pH 7.4, 37°	(2)
	laurate	1.87	1.3×10^{-3}		
	oleate	5.20	4.0×10^{-3}		
Rat liver	ATP[a]	-	5×10^{-4}	} pH 7.6, Tris, 30°	(3)
	CoA[a]	-	$<1 \times 10^{-5}$		
	CoA[a]	-	4×10^{-5}		

[a] With palmitate as the fatty acid substrate

References

1. Kornberg, A. & Pricer, W. E. Jr. (1953) JBC, 204, 329.
2. Borgstrøm, B. & Wheeldon, L. W. (1961) BBA, 50, 171.
3. Farstad, M. (1967) BBA, 146, 272.
4. Massaro, E. J. & Lennarz, W. J. (1965) B, 4, 85.

SUCCINYL-CoA SYNTHETASE

(Succinate: CoA ligase (GDP))

GTP + succinate + CoA $\rightleftharpoons$

GDP + orthophosphate + succinyl-CoA

Equilibrium constant

$$\frac{[GDP]\,[P_i]\,[succinyl\text{-}CoA]}{[GTP]\,[succinate]\,[CoA]} \quad \sim 0.27 \quad (pH\ 7.4,\ 20^\circ) \tag{3}$$

Molecular weight

source	value	conditions	
Pig heart	70,000	Sephadex G-100, pH 8.0	(2)

Specific activity

Pig heart (800 x) 110 succinate (pH 7.4, Tris, 30°) (2)

Specificity and Michaelis constants

The mammalian enzyme can utilize ITP (but not ATP) in the place of GTP and itaconate in the place of succinate.

In addition to the normal reaction (1.000), the enzyme also catalyzes the following:

(a) a magnesium dependent arsenolysis of succinyl-CoA (0.200)

(b) a CoA dependent arsenolysis of GTP (0.008)

(c) a succinate dependent hydrolysis of GTP (0.0004) (1,2,4)

source	substrate	reaction[a]	$K_m(M)$	conditions	
Pig	GTP	F	$5\text{-}10 \times 10^{-6}$		
heart	succinate	F	$4\text{-}8 \ \times 10^{-4}$	pH 7.4,	
	CoA	F	$5\text{-}20 \times 10^{-6}$	Tris-ace-	(3)
	GDP	R	$2\text{-}8 \ \times 10^{-6}$	tate, 30°	
	P_i	R	$2\text{-}7 \ \times 10^{-4}$		

Specificity and Michaelis constants contd.

source	substrate	reaction[a]	$K_m(M)$	conditions	
Pig heart	succinyl-CoA	R	$1\text{-}6 \times 10^{-5}$		
	8-aza GDP	R	$3\text{-}11 \times 10^{-5}$	pH 7.4,	
	8-aza GTP	F	$7\text{-}20 \times 10^{-5}$	Tris-ace-	(3)
	succinyl-CoA	A	1×10^{-5}	tate, 30°	
	arsenate	A	1.0×10^{-3}		
Pig kidney	GTP	F	3.3×10^{-3}		
	ITP	F	3.3×10^{-3}		
	succinate	F	5.8×10^{-3}	pH 7.4,	(4)
	CoA	F	1×10^{-4}	Tris, 30°	
	Mg^{2+}	F	1.9×10^{-3}		
	GDP	R	1.7×10^{-5}		
	IDP	R	3.8×10^{-5}		

[a] F   forward reaction
R   reverse reaction
A   arsenolysis of succinyl-CoA reaction

Inhibitors

source	inhibitor	type	$K_i(M)$	conditions	
Pig heart	GDP	C(GTP)	1×10^{-5}		
	succinyl-CoA	C(CoA)	2×10^{-5}		
	succinyl-CoA	NC(succinate)	-		
	P_i	UC(CoA)	7×10^{-3}	pH 7.4,	
	P_i	C(succinate)	2×10^{-3}	Tris-ace-	(3)
	P_i[a]	C(arsenate)	3×10^{-5}	tate, 30°	
	GTP[a]	C(arsenate)	$\sim 5 \times 10^{-6}$		
	GDP[a]	C(arsenate)	4×10^{-4}		
	succinate[a]	C(arsenate)	$\sim 6.7 \times 10^{-2}$		

[a] In the arsenolysis of succinyl-CoA reaction.

Light absorption data

Δ_ε(Succinyl-CoA - CoA), at (235 mμ) = 4000 M^{-1} cm^{-1} (pH 7.4)   (3)

References

1. Hager, L. P. (1963) The Enzymes, 6, 387.
2. Cha, S., Cha, C.-J. M. & Parks, R. E. Jr. (1967) JBC, 242, 2577.
3. Cha, S. & Parks, R. E. Jr. (1964) JBC, 239, 1961, 1968.
4. Mazumder, R., Sanadi, D. R. & Rodwell, V. W. (1960) JBC, 235, 2546.

SUCCINYL-CoA SYNTHETASE

(Succinate: CoA ligase (ADP))

ATP + succinate + CoA =

ADP + orthophosphate + succinyl-CoA

Equilibrium constant

$$\frac{[ADP]\ [P_i]\ [succinyl\text{-}CoA]}{[ATP]\ [succinate]\ [CoA]} = 0.27\ (\text{pH 7.4, Tris, 20}^\circ) \tag{2}$$

Molecular weight

source	value	conditions	
Escherichia coli	160,000	pH 7.2	(3)

Specific activity

E. coli (55 x)   49   succinate (pH 7.2, Tris, 37°)   (3)

Jerusalem artichoke (mitochondria) (47 x) 18.7 succinate   (4)
(pH 7.2, Tris-P$_i$, 27°)

Specificity

The enzyme (E. coli) is highly specific. Thus, ATP could not
be replaced by GTP or ITP and succinate could not be replaced by
acetate, propionate, butyrate, oxalate, malonate, glutarate, adipate,
aspartate, glutamate, malate, 2,2,3-trimethyl succinate, fumarate
or maleate. (3)

The enzymes isolated from spinach leaf and Jerusalem artichoke
are similarly highly specific. (1,2,4)

Michaelis constants

source	substrate	$K_m(M)$	conditions	
Spinach	ATP	5×10^{-4}	pH 7.4, Tris, 20°	(2)
	succinate	1.5×10^{-2}		

Michaelis constants contd.

source	substrate	$K_m(M)$	conditions	
Spinach	CoA	1×10^{-4}	pH 7.4, Tris, 20°	(2)
	Mg^{2+}	3.5×10^{-3}		
Jerusalem artichoke	ATP	1.4×10^{-4}		
	succinate	2.0×10^{-3}		
	CoA	2.2×10^{-5}		
	Mg^{2+}	2.0×10^{-4}	pH 7.2, Tris-P_i, 27°	(4)
	ADP	1.2×10^{-4}		
	P_i	1.4×10^{-3}		
	succinyl-CoA	5.6×10^{-5}		
	Mg^{2+}	8.0×10^{-4}		

Inhibitors

The enzyme (Jerusalem artichoke) is inhibited by malonate
(C(succinate)).   (4)

References

1. Hager, L. P. (1962) The Enzymes, 6, 387.

2. Kaufman, S. & Alivisatos, S. G. A. (1955) JBC, 216, 141, 153.

3. Gibson, J., Upper, C. D. & Gunsalus, I. C. (1967) JBC, 242, 2474.

4. Palmer, J. M. & Wedding, R. T. (1966) BBA, 113, 167.

GLUTARYL-CoA SYNTHETASE

(Glutarate: CoA ligase (ADP))

ATP + glutarate + CoA =

ADP + orthophosphate + glutaryl-CoA

Ref.

Specificity

Glutaryl-CoA synthetase from pigeon liver was about equally reactive with ATP, GTP or ITP. Glutaconate reacted at 40% the rate of glutarate but adipate, muconate, 3-hydroxyglutarate, 3-hydroxy-3-methylglutarate, 2-methylglutarate, 2,2-dimethylglutarate, 3-methylglutarate and 3,3-dimethylglutarate were all inactive. The enzyme isolated from dog muscle had similar properties – this enzyme, however, could also utilize 2-methylglutarate, 2,2-dimethylglutarate, 3-methylglutarate or 3,3-methylglutarate in the place of glutarate. (1)

References

1. Menon, G. K. K., Friedman, D. L. & Stern, J. R. (1960) BBA, 44, 375.

CHOLOYL-CoA SYNTHETASE

(Cholate: CoA ligase (AMP))

ATP + cholate + CoA = AMP + pyrophosphate + choloyl-CoA

Ref.

Specificity and Michaelis constants

source	substrate	$K_m(M)$	conditions	
Guinea-pig liver (microsomes)	cholate ATP	4×10^{-4} 1.5×10^{-3} }	pH 7.4, glyoxaline, 37°	(1,2)

The enzyme also catalyzes the formation of choloylhydroxamate from cholate, ATP and hydroxylamine. (1,2)

References

1. Elliott, W. H. (1962) Methods in Enzymology, 5, 473.

2. Elliott, W. H. (1956) BJ, 56, 427, 433.

<u>BUTYRYL-CoA SYNTHETASE</u>

(Butyrate: CoA ligase (AMP))

ATP + butyrate + CoA = AMP + PP_i + butyryl-CoA

<u>Ref</u>.

Specificity

The enzyme (bovine heart) was somewhat less active with straight chain acids having 3,5 or 6 carbons than with butyrate. Isobutyrate and crotonate had about 20% of the activity with butyrate. The following were inactive: formate, acetate, heptanoate, octanoate, pyruvate, malate, acrylate, fumarate, succinate, 2-hydroxybutyrate, 2-oxobutyrate, 2-aminobutyrate, 3-hydroxybutyrate, acetoacetate, dl-3-methylbutyrate, 4-aminobutyrate, benzoate, phenylacetate, L-phenyl-alanine, L-tyrosine or L-tryptophan. GTP could not replace ATP and both ITP and CTP possessed but slight activities. Neither cysteine nor glutathione substituted for reduced CoA as acceptor.　(1)

Michaelis constants

source	substrate	$K_m(M)$	conditions
Bovine heart	butyrate	1.5×10^{-3}	
	Mg^{2+}	1.8×10^{-3}	pH 8.0, Tris,
	ATP	3.0×10^{-3}	$37°$ （1)
	CoA	8.5×10^{-4}	

Inhibitors

Mg^{2+} and CoA were inhibitory at high concentrations.　(1)

References

1. Webster, L. T. Jr., Gerowin, L. D. & Rakita, L. (1965) <u>JBC</u>, <u>240</u>, 29.

ASPARAGINE SYNTHETASE

(L-Aspartate: ammonia ligase (AMP))

$$ATP + L\text{-aspartate} + NH_3 = AMP + PP_i + L\text{-asparagine}$$

Ref.

Specificity

The enzyme (<u>Streptococcus bovis</u>) is highly specific. Thus, L-aspartate could not be replaced by the following amino acids: D-aspartate, D- or L-glutamate, L-serine, glycine or L-valine. Hydroxylamine could replace ammonia. (1)

Michaelis constants

source	substrate	K_m(M)	conditions	
S. bovis	L- aspartate	2.6×10^{-2}		
	NH_4^+	4×10^{-3}	pH 7.2, Tris,	(1)
	Mg^{2+}	4.5×10^{-2}	38°	
	ATP	4×10^{-3}		

Inhibitors

source	inhibitor	type	K_i(M)	conditions	
S. bovis	L-asparagine	C (L-aspartate)	1.8×10^{-4}	pH 7.2, Tris,	(1)
				38°	

The enzyme was not inhibited by D-asparagine or by L-glutamine. (1)

References

1. Burchall, J. J., Reichelt, E. C. & Wolin, M. J. (1964) <u>JBC</u>, <u>239</u>, 1794.

GLUTAMINE SYNTHETASE

(L-Glutamate: ammonia ligase (ADP))

ATP + L-glutamate + NH_3 = ADP + orthophosphate + L-glutamine

Ref.

Equilibrium constant

$$\frac{[ADP]\,[L\text{-glutamine}]\,[P_i]}{[ATP]\,[L\text{-glutamate}]\,[NH_3]} = 1.2 \times 10^{-3} \quad \text{(pH 7.0, imidazole, 37}^\circ) \tag{1}$$

Molecular weight

source	value	conditions	
Escherichia coli	680,000 [12]	pH 6.5, also by electron microscopy.	(2,3,6)
Sheep brain	450,000	pH 7.1	(4)
Pea seedling	450,000	0.15M NaCl	(5)

Specific activity

E. coli (180 x)	127	L-glutamate[a]	(pH 7.7, imidazole, 37°. Activating ion = Mg^{2+})	(2)
Sheep brain (3000 x)	152	L-glutamate[b]	(pH 7.2, imidazole, 37°. Activating ion = Mg^{2+})	(4)

[a] with NH_4^+ as the third substrate
[b] with hydroxylamine as the third substrate

Specificity and Michaelis constants

source	substrate	V (relative)	K_m(M)	third substrate	conditions	
Sheep brain	L-glutamate	1.00	3.9×10^{-3}	NH_4^+		
	L-glutamate	1.00	3.3×10^{-3}	hydroxylamine		
	D-glutamate	0.27	1.3×10^{-2}	NH_4^+		
	D-glutamate	0.54	3.8×10^{-3}	hydroxylamine		
	2-methyl L-glutamate	0.75	6.7×10^{-3}	NH_4^+		
	threo 3-methyl D-glutamate	0.02	2.5×10^{-2}	NH_4^+	pH 7.2, imidazole, 37°	(7)
	threo 4-methyl L-glutamate	0.27	3.6×10^{-3}	NH_4^+		
	threo 4-hydroxy L-glutamate	1.00	2.4×10^{-3}	NH_4^+		
	threo 4-hydroxy D-glutamate	<0.08	-	NH_4^+		
	erythro 4-hydroxy L-glutamate	0.81	5.6×10^{-3}	NH_4^+		
	erythro 4-hydroxy D-glutamate	0.38	2.2×10^{-2}	NH_4^+		
	NH_4^+	-	1.8×10^{-4}	L-glutamate		
	NH_4^+	-	1.4×10^{-2}	D-glutamate	pH 7.2, imidazole, 37°	(4)
	hydroxylamine	-	1.5×10^{-4}	L-glutamate		
	hydroxylamine	-	3.5×10^{-3}	D-glutamate		
	ATP	-	2.3×10^{-3}	L- or D-glutamate and hydroxylamine		

Specificity and Michaelis constants contd.

source	substrate	relative velocity	$K_m(M)$	second substrate	conditions	
E. coli	L-glutamate	1.00	2.4×10^{-3}	NH_4^+		
	D-glutamate	0.04	-	NH_4^+		
	DL-2-methyl-glutamate	0.10	-	NH_4^+		
	N-methyl-glutamate	0.04	-	NH_4^+		
	L-isoglutamine	0.01	-	NH_4^+	pH 7.0,	
	DL-3-hydroxy-glutamate	0	-	NH_4^+	imidazole, 37°	(2)
	ATP	1.00	6.8×10^{-4}	-	Activating ion = Mg^{2+}	
	GTP	0.30	-	-		
	ITP	0.30	-	-		
	CTP	0.11	-	-		
	UTP	0	-	-		
	NH_4^+	1.00	1.8×10^{-3}	L-glutamate		
	methylamine	0.09	-	L-glutamate		
	Mg^{2+}	-	1.7×10^{-2}	-	pH 7.0, imidazole, 37°	(2)

The properties of the enzyme from pea seedlings are similar to those of the sheep brain enzyme (4,7). The enzyme (sheep brain) can utilize several dicarboxylic amino acids in the place of glutamate but L-aspartate is inactive (1,7). The γ glutamyltransferase activity of the enzyme is discussed in reference (4).

The enzymes isolated from a variety of sources vary greatly in their ability to catalyze the reverse reaction. Thus, that from E. coli catalyzes the reverse reaction at one thousandth the rate of the forward reaction and that from Bacillus licheniformis does not catalyze the reverse reaction at all. With the mammalian enzyme, however, the forward rate relative to the reverse rate is about 10 to 1. (2)

Inhibitors

The glutamine synthetase of E. coli possesses separate, noninteracting binding sites for each of the following eight inhibitors: alanine, AMP and carbamoyl phosphate (NC (any substrate)), glycine, CTP and tryptophan (partially competitive with glutamine) and histidine and glucosamine 6-phosphate (partially competitive with NH_4^+). At saturating concentrations the inhibitors are individually able to cause only partial inhibition of the enzyme activity; collectively, however, they are able to cause almost complete inhibition of the enzyme. This type of inhibition is termed "cumulative inhibition". (2,3)

References
1. Meister, A. (1962) The Enzymes, 6, 443.
2. Woolfolk, C. A., Shapiro, B. & Stadtman, E. R. (1966) ABB, 116, 177.
3. Woolfolk, C. A. & Stadtman, E. R. (1967) ABB, 118, 736.
4. Pamiljans, V., Krishnaswamy, P. R., Dumville, G. & Meister, A. (1962) B, 1, 153.
5. Levintow, L., Meister, A., Hogeboom, G. H. & Kuff, E. L. (1955) JACS, 77, 5304.
6. Shapiro, B., Valentine, R. & Stadtman, E. R. (1967) FP, 26, 559.
7. Kagan, H. M. & Meister, A. (1966) B, 5, 2423.

PHOSPHORIBOSYL-GLYCINEAMIDE SYNTHETASE

(Ribosylamine-5-phosphate: glycine ligase (ADP))

ATP + glycine + ribosylamine 5-phosphate =

ADP + orthophosphate + ribosyl-glycineamide 5-phosphate

Ref.

Equilibrium constant

The reaction is reversible. The reverse reaction is favoured. (1)

Molecular weight

source	value	conditions	
Aerobacter aerogenes	48,000	sucrose gradient	(2)

Specificity

With the enzyme from chicken liver arsenate could take the place of P_i in the reverse reaction. (1)

Michaelis constants

source	substrate	$K_m(M)$	conditions	
A. aerogenes	ATP	5.6×10^{-5}		
	glycine	1.9×10^{-4}		
	PRA	7.8×10^{-6}	pH 8.0,	(2)
	ribose 5-phosphate (a)	5.4×10^{-3}	Tris, $37°$	
	NH_3 (a)	1.32×10^{-3}		

(a) PRA is formed nonenzymically from ribose 5-phosphate and NH_3 and may be replaced by these compounds. The equilibrium constant for this reaction is approximately 1.

Abbreviations

PRA   ribosylamine 5-phosphate

References

1. Hartman, S. C. & Buchanan, J. M. (1958) JBC, 233, 456.
2. Nierlich, D. P. & Magasanik, B. (1965) JBC, 240, 366.

PANTOTHENATE SYNTHETASE

(L-Pantoate: β-alanine ligase (AMP))

ATP + L-pantoate + β-alanine =

AMP + pyrophosphate + L-pantothenate

Equilibrium constant

The forward reaction is favoured. (1)

Specificity

The enzyme from Escherichia coli or Brucella abortus is specific for L-pantoate which could not be replaced by pantoyl lactone. (1,2)

Michaelis constants

source	substrate	$K_m(M)$	conditions	
E. coli	β-alanine	$3.8 - 7.4 \times 10^{-4}$[a]	pH 8.5, Tris, 25°	(1)
	pantoate	$1.52 - 3.54 \times 10^{-3}$[a]		
B. abortus	β-alanine	4×10^{-5}	pH 7.4, P_i.	(2)
	pantoate	5×10^{-2}		

[a] Values of "0.38 - 0.74" for β-alanine and "1.52 - 3.54" for pantoate are reported in reference 1. It is assumed here that the units are 1×10^{-3}M.

References

1. Novelli, G. D. (1955) Methods in Enzymology, 2, 619.
2. Ginoza, H. S. & Altenbern, R. A. (1956) ABB, 56, 537.

γ-GLUTAMYL-CYSTEINE SYNTHETASE

(L-Glutamate: L-cysteine γ-ligase (ADP))

ATP + L-glutamate + L-cysteine =

ADP + orthophosphate + γ-L-glutamyl-L-cysteine

Ref.

Specificity and Michaelis constants

The enzyme (bovine lens) could utilize the following compounds in the place of L-glutamate (1.00): DL-2-methylglutamate (0.52), DL-allohydroxyglutamate (0.24), DL-3-hydroxyglutamate (0.10) and L-2-aminoadipate. The following compounds were inactive: L-aspartate, D-glutamate, N-acetyl-L-glutamate, glutarate, 2-oxoglutarate, L-glutamine, L-glutamine-γ-ethyl ester and L-2-pyrrolidone-5-carboxylate. The following compounds could not replace L-cysteine: N-formyl-2-aminobutyrate, D-threonine, D-cycloserine or ammonium sulphate (1). The ability of 71 compounds to couple with L-glutamate to form a series of γ-glutamyl peptides is discussed in reference (2).

source	substrate	$\frac{V}{(relative)}$	$K_m(M)$	conditions
Bovine lens	ATP	-	2.0×10^{-4}	
	L-glutamate	-	5.8×10^{-4}	
	L-cysteine	1.00	4.4×10^{-5}	
	L-2-aminobutyrate[a]	0.77	5.9×10^{-4}	
	DL-allylglycine[a]	0.58	1.2×10^{-3}	
	β-chloro-L-alanine[a]	1.16	7.0×10^{-5}	pH 7.6, Tris, 37° (1,2)
	L-cycloserine[a]	0.72	7.7×10^{-3}	
	DL-allothreonine[a]	0.51	2.2×10^{-3}	
	L-norvaline[a]	0.96	8.2×10^{-3}	
	DL-3-aminoisobutyrate[a]	0.53	2.5×10^{-3}	
	S-methyl-L-cysteine[a]	0.73	1.6×10^{-3}	
	L-homocysteine[a]	0.37	1.6×10^{-3}	

[a] In the place of L-cysteine.

References

1. Rathbun, W. B. (1967) ABB, 122, 62.
2. Rathbun, W. B. (1967) ABB, 122, 73.

GLUTATHIONE SYNTHETASE

(γ-L-Glutamyl-L-cysteine: glycine ligase (ADP))

ATP + γ-L-glutamyl-L-cysteine + glycine =

ADP + orthophosphate + glutathione

Ref.

Molecular weight

source	value	conditions	
Baker's yeast	123,000	pH 7.4	(1)

Specific activity

Baker's yeast (5000 x) 40[a] γ-L-glutamyl-L-cysteine   (1)
                          (pH 8.3, Tris, 37°)

---

[a] With glycine as the amino acid substrate. With hydroxylamine a value of 20 was obtained.

Specificity

The enzyme (baker's yeast) has the following specificity properties in the forward reaction:-

dipeptide substrate: γ-L-glutamyl-L-2-aminobutyrate (1.00), γ-L-glutamyl-L-cysteine (1.77), γ-L-glutamyl-L-alanine (0.39) and γ-L-glutamylglycine (0.01). The following were inactive: γ-L-glutamyl-L-leucine, γ-L-glutamyl-β-alanine, γ-D-glutamylglycine, α-L-glutamyl-L-leucine, α-L-glutamyl-L-alanine and L-aspartyl-L-alanine.

amino acid substrate: glycine could not be replaced by β-alanine, L-aspartate or L-alanine.   (1)

The enzyme from pigeon liver is highly specific for glycine which could not be replaced by ammonia, ethanolamine, sarcosine, methylamine, DL-alanine or glycollate. At high concentrations hydroxylamine was active.   (2)

Michaelis constants

source	substrate	$K_m(M)$	conditions	
Baker's yeast	γ-glutamyl-2-aminobutyrate[a] hydroxylamine[a] ATP[a] ATP glycine	5×10^{-4} 8.0×10^{-5} 8.3×10^{-5} 1.0×10^{-4} 2.0×10^{-3}	pH 8.3, Tris, 37°	(1)
Brewer's yeast	γ-glutamyl-L-cysteine ATP glycine	2.9×10^{-4} 1.1×10^{-4} 5.8×10^{-4}	pH 8.3, Tris, 37°	(3)
Pigeon liver	γ-glutamyl-L-cysteine glycine ATP	2.5×10^{-4} 6.0×10^{-4} 1.1×10^{-4}	pH 8.3, Tris, 37°	(2)

---

[a] In the reaction: ATP + γ-glutamyl-2-aminobutyrate + hydroxylamine = ADP + Pi + γ-glutamyl-2-aminobutyryl hydroxamate.

References

1. Mooz, E. D. & Meister, A. (1967) B, 6, 1722.
2. Snoke, J. E., Yanari, S. & Bloch, K. (1953) JBC, 201, 573.
3. Snoke, J. E. (1955) JBC, 213, 813.

D-ALANYLALANINE SYNTHETASE

(D-Alanine: D-alanine ligase (ADP))

ATP + D-alanine + D-alanine =

ADP + orthophosphate + D-alanyl-alanine

Ref.

Specificity and kinetic properties

The synthetase is highly specific for the D configuration. Thus, the enzyme from <u>Streptococcus faecalis</u> could utilize D-alanine (1.00), D-2-amino-<u>n</u>-butyrate (0.26) and D-serine (0.04) as substrates. Mixed dipeptides were produced with mixed amino acid substrates. The corresponding L-amino acids were inactive. The following compounds were also inactive: D-threonine, D-phenylalanine, D-valine, glycine, β-alanine, D-2-amino-<u>iso</u>butyrate, D-norvaline, D-methionine, D-norleucine, D-leucine and D-isoleucine. Of the nucleotide triphosphates tested, only ATP was active. (1,2)

It is thought that D-alanylalanine synthetase possesses two sites for D-alanine and the reaction catalyzed by the enzyme can be described by the following equations:

$$\underline{(a)} \quad E + A = EA$$
$$\underline{(b)} \quad EA + A = EAA$$

where E is enzyme, A is D-alanine and EA and EAA are binary and ternary complexes, respectively. K_A is the Michaelis constant for reaction (a) and K_{AA} that for reaction (b). (2)

source	substrate	$K_m(M)$	V (relative)	$K_A(M)$	$K_{AA}(M)$	conditions	
S. <u>fae-calis</u>	D-alanine	-	1.00	6.6×10^{-4}	1.0×10^{-2}	pH 7.8, Tris, 37°	(2)
	D-2-amino-<u>n</u>-butyrate	-	0.80	1.1×10^{-2}	3.3×10^{-2}		
	ATP	1.4×10^{-3}	-	-	-	pH 7.8, Tris, 37°	(1)
	Mn^{2+}	4.8×10^{-3}	-	-	-		

Inhibitors

source	inhibitor	type	$K_i(M)^{(a)}$	$K_i'(M)^{(a)}$	conditions	
S. <u>fae-calis</u>	D-cycloserine	C(D-alanine)	2.2×10^{-5}	1.4×10^{-4}	pH 7.8, Tris, 37°	(3)
	cis-DL-cyclothreonine	C(D-alanine)	1.2×10^{-4}	1.9×10^{-4}		
	trans-DL-cyclo-threonine	C(D-alanine)	5.4×10^{-4}	5.6×10^{-4}		

(a) K_i is the dissociation constant for the complex EI and K_i' that for the complex EAI where E is enzyme, A is D-alanine and I is inhibitor.

Other inhibitors (e.g. the product D-alanylalanine) are discussed in references (1) and (3).

References

1. Neuhaus, F. C. (1962) JBC, <u>237</u>, 778.
2. Neuhaus, F. C. (1962) JBC, <u>237</u>, 3128.
3. Neuhaus, F. C. & Lynch, J. L. (1964) B, <u>3</u>, 471.

PHOSPHORIBOSYL-AMINOIMIDAZOLE-
SUCCINOCARBOXAMIDE SYNTHETASE

(5'-Phosphoribosyl-4-carboxy-5-aminoimidazole:

L-aspartate ligase (ADP))

ATP + 5'-phosphoribosyl-4-carboxy-5-aminoimidazole + L-aspartate =
ADP + orthophosphate + 5'-phosphoribosyl-4-(N-succinocarboxamide)-
5-aminoimidazole

Ref.

Equilibrium constant

The equilibrium of the reaction is in the direction of succino-
AICAR production. (1)

Specificity

The enzyme (chicken liver) could utilize UTP or CTP in the
place of ATP in the forward reaction but GTP and ITP were inactive.
In the reverse reaction, arsenate could replace P_i and ADP could be
replaced, albeit to a limited extent, by CDP or UDP. Mg^{2+} was required in both the forward and reverse reactions. (1)

The enzyme is highly specific for L-aspartate which could not
be replaced by L-glutamate, D-aspartate or carbamoylphosphate. (2)

Abbreviations

succino-AICAR	5'-phosphoribosyl-4-(N-succinocarboxamide)-5-aminoimidazole
carboxy-AIR	5'-phosphoribosyl-4-carboxy-5-amino-imidazole

References

1. Flaks, J. G. & Lukens, L. N. (1963) Methods in Enzymology, 6, 82.
2. Lukens, L. N. & Buchanan, J. M. (1959) JBC, 234, 1791.

UDP-N-ACETYLMURAMOYL-ALANYL-D-GLUTAMYL-LYSINE SYNTHETASE

(UDP-N-acetylmuramoyl-L-alanyl-D-glutamate:

L-lysine ligase (ADP))

ATP + UDP-N-acetylmuramoyl-L-alanyl-D-glutamate + L-lysine = ADP +
orthophosphate + UDP-N-acetylmuramoyl-L-alanyl-D-glutamyl-L-lysine

Ref.

Equilibrium constant

The reaction is essentially irreversible [F].   (1)

Specificity

The enzyme (Staphylococcus aureus) is highly specific for its
substrates. Thus, ATP could not be replaced by ADP, ITP, GTP, UTP
or CTP and UDP-N-acetylmuramoyl-L-alanyl-D-glutamate could not be
replaced by UDP-N-acetylmuramoyl-L-alanyl-D-glutamyl-L-lysine or
UDP-N-acetylmuramoyl-L-alanyl-D-glutamyl-L-lysyl-D-alanyl-D-ala-
nine. L-Lysine could not be replaced by meso-diaminopimelate.   (1)

Michaelis constants

source	substrate	$K_m(M)$	conditions	
S. aureus	ATP	3×10^{-4}		
	UDP-N-acetylmuramoyl-L-alanyl-D-glutamate	4×10^{-4}	pH 8.4, Tris, 37°	(1)
	L-lysine	5×10^{-4}		

References

1. Ito, E. & Strominger, J. L. (1964) JBC, 239, 210.

UDP-N-ACETYLMURAMOYL-ALANYL-D-GLUTAMATE SYNTHETASE

(UDP-N-acetylmuramoyl-L-alanine: D-glutamate ligase (ADP))

ATP + UDP-N-acetylmuramoyl-L-alanine + D-glutamate =
ADP + orthophosphate + UDP-N-acetylmuramoyl-L-alanyl-D-glutamate

Ref.

Equilibrium constant

The reaction is reversible. (1)

Specificity

The enzyme from Staphylococcus aureus is highly specific for its substrates. Thus D-glutamate could not be replaced by the following compounds: L-glutamate, L-lysine, D-alanine, L-alanine, D-aspartate, DL-2-aminoadipate, DL-2-aminopimelate, DL-methionine sulphoxamine, DL-methionine sulphonium chloride or DL-methionine sulphoxide. ATP could not be replaced by CTP. (1)

Michaelis constants

source	substrate	$K_m(M)$	conditions	
S. aureus	ATP-Mn^{2+}	4.0×10^{-4}		
	UDP-N-acetyl-muramoyl-L-alanine	1.6×10^{-4}	pH 8.7, Tris, 37°	(1)
	D-glutamate	1.55×10^{-4}		

References

1. Nathenson, S. G., Strominger, J. L. & Ito, E. (1964) JBC, 239, 1773.

UDP-N-ACETYLMURAMOYL-L-ALANYL-D-GLUTAMYL-
L-LYSYL-D-ALANYL-D-ALANINE SYNTHETASE

(UDP-N-acetylmuramoyl-L-alanyl-D-glutamyl-L-lysine:
D-alanyl-D-alanine ligase (ADP))

ATP + UDP-N-acetylmuramoyl-L-alanyl-D-glutamyl-L-lysine + D-alanyl-
D-alanine = ADP + orthophosphate + UDP-N-acetylmuramoyl-L-alanyl-D-
glutamyl-L-lysyl-D-alanyl-D-alanine

Ref.

Specificity and Michaelis constants[a]

The synthetase (Streptococcus faecalis) is not specific for D-alanyl-D-alanine which can be replaced by a number of related dipeptides. In general, substitution at the N-terminal residue enhances binding of the dipeptide whereas substitution at the C-terminal residue decreases binding of the dipeptide to the enzyme.

source	substrate	$\frac{V}{(\text{relative})}$	$K_m (M)$
S. faecalis	D-alanyl-D-alanine	1.0	1.6×10^{-4}
	D-alanyl-D-2-amino-n-butyrate	1.0	7.6×10^{-4}
	D-alanyl-D-serine	1.0	9.1×10^{-4}
	D-alanyl-D-threonine	1.0	3.3×10^{-3}
	D-2-amino-n-butyryl-D-alanine	-	9×10^{-5}
	D-2-amino-n-butyryl-D-2-amino-n-butyrate	-	7×10^{-4}
	D-norvalyl-D-alanine	-	1.2×10^{-4}
	D-valyl-D-alanine	-	3.9×10^{-4}
	D-seryl-D-alanine	-	2.6×10^{-4}
	D-alanyl-D-valine	-	2.6×10^{-3}
	D-alanyl-D-norvaline	-	$>5.0 \times 10^{-3}$

[a]From reference (1). The conditions were: pH 7.8, Tris, 37°.

References

1. Neuhaus, F. C. & Struve, W. G. (1965) B, 4, 120.

N^5-FORMYLTETRAHYDROFOLATE CYCLODEHYDRASE

(N^5-Formyltetrahydrofolate cyclo-ligase (ADP))

$ATP + N^5$-formyltetrahydrofolate $= ADP + P_i + N^5, N^{10}$-methenyltetrahydrofolate

Ref.

Equilibrium constant

    The reaction is essentially irreversible [F].   (1)

Specificity

    The enzyme (sheep liver) can utilize GTP, UTP, or CTP in the place of ATP.   (1)

Michaelis constants

source	substrate	K_m(M)	conditions
Sheep liver	N^5-formyltetrahydrofo-late	1.43×10^{-4}	pH 6.0, citrate, (1) 30°
	ATP	4.5×10^{-4}	

Light absorption data

    Methenyltetrahydrofolate $\varepsilon,(343 \text{ m}\mu) = 23,600 \text{ M}^{-1}\text{cm}^{-1}$ (pH 6.0)   (1)

References

1. Greenberg, D. M., Wynston, L. K. & Nagabhushanam, A. (1965) B, 4, 1872.

GMP SYNTHETASE

(Xanthosine-5'-phosphate: ammonia ligase (AMP))

ATP + xanthosine 5'-phosphate + NH$_3$ =

AMP + pyrophosphate + GMP

Equilibrium constant

The reaction is essentially irreversible [F].   (1)

Specificity

The synthetase from _Aerobacter aerogenes_ is specific for NH$_3$ which cannot be replaced by L-glutamine. The enzyme requires Mg^{2+} for activity (K_m = 1.93 x 10^{-3}. Conditions: pH 8.52, Tris, room temperature).   (1)

Inhibitors

Hydroxylamine is a potent inhibitor of the enzyme.   (1)

Light absorption data

GMP ε, (290 mμ) = 6.0 x 10^3 M^{-1}cm^{-1} (acid)   (1)

References

1. Magasanik, B. (1963) _Methods in Enzymology_, 6, 111.

CTP SYNTHETASE

(UTP: ammonia ligase (ADP))

$$ATP + UTP + NH_3 = ADP + P_i + CTP$$

Ref.

Molecular weight

source	value	conditions	
Escherichia coli	~115,000	Sephadex G150, pH 7.4	(2)

Specificity

The enzyme (E. coli) can utilize ammonia or glutamine as the nitrogen donor. With glutamine as the donor, GTP is also required for activity.

(1)

Michaelis constants

source	substrate	$K_m(M)$	conditions	
E. coli (glutamine as nitrogen donor)	UTP	1.5×10^{-4}	pH 7.1, Tris, 38°	(1)
	ATP	2.0×10^{-4}		
	GTP	8.0×10^{-5}		
	glutamine	2.2×10^{-4}		

At low substrate concentrations the kinetics are strongly sinusoidal, but at high concentrations they follow Michaelis-Menton kinetics. With ammonia as the nitrogen donor, sinusoidal kinetics are exhibited whether the substrates are at low or high concentrations.

(1)

Inhibitors

source	inhibitor	type	$K_i(M)$	conditions	
E. coli	CTP	C (UTP)	1.1×10^{-4}	pH 7.1, Tris, 38°	(1)

Light absorption data

Δ_ϵ(CTP - UTP) at 291 mμ = 1338 $M^{-1}cm^{-1}$ (pH 7.1) (1)

References

1. Long, C. W. & Pardee, A. B. (1967) JBC, 242, 4715.
2. Long, C. W. (1967) Personal communication.

FORMYLTETRAHYDROFOLATE SYNTHETASE

(Formate:tetrahydrofolate ligase (ADP))

ATP + formate + tetrahydrofolate = ADP + P_i + 10-formyltetrahydrofolate

Ref.

Equilibrium constant

$$\frac{[ADP]\,[P_i]\,[10\text{-formyltetrahydrofolate}]}{[ATP]\,[formate]\,[tetrahydrofolate]} = 41 \qquad \text{(pH 7.7, triethanol-amine, } 37^\circ)$$ (2)

Molecular weight

source	value	conditions	
Clostridium cylindrosporum	230,000	pH 7.0	(2)

Specific activity

C. cylindrosporum	420 tetrahydrofolate	(pH 7.8, triethanol-amine, 37°)	(2)
Pigeon liver (180 x) 5.8 tetrahydrofolate		(pH 7.4, Tris, 37°)	(3)

Specificity

The enzyme isolated from C. cylindrosporum is highly specific. Thus, formate could not be replaced by methanol, formaldehyde, formamide, acetate, pyruvate, glycine, formamidine, formylglycine, formylaspartate, formylglutamate, formylanthranilate, formimino aspartate, formimino glutamate, DL-serine, xanthine or inosinate and ATP could not be replaced by AMP, ADP, UTP, GTP, ITP, CTP, GDP, UDP, CDP or IDP. dl-Tetrahydropteroyl-L-glutamate could be replaced to a limited extent by other derivatives of tetrahydrofolate -- see Michaelis constant section (5). The properties of the pigeon liver enzyme are discussed in reference (3).

Michaelis constants

source	substrate	V (relative)	K_m(M)	conditions	
C. cylindrosporum	formate	-	6.7×10^{-3}	pH 8, tri-ethanol-amine, 37°	(2)
	ATP	-	2.9×10^{-4}		
	Mg^{2+}	-	2.3×10^{-3}		

Michaelis constants (cont.)

	dl-tetrahydropteroyl- -L-glutamate	1.00	5.2×10^{-4}	pH 8.0, tri-
	-D-glutamate	0.06	6.8×10^{-4}	ethanol-
	-L-aspartate	0.20	1.56×10^{-3}	amine,
	dl-tetrahydropteroate	0.005	2.34×10^{-3}	37°

(2)

Lactobacillus arabinosus	formate	-	8×10^{-3}
	ATP	-	4.5×10^{-4}
	dl-tetrahydrofolate	-	1.5×10^{-3}

pH 8.5, Tris, 37° (4)

Pigeon liver	formate	-	1.2×10^{-3}
	ATP	-	1.1×10^{-4}
	dl-tetrahydrofolate	-	1.6×10^{-3}

pH 7.4, Tris, 37° (3)

Inhibitors

source	inhibitor	type	K_i (M)	conditions	
C. cylindro- sporum	P_i	NC (ATP)	1.2×10^{-2}		
		NC (Mg^{2+})	1.4×10^{-2}		
		NC (formate)	1.4×10^{-2}	pH 8, tri-	
	ADP	NC (l-tetrahydro- folate)	1.8×10^{-3}	ethanol-	(2)
		NC (formate)	4.3×10^{-3}	amine, 37°	
		C (Mg^{2+})	4.8×10^{-3}		
		C (ATP)	2.7×10^{-4}		

References

1. Rabinowitz, J. C. (1960) The Enzymes, 2, 206.

2. Himes, R. H. & Rabinowitz, J. C. (1962) JBC, 237, 2903.

3. Jaenicke, L. & Brode, E. (1961) BZ, 334, 108.

4. Lansford, E. M. Jr., Turner, R. B., Weathersbee, C. J. & Shive, W.
   (1964) JBC, 239, 497.

5. Rabinowitz, J. C. & Pricer, W. E. Jr. (1963) Methods in Enzymology, 6, 375.

ADENYLOSUCCINATE SYNTHETASE

(IMP: L-aspartate ligase (GDP))

GTP + IMP + L-aspartate = GDP + orthophosphate + adenylosuccinate

Ref.

Equilibrium constant

$$\frac{[GDP]\ [P_i]\ [adenylosuccinate]}{[GTP]\ [IMP]\ [L\text{-}aspartate]} = 2.9 - 10.0 \ (pH\ 8.0,\ glycine,\ 37°) \quad (5)$$

Specificity

The enzyme (Escherichia coli) is highly specific for its substrates. Thus, IMP could not be replaced by inosine or hypoxanthine and of a number of compounds tested (ammonia, hydroxylamine, L-asparagine, D-aspartate, L-glutamate, L-glutamine, β-alanine and DL-alanine), only hydroxylamine could replace L-aspartate (forming 6-N-hydroxy-AMP). GTP could not be replaced by any of the common mono-, di- or tri-nucleotides. (1,2,3)

Michaelis constants

source	substrate	$K_m(M)$	conditions	
E. coli	GTP	4×10^{-5}	pH 8.0,	
	IMP	3×10^{-5}	glycine,	(3)
	L-aspartate	1×10^{-4}	30°	
	GTP	4.8×10^{-5}	pH 8.0,	
	IMP	5.4×10^{-5}	glycine,	(4)
	L-aspartate	2.7×10^{-4}	25°	

Inhibitors

source	inhibitor	type	$K_i(M)$	conditions	
E. coli	AMP[a]	C(IMP)	9.5×10^{-5}		
	dAMP	NC(IMP)	-		
	adenylosuccinate	C(IMP)	2.7×10^{-4}		
		C(L-aspartate)	4.7×10^{-4}	pH 8.0,	
	GMP[b]	C(GTP)	9.2×10^{-5}	glycine,	(4)
		C(IMP)	7.4×10^{-5}	25°	
	dGMP[c]	C(IMP)	7.9×10^{-5}		
	GDP[d]	C(GTP)	2.2×10^{-5}		

[a] Also NC(GTP and L-aspartate)
[b] Also NC(L-aspartate)
[c] Also NC(GTP)
[d] Also NC(IMP and L-aspartate)

References

1. Ratner, S. (1962) The Enzymes, 6, 505.
2. Lieberman, I. (1963) Methods in Enzymology, 6, 100.
3. Lieberman, I. (1956) JBC, 223, 327.
4. Wyngaarden, J. B. & Greenland, R. A. (1963) JBC, 238, 1054.
5. Fromm, H. J. (1958) BBA, 29, 255.

ARGININOSUCCINATE SYNTHETASE

(L-Citrulline: L-aspartate ligase (AMP))

ATP + L-citrulline + L-aspartate =

AMP + pyrophosphate + L-argininosuccinate

Equilibrium constant

$$\frac{[AMP]\ [PP_i]\ [L\text{-argininosuccinate}]}{[ATP]\ [L\text{-citrulline}]\ [L\text{-aspartate}]} = 8.9\ (pH\ 7.5,\ 38^\circ) \tag{2}$$

Specificity

The enzyme is highly specific. Thus only the natural isomers of citrulline and aspartate are active and of many natural amino acids and analogs of L-aspartate, only L-aspartate and threo-β-methyl-L-aspartate are active as substrates. At optimum conditions for each direction the forward reaction proceeds at a rate twenty times that of the reverse reaction.

(1,3)

Michaelis constants

source	substrate	$K_m(M)$	conditions	
Steer liver	L-citrulline	4.6×10^{-5}		
	L-aspartate	3.5×10^{-5}		
	threo-β-methyl L-aspartate	8.8×10^{-4}		
	PP$_i$	7.9×10^{-5}		
	L-argininosuccinate	2.8×10^{-5}	pH 7.5, Tris, 38°	(3)
Hog kidney	Mg-ATP^{2-}	3.2×10^{-4}		
	L-citrulline	4.4×10^{-5}		
	L-aspartate	3.8×10^{-5}		
	AMP	2.1×10^{-4}		
	PP$_i$	8.2×10^{-5}		
	L-argininosuccinate	3.5×10^{-5}		

Inhibitors

source	inhibitor	type	$K_i(M)$	conditions
Steer liver	D-aspartate	C(L-aspartate)	2.0×10^{-2}	
	α-methyl-DL-aspartate	C(L-aspartate)	1.8×10^{-3}	
	PP_i	NC(ATP)	6.2×10^{-5}	
	PP_i	NC(L-citrulline)	7.9×10^{-5}	
	PP_i	NC(L-aspartate)	2.2×10^{-4}	
	L-arginine	C(L-citrulline)	2.0×10^{-2}	pH 7.5, Tris, 38° (3)
	L-argininosuccinate	C(ATP)	1.1×10^{-3}	
	L-argininosuccinate	C(L-citrulline)	3.0×10^{-4}	
	L-argininosuccinate	C(L-aspartate)	4.6×10^{-4}	
Hog kidney	AMP	C(ATP)	3.5×10^{-4}	
	PP_i	NC(ATP)	5.7×10^{-5}	
	PP_i	NC(citrulline)	8.5×10^{-5}	
	PP_i	NC(L-aspartate)	2.0×10^{-4}	
Beef liver	δ-acetylornithine	C(L-citrulline)	1.5×10^{-3}	pH 7.4, P_i, 38° (4)

References

1. Ratner, S. (1962) The Enzymes, 6, 499.

2. Schuegraf, A., Ratner, S. & Warner, R. C. (1960) JBC, 235, 3597.

3. Rochovansky, O. & Ratner, S. (1967) JBC, 242, 3839.

4. Tigier, H., Kennedy, J. & Grisolia, S. (1965) BBA, 110, 423.

5'-PHOSPHORIBOSYLIMIDAZOLEACETATE SYNTHETASE

(Imidazoleacetate:5'-phosphoribose ligase (ADP))

ATP + imidazoleacetate +5'-phospho-α-D-ribosyl-pyrophosphate =

ADP + P_i + PP_i + 5-phospho-α-D-ribosyl-imidazole acetate

Ref.

Equilibrium constant

The reaction is essentially irreversible [F].   (1)

Michaelis constants

source	substrate	$K_m(M)$	conditions	
Rabbit liver	5'-phosphoribosyl-pyrophosphate	3.4×10^{-6}	pH 8.15, Tris, 37°	(1)
	imidazoleacetate	3.72×10^{-4}		
	ATP	3.18×10^{-4}		

References

1. Crowley, G. M. (1964)   JBC, 239, 2593.

NAD SYNTHETASE

(Deamido-NAD: L-glutamine amido-ligase (AMP))

ATP + deamido-NAD + L-glutamine + H_2O =

AMP + pyrophosphate + NAD + L-glutamate

Ref.

Specificity

NAD synthetase, isolated from Escherichia coli or yeast, is highly specific for ATP which could not be replaced by CTP, UTP, ITP or GTP. The enzymes differ markedly in their specificity for the nitrogen donor; thus that from E. coli utilizes ammonia more effectively than L-glutamine whereas that from yeast utilizes L-glutamine much more effectively than ammonia. L-Glutamate, L-aspartate and L-asparagine are inactive with either enzyme.

(1,3)

Michaelis constants

source	substrate	$\frac{V}{(relative)}$	$K_m(M)$	conditions	
E. coli	ATP	–	2.0×10^{-4}		
	deamido-NAD	–	1.1×10^{-4}	pH 8.5,	
	NH_4^+	1.00	6.5×10^{-5}	Tris, 37°	(1)
	L-glutamine	0.68	1.6×10^{-2}		
Yeast	ATP	–	6.0×10^{-4}		
	deamido-NAD	–	1.4×10^{-4}		
	NH_4^+	–	1.4×10^{-1}	pH 7.4,	
	L-glutamine	–	3.5×10^{-3}	Tris, 37°	(2)
	Mg^{2+}	–	1.3×10^{-3}		

Inhibitors

source	inhibitor	type	$K_i(M)$	conditions	
E. coli	adenosine psicofuranine	⟩ "mixed"	⟨ 1.5×10^{-3} 6.0×10^{-4} ⟩	pH 8.5, Tris, 37°	(1)

The enzyme (E. coli) was also inhibited by AMP, ADP, cordycepin, and decoyinine, but not by azaserine, adenine, guanosine, cytidine, uridine, thymidine or inosine. The enzyme isolated from yeast was inhibited by azaserine, adenosine and AMP but decoyinine and psicofuranine were poor inhibitors.   (1)

References

1. Spencer, R. L. & Preiss, J. (1967) JBC, 242, 385.

2. Imsande, J., Preiss, J. & Handler, P. (1963) Methods in Enzymology, 6, 350.

3. Preiss, J. & Handler, P. (1958) JBC, 233, 493.

PHOSPHORIBOSYL-FORMYLGLYCINEAMIDINE SYNTHETASE

(5'-Phosphoribosyl-formylglycineamide:

L-glutamine amido-ligase (ADP))

ATP + 5'-phosphoribosyl-formylglycineamide + L-glutamine + H$_2$O =

ADP + orthophosphate + 5'-phosphoribosyl-formylglycineamidine +

L-glutamate

Ref.

Equilibrium constant

The reaction is essentially irreversible [F]. (3)

Molecular weight

source	value	conditions	
Salmonella typhimurium	135,000	0.15 M KCl	(1)

Michaelis constants

source	substrate	$K_m(M)$	conditions	
Chicken liver	FGAR	6.4×10^{-5}	pH 7.4, P$_i$, 38°	(2,3)
	L-glutamine	6.2×10^{-4}		

Inhibitors

source	inhibitor	type	$K_i(M)$	conditions	
Chicken liver	L-azaserine	complex	3.4×10^{-5}	pH 7.4, P$_i$, 38°	(2)
	6-diazo-5-oxo-L-norleucine	C(L-glutamine)	1.1×10^{-6}		

The enzyme from S. typhimurium is also inhibited by L-azaserine and 6-diazo-5-oxo-L-norleucine. (1,3)

Abbreviations

FGAR   5'-phosphoribosyl-formylglycine amide

References

1. French, T. C., Dawid, I. B., Day, R. A. & Buchanan, J. M. (1963) JBC, 238, 2171.
2. Levenberg, B., Melnick, I. & Buchanan, J. M. (1957) JBC, 225, 163.
3. Flaks, J. G. & Lukens, L. N. (1963) Methods in Enzymology, 6, 69.

PYRUVATE-CARBOXYLASE

(Pyruvate:carbon dioxide ligase (ADP))

$$ATP + pyruvate + CO_2 + H_2O = ADP + P_i + oxaloacetate$$

Ref.

Equilibrium constant

The reaction is reversible. (1)

Molecular weight

source	value	conditions
Chicken liver mitochondria	655,000 [4]	pH 7.2, also by (1,2) electron microscopy

Specific activity

Chicken liver mitochondria (200 x) 32 pyruvate (pH 7.4, Tris, $25°$) (1)

Specificity and Michaelis constants

source	substrate	relative velocity	$K_m(M)$	conditions
Chicken liver mitochondria (requires acetyl-CoA for activity)	ATP (F)	10.0	5.8×10^{-5}	
	pyruvate (F)	-	4.4×10^{-4}	
	bicarbonate (F)	-	1.0×10^{-3}	
	acetyl-CoA (F)	-	2.3×10^{-5}	
	Mg^{2+} (F)	-	2.8×10^{-3}	pH 7.8, P_i, $25°$ (1)
	ADP (R)	1.0	6.3×10^{-5}	
	oxaloacetate (R)	-	5.0×10^{-5}	
	P_i (R)	-	1.2×10^{-2}	
	acetyl-CoA (R)	-	1.5×10^{-5}	
	Mg^{2+} (R)	-	1.4×10^{-3}	
Saccharomyces cerevisiae (yeast) (requires acetyl-CoA for activity)	pyruvate (F)	-	8×10^{-4}	pH 8.4, Tris, $30°$ (3)
	ATP (F)	-	2.4×10^{-4}	
	bicarbonate (F)	-	2.7×10^{-3}	
	Mg^{2+} (F)	-	4.2×10^{-3}	

F = forward reaction
R = reverse reaction

The enzyme (chicken liver) utilizes ATP and dATP equally well but other trinucleotides tested were inactive (4). Orthophosphate could not be replaced by arsenate (5). The mechanism of the acetyl-CoA activation is discussed in reference (5).

Inhibitors

source	inhibitor	type	$K_i(M)$	conditions
S. cerevisiae	oxalate	NC (pyruvate, bicarbonate or ATP)	7×10^{-5}	pH 8.4, Tris, 30° (3)
Chicken liver mitochondria	ADP	C (ATP)	7.5×10^{-5}	pH 7.8, Tris, 23° (4)
	5'-AMP		9.3×10^{-3}	
	3'-AMP		1.3×10^{-2}	
	CTP		9.6×10^{-5}	
	dCTP		7.7×10^{-5}	
	GTP	NC (ATP)	2.3×10^{-4}	
	UTP		4.5×10^{-4}	
	ITP		6.8×10^{-4}	
	TTP		1.3×10^{-3}	
	CDP		1.6×10^{-3}	
	5'-CMP		1.2×10^{-2}	

References

1. Scrutton, M. C. & Utter, M. F. (1965) JBC, 240, 1.

2. Valentine, R. C., Wrigley, N. G., Scrutten, M. C., Irias, J. J. & Utter, M. F. (1966) B, 5, 3111.

3. Ruiz-Amil, M., deTorrontegui, G., Palacián, E., Catalina, L. & Losada, M. (1965) JBC, 240, 3485.

4. Scrutton, M. C. & Utter, M. F. (1965) JBC, 240, 3714.

5. Scrutton, M. C., Keech, D. B. & Utter, M. F. (1965) JBC, 240, 574.

ACETYL-COA CARBOXYLASE

(Acetyl-CoA:carbon-dioxide ligase (ADP))

$$ATP + acetyl\text{-}CoA + CO_2 + H_2O = ADP + P_i + malonyl\text{-}CoA$$

Ref.

Equilibrium constant

The reaction is essentially irreversible [F]. (1)

Molecular weight

source	value	conditions		Ref.
Rat epididymyl adipose tissue	~540,000	no citrate	sucrose gradient	(3)
	~1,800,000	5×10^{-3} M citrate	sucrose gradient	(3)

Specificity

The enzyme isolated from chicken liver utilizes acetyl-CoA (1.00), propionyl-CoA (0.60), butyryl-CoA (0.10), crotonoyl-CoA (0.05) and 3-hydroxybutyryl-CoA (0.02). UTP is about 30% as effective as ATP but CTP and GTP are inactive. A number of polycarboxylic acids stimulate the enzyme - of these isocitrate and citrate are the most effective. (4)

Michaelis constants

source	substrate	K_m(M)	conditions		Ref.
Rat liver	acetyl-CoA	1.9×10^{-5}	pH 7.5, Tris, 25°		(2)
Chicken liver	ATP	5.4×10^{-3}	no isocitrate	pH 6.3, P_i, 37°	(4)
	UTP	8.0×10^{-3}	no isocitrate	pH 6.3, P_i, 37°	(4)
	ATP	1.0×10^{-3}	5×10^{-2} M isocitrate	pH 6.3, P_i, 37°	(4)
	UTP	1.5×10^{-3}	5×10^{-2} M isocitrate	pH 6.3, P_i, 37°	(4)
	acetyl-CoA	4.7×10^{-6}	with or without 5×10^{-2} M isocitrate	pH 6.3, P_i, 37°	(4)
	propionyl-CoA	8.8×10^{-6}	with or without 5×10^{-2} M isocitrate	pH 6.3, P_i, 37°	(4)

Inhibitors

source	inhibitor	type	K_i(M)	conditions	Ref.
Rat liver	caproyl-CoA	C (acetyl-CoA)	1.4×10^{-4}	pH 7.5, Tris, 25°	(2)
	lauroyl-CoA	C (acetyl-CoA)	7.4×10^{-5}	pH 7.5, Tris, 25°	(2)
	myristoyl-CoA	C (acetyl-CoA)	1.1×10^{-5}	pH 7.5, Tris, 25°	(2)
	palmitoyl-CoA	C (acetyl-CoA)	7.2×10^{-6}	pH 7.5, Tris, 25°	(2)
	marginoyl-CoA	C (acetyl-CoA)	4.3×10^{-6}	pH 7.5, Tris, 25°	(2)
	stearoyl-CoA	C (acetyl-CoA)	7.1×10^{-7}	pH 7.5, Tris, 25°	(2)
	oleoyl-CoA	C (acetyl-CoA)	1.3×10^{-6}	pH 7.5, Tris, 25°	(2)

References

1. Utter, M. F. (1961) The Enzymes, 5, 336.
2. Bortz, W. M. & Lynen, F. (1963) BZ, 337, 505.
3. Vagelos, P. R., Alberts, A. W. & Martin, D. B. (1963) JBC, 238, 533.
4. Waite, M. & Wakil, S. J. (1962) JBC, 237, 2750.

PROPIONYL-CoA CARBOXYLASE

(Propionyl-CoA:carbon-dioxide ligase (ADP))

$$ATP + \text{propionyl-CoA} + CO_2 + H_2O = ADP + P_i + \text{methylmalonyl-CoA}$$

Ref.

Equilibrium constant

$$\frac{[ADP]\,[P_i]\,[\text{methylmalonyl-CoA}]}{[ATP]\,[\text{propionyl-CoA}]\,[HCO_3^-]} = 5.7 \qquad \text{pH 8.1, Tris, } 28^\circ \qquad (2)$$

(also see reference 6)

Molecular weight

source	value	conditions	
Pig heart	700,000 [4]	pH 6.5	(3)
Bovine liver mitochondria	$S_{20,w}$ = 19.0	pH 7.2	(6)

Specific activity

Pig heart (800 x)	28.6 propionyl-CoA 4.3 methylmalonyl-CoA	(pH 8, Tris, 30°)	(2,3)
Bovine liver mitochondria (192 x)	16.5 propionyl-CoA	(pH 8.5, Tris, 37°)	(6)

Specificity

The enzyme isolated from pig heart is specific - thus, GTP, UTP, CTP, or ITP could not replace ATP and butyryl-CoA, acetyl-CoA and crotonoyl-CoA could replace propionyl-CoA only to a limited extent. (3,7)

Michaelis constants

source	substrate	V (relative)	K_m (M)	conditions	
Pig heart	CO_2	–	2.5×10^{-3}	pH 8, Tris, 25°	(4)
	ATP	–	8.0×10^{-5}		
	propionyl-CoA	1.000	2.0×10^{-4}	pH 8, Tris, 25°	(3)
	butyryl-CoA	0.060	1.5×10^{-3}		
	acetyl-CoA	0.007	–		
	crotonoyl-CoA	0.030	–		
Bovine liver mitochondria	propionyl-CoA	1.00	2.6×10^{-4}	pH 8.5, Tris, 37°	(6)
	acetyl-CoA	0.01	3.5×10^{-4}		
	butyryl-CoA	0.05	3.5×10^{-4}		
	valeryl-CoA	0.005	5.1×10^{-4}		
	ATP	1.00	5.5×10^{-5}		
	HCO_3	1.00	1.9×10^{-3}		

Inhibitors

source	inhibitor	type	K_i(M)	conditions
Pig heart	ADP	C (ATP)	5.72×10^{-4}	pH 7.5, Tris, (5) 30°

References

1. Utter, M. F. (1961) The Enzymes, 5, 335.

2. Kaziro, Y., Grossman, A. & Ochoa, S. (1965) JBC, 240, 64.

3. Kaziro, Y., Ochoa, S., Warner, R. C. & Chen, J-Y. (1961) JBC, 236, 1917.

4. Tietz, A. & Ochoa, S. (1959) JBC, 234, 1394.

5. Kaziro, Y., Hass, L. F., Boyer, P. D. & Ochoa, S. (1962) JBC, 237, 1460.

6. Halenz, D. R., Feng, J-Y., Hegre, C. S. & Lane, M. D. (1962) JBC, 237, 2140.

7. Tietz, A. & Ochoa, S. (1962) Methods in Enzymology, 5, 570.

8. Lane, M. D., & Halenz, D. R. (1962) Methods in Enzymology, 5, 576.

METHYLCROTONOYL-CoA CARBOXYLASE

(3-Methylcrotonoyl-CoA:carbon-dioxide ligase (ADP))

$$ATP + 3\text{-methylcrotonoyl-CoA} + CO_2 + H_2O = ADP + P_i + 3\text{-methylglutaconyl-CoA}$$

Ref.

Equilibrium constant

The reversibility of the reaction has been demonstrated. (1)

Molecular weight

source	value	conditions	
Achromobacter sp.	184,000	minimum: biotin content	(2)
	$S_{20,w} = 19.4$	pH 7.5	(2)

Specific activity

Achromobacter sp. (63 x) 10.7 3-methylcrotonoyl-(pH 8.0, Tris, 25°) (2)
CoA

Specificity

The enzyme (Achromobacter sp.) utilizes the following acyl-CoA derivatives: 3-methylcrotonoyl-CoA (1.000), acetyl-CoA (0.020), propionyl-CoA (0.026), acetoacetyl-CoA (0.140), crotonoyl-CoA (0.200), but not capronoyl-CoA or stearoyl-CoA. (2)

The enzyme purified from Mycobacterium sp. is described in reference (1).

Michaelis constants

source	substrate	$K_m(M)$	conditions	
Achromobacter sp.	ATP	8.3×10^{-5}	pH 8.0, Tris,	(2)
	3-methylcrotonoyl-CoA	1.2×10^{-5}	25°	
	HCO_3^-	2.17×10^{-3}	pH 7.2, 25°	(1)
Chicken liver	ATP	2.9×10^{-4}	pH 7.4, EDTA,	(3)
	3-methylcrotonoyl-CoA	3×10^{-4}	37°	

References

1. Lynen, F., Knappe, J., Lorch, E., Jütting, G., Ringelmann, E. & Lachance, J-P. (1961) BZ, 335, 123.

2. Himes, R. H., Young, D. L., Ringelmann, E. & Lynen, F. (1963) BZ, 337, 48.

3. Coon, M. J. (1962) Methods in Enzymology, 5, 896.

ENZYME INDEX

The following trivial names often occur in the literature: carboxy-kinase and carboxytransphosphorylase (see sub-subgroup 4.1.1.); dehydrase (dehydratase or hydratase : 4.2.1); kinase (phosphotransferase : 2.7.1-6); kinosynthetase (synthetase : 6.3.2, 6.3.4); methylpherase (methyltrans-ferase : 2.1.1); oxidase (often dehydrogenase - see group 1); phosphorylase (2.4.1, 2.4.2, 2.7.7); pyrophosphorylase (2.4.2, 2.7.7); synthetase (often synthase or lyase: 2.1.1, 2.3.1, 2.4.1, 2.7.7, 4.1.2, 4.1.3) and thiokinase (synthetase : 6.2.1). The names amidinotransferase, formyltransferase, glucosyltransferase etc. are often replaced by transamidinase, transformy-lase or transglucosylase etc. Systematic names have not been included in the Enzyme Index.

Acetamidase	3.5.1.4	Acid deoxyribonuclease	3.1.4.6
Acetate kinase	2.7.2.1	Acid phosphatase	3.1.3.2
Acetate thiokinase	6.2.1.1	Acid phosphomonoesterase	3.1.3.2
Acetoacetate decarboxylase	4.1.1.4	Aconitase	4.2.1.3
Acetoacetate succinate		Aconitate hydratase	4.2.1.3
thiophorase	2.8.3.5	Acyl-CoA dehydrogenase	1.3.99.3
Acetoacetyl-CoA reductase	1.1.1.36	Acyl-CoA synthetase 6.2.1.2,	6.2.1.3
Acetoacetyl-CoA thiolase	2.3.1.9	Acyl dehydrogenase	1.3.99.3
Acetokinase	2.7.2.1	N-Acylglucosamine 2-epimerase	5.1.3.a
Acetyl activating enzyme	6.2.1.1	N-Acylglucosamine-6-phosphate	
Acetylcholinesterase	3.1.1.7	2-epimerase	5.1.3.b
Acetyl-CoA acetyltransferase	2.3.1.9	Acyl-lysine deacylase	3.5.1.17
Acetyl-CoA carboxylase	6.4.1.2	N-Acyl-D-mannosamine kinase	2.7.1.b
Acetyl-CoA synthetase	6.2.1.1	Acylphosphatase	3.6.1.7
Acetylesterase	3.1.1.6	Acylphosphate: hexose	
Acetylglucosamine		phosphotransferase	2.7.1.g
phosphomutase	2.7.5.2	Adenase	3.5.4.2
N-Acetyl-D-glucosamine kinase	2.7.1.f	Adenine deaminase	3.5.4.2
β-Acetylglucosaminidase	3.2.1.30	Adenine phosphoribosyl-	
N-Acetyl-β-glucosaminidase	3.2.1.29	transferase	2.4.2.7
N-Acetyllactosamine synthetase		Adenosine deaminase	3.5.4.4
see	2.4.1.22	Adenosine kinase	2.7.1.20
N-Acetylneuraminate lyase		Adenosine nucleosidase	3.2.2.a
	4.1.3.3, 4.1.3.b	Adenosylhomocysteinase	3.3.1.1
N-Acetylneuraminate-9-		Adenosylmethionine	
phosphatase	3.1.3.a	cyclotransferase	2.5.1.4
N-Acetylneuraminate-9-		Adenylate kinase	2.7.4.3
phosphate synthase	4.1.3.a	Adenylate pyrophosphorylase	2.4.2.7
N-Acetylneuraminate synthase	4.1.3.b	Adenylic acid ribosidase	3.2.2.4
N-Acetyl-neuraminic acid		Adenylosuccinase	4.3.2.2
aldolase	4.1.3.3	Adenylosuccinate lyase	4.3.2.2
Acetylornithine		Adenylosuccinate synthetase	6.3.4.4
aminotransferase	2.6.1.11	ADPglucose-glycogen glucosyl-	
Acetylornithine deacetylase	3.5.1.16	transferase	2.4.1.a
Acetylserotonin		ADPglucose pyrophosphorylase	2.7.7.b
methyltransferase	2.1.1.4	ADPglucose-starch glucosyl-	
		transferase	2.4.1.b

A-esterase	3.1.1.2	5-Amino-4-imidazolecarboxamide	
D-Alanine aminotransferase	2.6.1.b	ribotide transferase	2.1.2.3
Alanine aminotransferase	2.6.1.2	5-Amino-4-imidazole-N-succino-	
β-Alanine aminotransferase	2.6.1.18	carboxamide ribotide	
Alanine dehydrogenase	1.4.1.1	kinosynthetase	6.3.2.6
Alanine-ketoacid amino-		Aminolaevulinate dehydratase	4.2.1.24
transferase	2.6.1.12	Aminomalonate decarboxylase	4.1.1.10
Alanine racemase	5.1.1.1	Aminopeptidase 3.4.1.2,	3.4.1.3
D-Alanylalanine synthetase	6.3.2.4	AMP deaminase	3.5.4.6
β-Alanyl-CoA ammonia-lyase	4.3.1.6	AMP nucleosidase	3.2.2.4
D-Alanyl-polyphosphoribitol		AMP pyrophosphorylase	2.4.2.7
synthetase	6.1.1.13	α-Amylase	3.2.1.1
Alanyl-sRNA synthetase	6.1.1.7	β-Amylase	3.2.1.2
Alcohol dehydrogenase	1.1.1.1	Amylo-1,6-glucosidase	3.2.1.33
Alcohol dehydrogenase (NADP)	1.1.1.2	Amylomaltase	2.4.1.3
Aldehyde dehydrogenase	1.2.1.3	Amylosucrase	2.4.1.4
Aldehyde dehydrogenase		Apyrase	3.6.1.5
(acylating)	1.2.1.10	D-Arabinitol dehydrogenase	1.1.1.11
Aldehyde dehydrogenase (NADP)	1.2.1.4	Arabinokinase	2.7.1.c
Aldehyde dehydrogenase (NAD(P))	1.2.1.5	L-Arabinose dehydrogenase	1.1.1.46
Aldehyde oxidase	1.2.3.1	Arabinose isomerase	5.3.1.3
Aldehyde reductase	1.1.1.1	L-Arabinose isomerase	5.3.1.4
Aldolase 4.1.2.7,	4.1.2.13	Arabinosephosphate isomerase	5.3.1.13
Aldonolactonase	3.1.1.18	Arginase	3.5.3.1
Aldose 1-epimerase	5.1.3.3	Arginine decarboxylase	4.1.1.19
Aldose mutarotase	5.1.3.3	Arginine deiminase	3.5.3.6
Aldose reductase	1.1.1.21	Arginine desiminase	3.5.3.6
Ali-esterase	3.1.1.1	Arginine kinase	2.7.3.3
Alkaline phosphatase	3.1.3.1	Arginine oxidase	1.4.3.b
Alkaline phosphomonoesterase	3.1.3.1	Argininosuccinase	4.3.2.1
S-Alkyl cysteinase	4.4.1.6	Argininosuccinate lyase	4.3.2.1
S-Alkylcysteine lyase	4.4.1.6	Argininosuccinate synthetase	6.3.4.5
ε-Alkyllysinase	1.5.3.a	Arginyl-sRNA synthetase	6.1.1.a
Allantoinase	3.5.2.5	Aromatic L-amino-acid	
Alliinase	4.4.1.4	decarboxylase	4.1.1.26
Alliin lyase	4.4.1.4	Aryl acylamidase	3.5.1.13
Allothreonine aldolase	4.1.2.6	Arylamine acetylase	2.3.1.5
Altronate dehydratase	4.2.1.7	Arylamine acetyltransferase	2.3.1.5
Amidase	3.5.1.4	Arylesterase	3.1.1.2
Amidophosphoribosyltransferase	2.4.2.14	Aryl 4-hydroxylase	1.14.1.1
Amine oxidase	1.4.3.4	Arylsulphatase	3.1.6.1
D-Aminoacid acetyltransferase	2.3.1.d	Aryl sulphotransferase	2.8.2.1
D-Amino-acid oxidase	1.4.3.3	Ascorbate oxidase	1.10.3.3
L-Amino-acid oxidase	1.4.3.2	Ascorbate oxidase (producing	
Aminoacylase	3.5.1.14	oxalate and threonate) see	1.10.3.3
Aminoacylase I	3.5.1.14	Asparaginase	3.5.1.1
Amino-acylhistidine dipeptidase	3.4.3.3	Asparagine synthetase	6.3.1.1
Aminobutyraldehyde		Asparaginyl-sRNA synthetase	
dehydrogenase	1.2.1.19	see	6.1.1.12
Aminobutyrate aminotransferase	2.6.1.19	Aspartase	4.3.1.1
Aminodeoxygluconate		Aspartate acetyltransferase	2.3.1.17
dehydratase	4.2.1.26	Aspartate aminotransferase	2.6.1.1
Aminoimidazolase	3.5.4.8	Aspartate ammonia-lyase	4.3.1.1

Glutamate formiminotransferase	2.1.2.5	Glycosulphatase	3.1.6.3
Glutamate mutase	5.4.99.1	Glycyl-glycine dipeptidase	3.4.3.1
Glutamate racemase	5.1.1.3	Glycyl-sRNA synthetase	6.1.1.e
Glutamic-alanine transaminase	2.6.1.2	Glyoxalase I	4.4.1.5
Glutamic-aspartic transaminase	2.6.1.1	Glyoxalase II	3.1.2.6
Glutamic-oxaloacetic		Glyoxylate carboligase	4.1.1.b
transaminase	2.6.1.1	Glyoxylate dehydrogenase	1.2.1.17
Glutamic-pyruvic transaminase	2.6.1.2	Glyoxylate reductase	1.1.1.26
Glutaminase	3.5.1.2	Glyoxylate transacetase	4.1.3.2
Glutamine-fructose-6-phosphate		GMP pyrophosphorylase	2.4.2.8
aminotransferase	2.6.1.16	GMP reductase	1.6.6.8
Glutamine synthetase	6.3.1.2	GMP synthetase	6.3.4.1
Glutaminyl-sRNA synthetase see	6.1.1.d	dGTPase	3.1.5.1
γ-Glutamyl-cysteine synthetase	6.3.2.2	Guanase	3.5.4.3
Glutamyl-sRNA synthetase	6.1.1.d	Guanidinoacetate kinase	2.7.3.1
D-Glutamyltransferase	2.3.2.1	Guanine deaminase	3.5.4.3
γ-Glutamyl transpeptidase	2.3.2.1	Guanosine phosphorylase	2.4.2.15
Glutaryl-CoA synthetase	6.2.1.6	Guanylate kinase	2.7.4.8
Glutathione dehydrogenase	1.8.5.1	Guanyloribonuclease	2.7.7.26
Glutathione reductase	1.6.4.2	L-Gulonolactone oxidase	1.1.3.8
Glutathione synthetase	6.3.2.3		
Glyceraldehydephosphate		Heptanoyl thiokinase	6.2.1.2
dehydrogenase	1.2.1.9, 1.2.1.12	Hexokinase	2.7.1.1
Glyceraldehydephosphate		Hexosediphosphatase	3.1.3.11
dehydrogenase (NADP)	1.2.1.13	Hexosephosphate amino-	
Glycerate dehydrogenase	1.1.1.29	transferase	2.6.1.16
Glycerate kinase	2.7.1.31	Hexosephosphate isomerase	5.3.1.9
Glycerate phosphomutase	2.7.5.3, 2.7.5.4	Hexose 1-phosphate nucleo-	
Glycerol dehydrogenase	1.1.1.6	tidyltransferase	2.7.7.d
Glycerol kinase	2.7.1.30	Hexose-1-phosphate uridylyl-	
Glycerol-2-phosphatase	3.1.3.19	transferase	2.7.7.12
Glycerolphosphate		Hippuricase	3.5.1.14
dehydrogenase	1.1.99.5	Histaminase	1.4.3.6
Glycerol-3-phosphate		Histamine methyltransferase	2.1.1.8
dehydrogenase	1.1.1.8	Histidase	4.3.1.3
Glycerophosphorylcholine		Histidinase	4.3.1.3
diesterase	3.1.4.2	Histidine ammonia-lyase	4.3.1.3
Glycinamide ribotide		Histidine α-deaminase	4.3.1.3
transformylase	2.1.2.2	Histidine decarboxylase	4.1.1.22
Glycine acyltransferase	2.3.1.13	Histidinol dehydrogenase	1.1.1.23
Glycineamide ribonucleotide		Histidinolphosphatase	3.1.3.15
synthetase	6.3.1.3	Histidinolphosphate amino-	
Glycine amidinotransferase	2.1.4.1	transferase	2.6.1.9
Glycine aminotransferase	2.6.1.4	Homocysteine methyl-	
Glycine dehydrogenase	1.4.1.a	transferase	2.1.1.10
Glycine formiminotransferase	2.1.2.4	Homocysteine synthase	4.2.1.22
Glycocyamine kinase	2.7.3.1	Homogentisate oxygenase	1.13.1.5
Glycogen phosphorylase	2.4.1.1	Homogentisicase	1.13.1.5
Glycogen-UDP glucosyl-		Homoserine deaminase	4.2.1.15
transferase	2.4.1.11	Homoserine dehydratase	4.2.1.15
Glycogen synthetase	2.4.1.11	Homoserine dehydrogenase	1.1.1.3
Glycolaldehydetransferase	2.2.1.1	Homoserine kinase	2.7.1.39
Glycollate oxidase	1.1.3.1		